REX
WHISTLER

Cover device: see cat. no. 456

see cat. no. 296

From *THE EMPEROR HEART*. Cat. No. 481

Design for ceiling plasterwork : see cat. no. 337

SELF-PORTRAIT

C. 1934.   Oil on Canvas.   Cat. no. 116

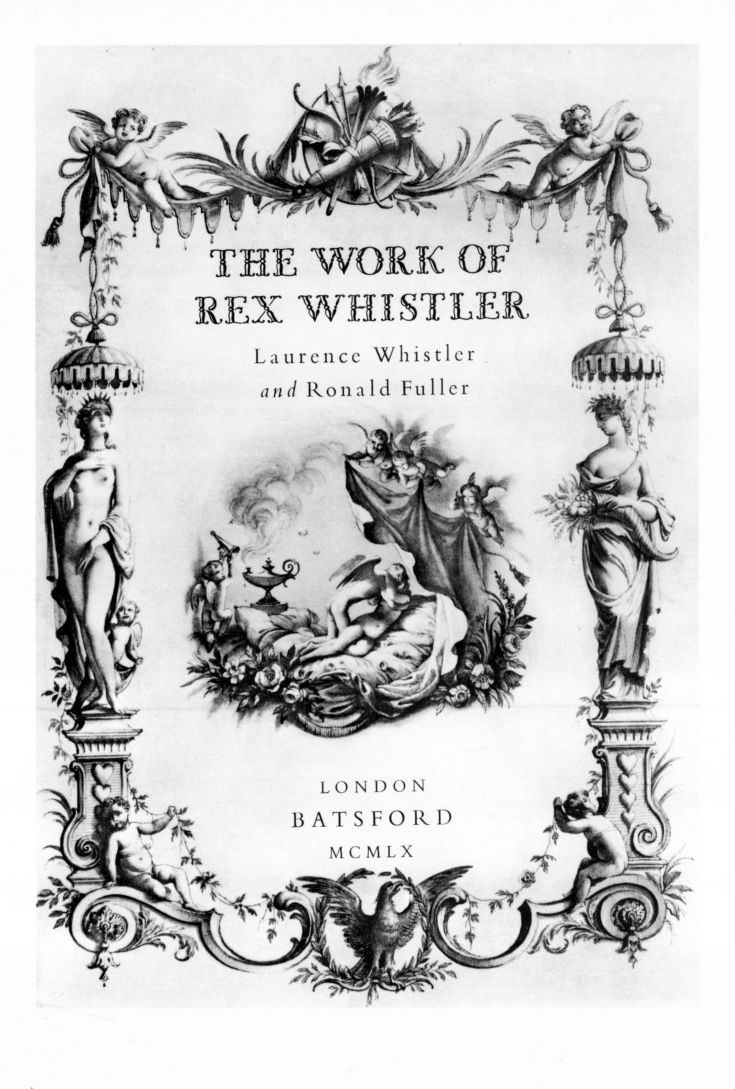

THE WORK OF
REX WHISTLER

Laurence Whistler
and Ronald Fuller

LONDON

BATSFORD

MCMLX

PAGODA WINKY

with love from Rex
1935.

Made and printed in Great Britain by William Clowes and Sons, Ltd, London and Beccles
Collotype Plates by L. Van Leer and Co. Ltd, London and Amsterdam for the publishers
B. T. BATSFORD LTD
4 Fitzhardinge Street, Portman Square, London, W.1

Title-page design : see cat. no. 522   *Design on this page : see cat. no. 264*

For his Mother

with Love

From *A THATCHED ROOF.* Cat. No. 455

CONTENTS

From *THE EMPEROR HEART*. Cat. No. 481

ACKNOWLEDGMENT

WE thank Her Majesty Queen Elizabeth the Queen Mother, Her Royal Highness the Duchess of Kent, Her Royal Highness Princess Alice, Countess of Athlone, and very many others who have enabled this book to be made, by allowing original work to be examined, by lending letters or giving information, and by lending paintings and drawings for reproduction. Much help has been received from those whose names are given in the catalogue as the owners of works; and we would record the particular kindnesses of the following: Christabel, Lady Aberconway; Mr. Richard Addinsell; Mrs. Herbert Agar; Mr. Robert Andrews; The Marquis of Anglesey; The Director of the Ashmolean Museum, Oxford; Mr. Archie Balfour; Mr. Cecil Beaton; Mr. Hugh Beaumont; Mrs. Jack Beddington; Sir Alfred and Lady Beit; Margaret, Countess of Birkenhead; Mrs. Blois; Mrs. Stephen Bone; Miss Grace Boyce; Mr. Braben, of Shell-Mex and B.P. Ltd.; The British Council (and Miss W. A. Ward); Mr. Marcus Brumwell; Sir Malcolm Bullock, Bt.; Mrs. Henzell Case; Lady Elizabeth Clyde; Mr. Richard Cobden-Sanderson; Lady Diana Cooper; The Marquesa de Casa Maury; Lady Ursula D'Abo; The Marquis Douro; Lady Caroline Duff; Lady Juliet Duff; Mrs. M. Egerton; Mr. Arthur Fanshawe; Mr. Michael Felmingham; Mr. Felix Fenston; Mrs. E. R. S. Fifoot; Mr. Simon Fleet; Sir John Gielgud; Mr. Donald Gilchrist; Mr. Thomas Goff; Mr. David Grieg; The Lady Elizabeth von Hofmannsthal; The Lord Herbert; The Hon. Mrs. Hore-Ruthven; Mr. David Horner; Mrs. Huskinson; The Earl and Countess of Iddesleigh; Mr. Ian Jenkin; Lady Laycock; Miss Rosamund Lehmann; Mr. and Mrs. A. H. Lewes; Dr. David Lewes; Pamela, Countess of Lytton; Lady Mander; Mr. T. L. Marks; Dr. Anne McLaren; Mr. Gilbert Miller; Mr. Derrick Morley; The late Countess Mountbatten of Burma; Mr. Clifford Musgrave; The Director of the National Portrait Gallery, London; Mr. Willoughby Norman; Mr. Vernon Nye; Mrs. O'Cock; Odhams Press Ltd.; The Baron and Baroness Porcelli; Mr. Kenneth Rae; Lady Reed; The Viscountess Ridley; Miss Katherine Robinson; The Royal Ballet Benevolent Fund; Mrs. Gilbert Russell; The Hon. Lady Salmond; Mr. Mark Severin; Mr. and Mrs. Siegfried Sassoon; Dr. S. L. Simpson; Sir Osbert Sitwell, Bt.; Mr. Sacheverell Sitwell; The Hon. James Smith; the late Mrs. Constance Spry; The Trustees and Director of the Tate Gallery, London; The Hon. Stephen Tennant; Mr. Herbert Thearle; The Duke of Wellington; The Welsh Guards; Loelia, Duchess of Westminster; Mr. John Whiskard; Lady Davina Woodhouse; and the Ministry of Works.

We specially thank Miss Rosemary Olivier, in addition, for copying out from the unpublished Journal of her aunt, Edith Olivier, all references to the artist—comprising a book in themselves. These entries were often invaluable in identifying or dating works; for he kept virtually no records. We thank Mr. Ian Robertson for reading the catalogue in typescript, and Lord Anglesey for reading the proofs. And, in company with the publishers, we thank Mr. Thomas Goff, and Shell Mex and B.P. Ltd., for their generous contributions towards the cost of the colour plates. To the first we owe the reproduction of the clavichord built by Mr. Goff.

Grateful acknowledgment is made to the following publishers: The Cresset Press Ltd., J. M. Dent and Sons Ltd., Faber and Faber Ltd., Wm. Heinemann Ltd., John Lane, the Bodley Head Ltd., Putnam and Co. Ltd., The Richards Press Ltd.

On only a few works, known to exist, was full information sought in vain from the owners. These we have described as best we might. The artist's many true friends have witnessed by their helpfulness to the affection they once had for him, and still have.

L W : R F

M C M L X

From *THE LORD FISH*. Cat. No. 454

Introduction

WHATEVER position my brother Rex will finally be found to occupy among the artists of our country, it can hardly be disputed that he was one of the most versatile. In this he has been likened to William Kent; but he was more level in performance than Kent—that brilliant garden-designer, moderate architect, and very poor painter—and he had even wider versatility. A glance through the illustrations to this book, or simply at the contents page, confirms the thought. We cannot immediately say that he was less good at creating stage scenery than illustrating books; a better painter of murals than designer of book-plates; was better in water-colours than in oils; was happier on the large scale than on the small. In quality, the long dining-room at Plas Newydd (*Plates 22–24*) may rank with the miniature landscape in a printed head-piece.

In addition, there were talents he did not have time or opportunity to develop. He could have been an architect in the classical tradition, and a more exciting one than many who practise today with success. He was quite capable of designing a theatre, a church, a bridge, or of landscaping a new estate. His fanciful notions often recall Thomas Archer, being English baroque with a continental accent. But these were to please himself. He did, in fact, carry out a number of small alterations and improvements in private houses and gardens. And of course the architectural knowledge was put to good use in his theatrical designs, at once scholarly and romantic.

And still we have not mentioned the continuous current of minor work that flowed from his hand in the form of illustrations to periodicals, "reversible faces" for children, grotesques, advertisements, decorated fly-leaves, posters, Christmas cards, dust wrappers, dance programmes, telegraph forms, and many other inventions not a bit less hetero-geneous. These, mainly, are what the public knows of Rex Whistler. For every person who has seen an easel painting in his later manner, there are perhaps a hundred who associate him with some ephemeral gaiety, or at very best with the painting at Brighton called "Allegory"—a painting delightful enough but still only a joke for his fellow-officers, which he certainly never imagined as being so widely overheard (*Plate 31*). In short, he has paid for his versatility. He has been dismissed, or accepted (the words are virtually synonymous in this context), as a "mere" illustrator, a frivolous and witty entertainer.

It is the purpose of this book to suggest that he was a serious and permanent artist, unique in vision and unique in expression. Such a purpose can hardly be fulfilled by any book, however. We are confronted at once not merely with the problem of colour, as in representing any painter between boards, but with the problems of scale and place. He himself believed that the best would be found in one or two of his later mural paint-ings. But these are remote in private houses and depend for full effect on their setting, so sensitively did he marry them to the life of the house and its architecture, spilling out in *trompe l'œil* or appropriate ornament on to neighbouring walls and ceilings. It is sad, though inevitable, that his only murals known to the many should be almost the earliest. For he was twenty when he began to paint in the Tate Gallery Refreshment Room and twenty-two when he stopped (*Plate 3*). This playful room has, naturally

DAVID AND GOLIATH. Pencil. Drawn at the age of five

then, the note of youthfulness. Yet such was its impact that it established him as a slighter and more whimsical artist than he was destined to be in the fullness of time—a fullness, we should remember, hardly granted to him anyway.

To his own choice of the best paintings he would have added one or two stage designs and one or two illustrated books; and he would have been right. Here it is worth noting that he was a draughtsman long before he was a painter. His Rome sketch-book of 1928 contains some very accomplished drawings, made with obvious relish on days when he was not groaning over his landscapes in oil or water-colour. It is to the later nineteen-thirties that his finest paintings belong, or indeed, as we shall see, to the years of war. His finest illustrations, on the other hand, are those in *Gulliver's Travels* of 1930 (*Plate 60 et seq.*), and *The Next Volume* of 1932 (*Plates 81* and *82*). His big *Königsmark* drawings of 1941 (*Plate 88*) do not compare well with the *Gulliver*; but that reflects the difficulty, and speed, with which they were executed in army quarters, not an intrinsic falling-off of ability. In this genre he never did anything better than the two earlier books, or indeed as good. Alas, they were limited editions, and like the best murals, they remain unknown to the general public! It was *The New Forget-Me-Not* of 1929 (*Plates 55–58*), frivolous, impertinent, and youthful, which confirmed the reputation already won for him at the Tate.

He had in fact two manners—the second emerging from the first in the early nineteen-thirties—and in the war was developing a third. This would, I do not doubt, have been much in evidence had he come back to a peace which seemed, and still seems, to call for his contribution. Though certainly precocious with pencil and pen (see pages xiv, xv, xvi, for example), and obviously not unaware of his natural endowment, he described himself in 1935 as a "very late developer"—meaning partly, at least, that he had relied too long on that facility. In 1942 he declared that he was "only just beginning" to know how to paint in oils. A friend remembers him thus in uniform: "As he examined somewhat wistfully his pre-war paintings, he said, 'I can do much better than that now!'" It had always been easier for him to invent than to perceive, to weave fantasy than to penetrate reality. There was his inward vision on the one hand, and there was the object or landscape in front of him on the other: he had found the marriage of the two a slow and hard matter to negotiate. Easel-painting had been, on the whole, his least satisfactory sphere. Some of his earlier canvases might fairly be described as water-colours in terms of oils; others were finely accurate records of architecture, and not a great deal more. Suddenly, as it seems, he discovered a new imaginative freedom: ironically, when physical freedom was drastically curtailed—with his Welsh Guards cap in the grass for reminder. Painting to please himself, he escaped from the "tight" manner and the muted idealized palette. He used stronger colours. He painted light, and the rapture of light. His little landscape of 1943 in a backyard near Thetford is a sign-post to what would have followed. Nothing is romanticized here. All is only what he saw. Yet it glows with the poetry of English summer, poignant for him in the knowledge that it might be his last (*Plate 35*).

Then again, in 1940, he had written: "I am just finishing the best portrait I've yet done . . . one of little Laura Ridley" (*Plate 42*). And there followed a run of portraits which reflect a new zeal. It is curious that several owners should have told me they possess "the only portrait he ever did", or else "the first" (painted, perhaps, during the

THE ANGELS OF MONS. The troops in Indian ink, the angels in pencil. Drawn in 1915, at the age of ten

XV

war). They will be surprised to learn that about fifty are recorded, in oils alone, and from all periods, not to mention some half a dozen self-portraits. I infer that he rather allowed this impression to be given, by way of insurance against failure. Many of his numerous pencil portraits are exquisite drawings—here his master was Ingres—and several times he hit off a striking success on canvas, especially in later years. But for certain revelation of soul—indeed of physical appearance—he had not the necessary detachment of the born portraitist. He was too sensitive to the quivering mental ray that issued from his sitter (or her relations). That is why he was at his best when least concerned—in the fine image of the master-cook, for example (*Plate 53*), or in his portraits of children. He not only loved children but remembered and imagined childhood intensely. In the portrait of little Rosanagh Crichton, propped up on pillows doing paper cut-outs during an illness, it is the poetry of the long day in bed that moves us (*Plate 50*).

English art is for ever approximating to poetry, and for my brother the tendency was not altogether unconscious. He regarded poetry as supreme, and I think would have preferred to be a poet. He once told me so. The English and American verse he admired meant as much to him as ever Milton to Samuel Palmer. I think he would have expressed the poetry in him more, and not less, as time went on. I think all his painting would have become freer in technique and richer in colouring, less often humorous, or with more subtle humour, less mannered, less and less harking back to the 18th century, or

THE FUSE FACTORY, LUTON. 1917. Memory of a visit: drawn at the age of twelve

any other past century. This could be called speculation. It is certain that he was only in the middle of his course, and had much to say that he had not yet said or imagined.

He was born in 1905. He made, to my knowledge, no single enemy, but warm innumerable friends at every period of his life and in all parts of society. He encountered a preparatory school at the age of eight, the army at the age of thirty-five. Both institutions were quite alien to his imaginative, detached, and sensitive nature. In both he was universally liked, even loved. He died fighting in Normandy, a troop commander in the Guards Armoured Division, on July 18th, 1944, his first morning in action. He was thirty-nine.

For his fertility the catalogue answers by its length. It concerns only the more notable work of twenty-one years, to the exclusion of countless decorated letters, half-minute sketches, and much else that many people think worth preserving: to the exclusion, too, of all juvenilia, except one example I capriciously admit.

I thank Mr. Ronald Fuller, my brother's close friend at Haileybury and afterwards, for undertaking to list the greater part of the printed works, and otherwise generally helping me in the task of compiling this catalogue; and for making the index.

L W

From *THE NEW KEEPSAKE*. Cat. no. 435

From *THE EMPEROR HEART*. Cat. no. 481

Signatures and Hand-writing

THE artist's first signature as a schoolboy was REX WHISTLER (wholly or partly written in capital letters). About 1917 he began to sign himself *Rex J. Whistler* (or occasionally *Rex John Whistler*), and this was the more favoured alternative throughout student days, though *Rex Whistler* might also be used. At the same period he used a neat cipher of *RJW* invented by himself, the capitals having shared strokes. This was most in evidence *c.* 1923–4. About 1926, however, he dropped his middle name, and then the same cipher was used for a very short time without the loop representing the *J*.

After 1926, when he was twenty-one, his full signature was always *Rex Whistler*—sometimes in careful calligraphy, often in his normal hand (or, when a brush was used, in a style approximating to that). His initials, from this time, were a simple *R.W.*, not in cipher. Occasionally the form *Rex W.* is found.

The presence or absence of a signature has little significance. Nearly half his finished works were not signed—among them some of those that pleased him most.

His hand-writing was more or less upright through adolescence, and until the latter part of 1926—the year he ceased to be a student and went to work on the Tate Gallery murals—when it began to show slope. By about 1929 it had arrived at the angle that would be habitual (though later signatures with a brush might be less inclined). In the same year it became smaller, finer, and less rounded, chiefly as the result of a change of pen. In place of a writing nib in a normal-sized holder he preferred to use from this time forward, for convenience, the same very fine drawing nib in a small holder which he employed in his art. By about 1930 his hand was mature, and thereafter would show only slight development. This refers to his everyday writing. He might on occasion, at any period, adopt a more mannered style.

In pen and ink, 1924

In oils   *In oils*

For further signatures, see page xxi and *Plates 14, 41, 64–66, 85, 86* and *88*, etc. For hand-writing of 1923 and 1941 see pages xx and xxi respectively. Decorated letters to Sir Osbert Sitwell and Christabel Lady Aberconway were reproduced in *Noble Essences or Courteous Revelations* by Sir Osbert Sitwell, 1950.

W. De la Mare

Peacock Pie

Who said "Peacock Pie"?
The Old King to the sparrow.
Who said "Crops are ripe"?
Rust to the Harrow.
Who said "Where sleeps she now?
Where rests she now her head
Bathed in Eve's Loveliness?"
          That's what I said

Who said; "Aye, mum's the word"
Sexton to Willow.
Who said; "Green dusk for dreams
Moss for a pillow."
Who said; "All Time's Delight
Hath she for narrow bed,
Life's troubled bubble broken"
          That's what I said

Page from *AN ANTHOLOGY OF MINE*, 1923. Cat. no. 288

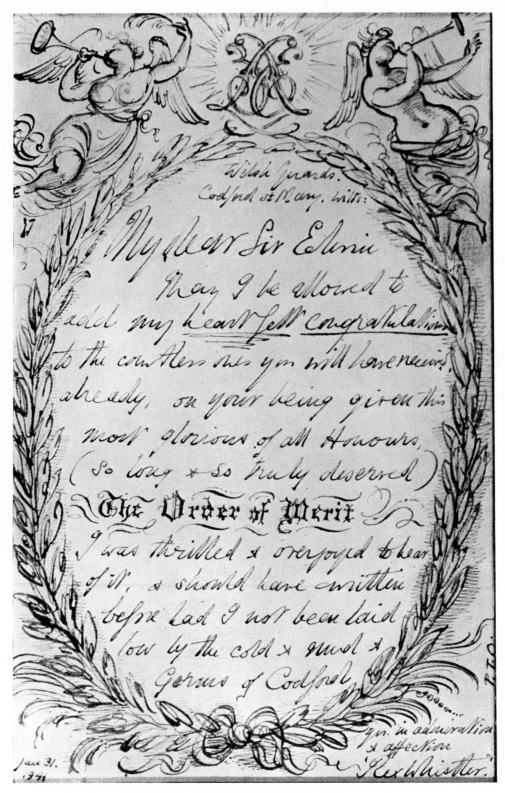

A LETTER TO SIR EDWIN LUTYENS, 1941

A REBUS LETTER TO LADY ROSE PAGET

xxii

From *HANS ANDERSEN*: 'Great Claus and Little Claus'. Cat. no. 475

A Note on the Illustrations

THE black and white plates are arranged as nearly as possible in chronological order within four separate groups:

Oil paintings, including murals
Portraits
Drawings, including illustrations to books
Designs for the theatre and cinema

A reference is given in each caption to the serial number of the work in the ensuing catalogue. Similar references will be found under the drawings reproduced in the text.

BACCHUS AND ARIADNE AFTER TITIAN. Cat. no. 665

1 SELF-PORTRAIT IN REGENT'S PARK, LONDON. Painted the day his uniform arrived:
before joining the Welsh Guards in 1940. Oil on canvas. Cat. no. 147

2 DORNEYWOOD, Buckinghamshire. Mural in the hall, for Sir Courtauld Thompson. 1928–1929. With a portrait bust of Sir Courtauld, and a medallion self-portrait. Oil on canvas. Cat. no. 3

3 THE TATE GALLERY RESTAURANT, LONDON. Departure scene in a series of murals encircling the room, entitled 'The Pursuit of Rare Meats'. 1927. Oil on canvas. Cat. no. 2

4 WESTON HALL, Northamptonshire. Mr. Sacheverell Sitwell
in the kitchen garden. 1929. Oil on canvas. Cat. no. 46

5 THE BUCKINGHAM ROAD IN THE RAIN. Near Whitchurch,
Buckinghamshire. ? 1936. Oil on canvas. Cat. no. 71

6 'THE TEMPLE OF REMUS', ROME. 1928. Oil on canvas. Cat. no. 33

7 'TIVOLI FROM THE ROAD'. 1929. Oil on canvas. Cat. no. 37

8 PORT LYMPNE, Kent. The main wall, showing real poles and tassels below painted tenting

9, 10 PORT LYMPNE, Kent. Painted room for Sir Philip Sassoon. 1930-1932. Oil on canvas and ceiling-plaster. General view, and detail of end-panel. Cat. no. 5

11 NO. 19 HILL ST., LONDON. Staircase mural for Mrs Euan Wallace. 1930-1931. Oil on canvas. Cat. no. 4

12 BROOK HOUSE, PARK LANE, LONDON. Painted room for Lady Louis Mountbatten. 1937.
Grisaille on a blue ground, with silver enrichments. Oil on canvas and plaster. Cat. no. 13

13 HADDON HALL, Derbyshire. For the Duke of Rutland. 1933. Oil on wood. Cat. no. 50

14 CRANBORNE MANOR, Dorset. 1935. Oil on canvas. Cat. no. 60

15 NO. 36 HILL ST., LONDON. Water-colour design for the panel opposite. Cat. no. 11

16 NO. 36 HILL ST., LONDON. One of eight mural panels

17, 18   NO. 36 HILL ST., LONDON.   Two of eight mural panels

19　NO. 36 HILL ST., LONDON.　One of eight mural panels for the Baroness Porcelli.　1936.
Oil on canvas.　Cat. no. 11

20 The Artist at work on the Plas Newydd murals

21 PLAS NEWYDD, Isle of Anglesey. The dining-room for the Marquis of Anglesey.
1936–1938. Cat. no. 12

22-24 PLAS NEWYDD

in the dining-room of the

Oil on canvas, and wall- and

Above: the main wall

To the left: part of the left-hand

the artist

To the right: part of the right

dogs on the steps

sle of Anglesey. Mural paintings

Marquis of Anglesey. 1936–1938.

eiling-surfaces. Cat. no. 12

2 ft 6 in x 47 ft

eturn wall, with a self-portrait of

gardener

and return wall, with the family

f the arcade

25 ULYSSES' FAREWELL. 1932-1933. For Sir Malcolm Bullock. Oil on canvas. Cat. no. 52

26 MOTTISFONT ABBEY, Hampshire. Pencil sketch for fireplace wall. Cat. no. 14

27 MOTTISFONT ABBEY, Hampshire. Trompe l'oeil niche and urn,
real and pretence ermine hangings, and the artist's candelabra

28 MOTTISFONT ABBEY, Hampshire. Alternative proposals for the fireplace wall. Grisaille landscape, and gold trophy. Pencil and water-colour. Cat. no. 14

29 MOTTISFONT ABBEY, Hampshire. Painted room for Mrs Gilbert Russell. 1938–1939. Oil on wall-surface. Cat. no. 14

30, 31 NO. 39 PRESTON PARK AVENUE, BRIGHTON, Sussex. 1944.
Below: 'Allegory: H.R.H. The Prince Regent awakening the Spirit of Brighton'.
Oil on wall–paper. Cat. no. 15

32 THE DAYE HOUSE, Wilton, Wiltshire. *c.* 1942. Oil on canvas. Cat. no. 93

33 CLAREMONT, Surrey. 1940. Oil on canvas. Cat. no. 87

34 THE DAYE HOUSE GATEWAY. Edith Olivier seated. 1940. Oil on canvas. Cat. no. 84

35 LANDSCAPE NEAR THETFORD, Norfolk.   With a self-portrait.   1943.   Oil on canvas.   Cat. no. 95

36 CONVERSATION PIECE AT THE DAYE HOUSE. 1937. Edith Olivier, Lord David Cecil,
Lady Ottoline Morrell and the artist (standing). Water-colour. Cat. no. 192

37 STUDIES FOR A STATUE-
FOUNTAIN. Blind-folded Eros
on a pedestal with a frieze of Cupids.
Undated. Pencil. Cat. no. 347

38 'DRAWN IN TRAIN TO
AULLA, MIDNIGHT'. In the
train from Rome. July 10th–11th,
1928. Pencil. Cat. no. 249

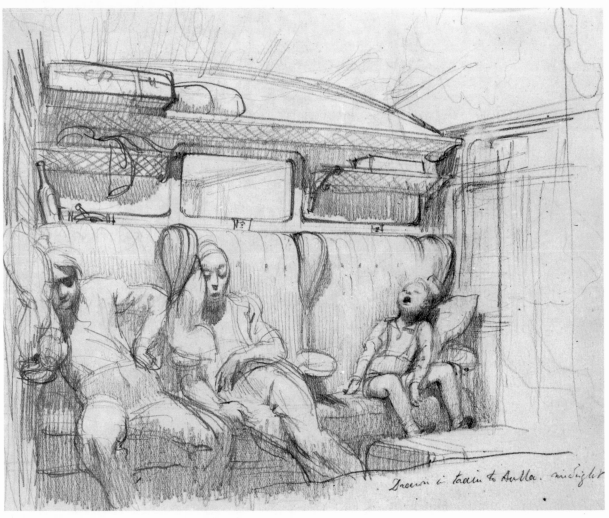

39 MR VALERIAN AND MISS ELIZABETH WELLESLEY
at Penns in the Rocks.   1932-1934.   Oil on canvas.   Cat. no. 105

40   MISS ANGELA AND MISS PENELOPE DUDLEY WARD. With a
self-portrait in the fountain mask.   1933-1934.   Oil on canvas.   Cat. no. 111

41   MISS PEGGY MORRISON.   1930.   Pencil.   Cat. no. 175

42   MISS LAURA RIDLEY AS A DRUMMER-BOY.   1940.   Oil on canvas.   Cat. no. 138

43   LAURENCE WHISTLER.   *c.* 1931.
Pencil.   Cat. no. 178

44   AN OLD LADY IN DEATH.   ? 1929.
Pencil.   Cat. no. 174

45   MISS ROSEMARY SALMOND.   1939.
Pencil.   Cat. no. 198

46   SIR WILLIAM WALTON.   1929.
Pencil.   Cat. no. 172

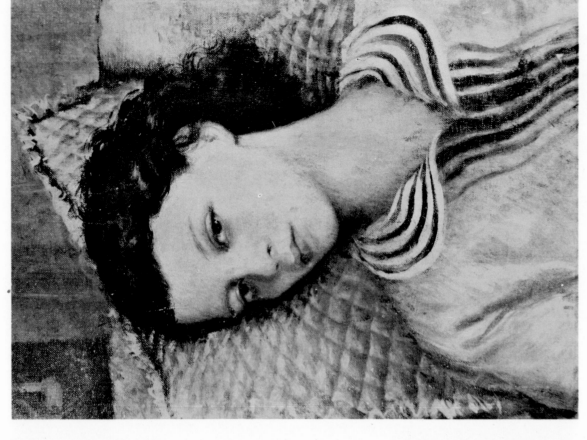

48 THE LADY CAROLINE PAGET. 1937.
Oil on canvas. Cat. no. 130

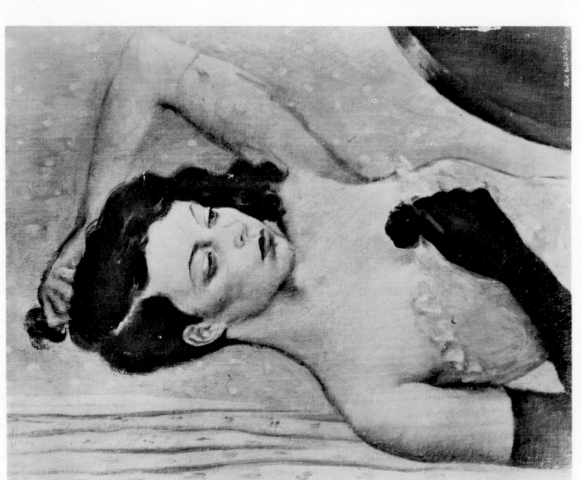

47 GIRL WITH A RED ROSE. 1935.
Oil on canvas. Cat. no. 120

49   IN THE WILDERNESS.   'As I was in the days of my youth. . .'   1939.   Oil on canvas.   Cat. no. 80

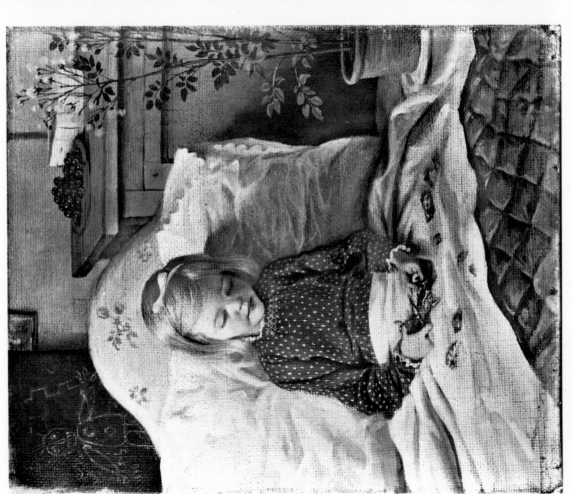

51 MISS ANNE McLAREN. 1940.
Oil on canvas. Cat. no. 140

50 MISS ROSANAGH CRICHTON. 1938.
Oil on canvas. Cat. no. 131

53 THE MASTER-COOK. ? 1941. Oil on canvas.
Cat. no. 153

52 JOCK LEWES, of the Special Air Service. 1940.
Oil on canvas. Cat. no. 150

54 SAMSON IN THE TEMPLE OF DAGON. 1928.
Sepia ink and Indian ink. Cat. no. 238

55-58   REJECTED DECORATIONS FOR *THE NEW FORGET-ME-NOT.*
1929.   Brown ink.   Cat. no. 419

59 'HIS MAJESTY'S BATH-CHAIR'. 1929. Sepia ink and wash. Cat. no. 254

60 THE MERMAID. *c.* 1935. Water-colour. Cat. no. 262

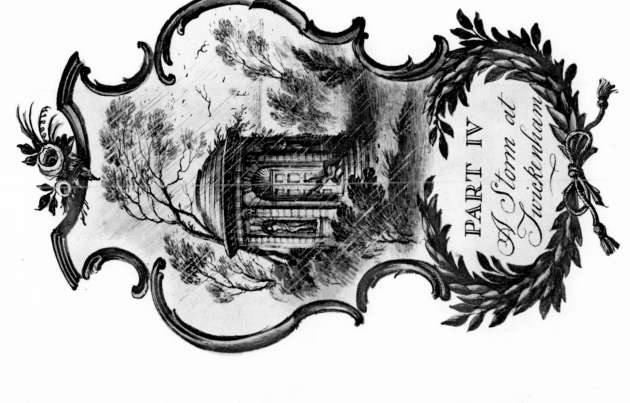

62 From *THE SILVER COLLAR BOY*
by C. Wright. 1934. Sepia ink and wash. Cat. no. 465

61 From *THE LORD FISH* by Walter de la Mare.
1933. Sepia ink and wash. Cat. no. 454

His Majesty
presents him with
fifty purses of two-
hundred Sprugs a-piece
together with his picture
at full length

63 ILLUSTRATION TO *GULLIVER'S TRAVELS*. 1930. Sepia pen and ink. Cat. no. 426

He screams as loud as
Fear can make him, where-
upon the huge Creature
at last espies him

Rex Whistler

64 ILLUSTRATION TO *GULLIVER'S TRAVELS.* 1930. Sepia pen and ink. Cat. no. 426

A·HERD·OF·ABOUT
FORTY·*Yahoos*·COME·
FLOCKING·ABOUT·HIM·
HOWLING·&·MAKING
·ODIOUS·FACES·

Rex Whistler 1930

65 ILLUSTRATION TO *GULLIVER'S TRAVELS*. 1930. Sepia pen and ink. Cat. no. 426

IN·THE·LOWEST·GALLERY·
HE·BEHOLDS·SOME·PEOPLE·
FISHING·WITH·LONG·ANGLING·
RODS·AND·OTHERS·
·LOOKING·ON·

66   ILLUSTRATION TO *GULLIVER'S TRAVELS*.   1930.   Sepia pen and ink.   Cat. no. 426

67 TAIL-PIECE TO *GULLIVER'S TRAVELS*. 1930. Sepia ink and wash. Cat. no. 426

68 HEAD-PIECE TO *GULLIVER'S TRAVELS*. Sepia ink and wash. Cat. no. 426

69 PROPOSED ALTERATIONS TO THE ARTIST'S HOME. Bolebec House. Whitchurch,
Buckinghamshire. *c.* 1934. Alterations to 'existing house' (between arrows). Water-colour. Cat. no. 331

70 IDEA FOR A LANDSCAPE GARDEN. *c.* 1933. Sepia ink and wash. Cat. no. 685

71-74 FOUR BOOKPLATES. Original drawings. Cat. nos 586, 587 (above); 600, 592 (below)

75 CLAVICHORD, made by Thomas Goff, and decorated for him by the artist.   Orpheus charming
the animals.   1939.   Oil on wood.   Cat. no. 356

76 DUST-WRAPPER. 1934. Indian ink and water-colour. Cat. no. 467

78 TEMPLE BAR. 1933. For Shell-Mex and B.P. Ltd.
Sepia ink and wash, heightened with white. Cat. no. 634

77 DECORATION in a book for Lord Herbert.
A view of Wilton. Water-colour. Cat. no. 531

80 FLY-LEAF INSCRIPTION in a
volume of Shakespeare. Sepia ink and
wash. Cat. no. 530

79 DECORATION in a book given by the artist to
the Queen (H.M. Queen Elizabeth the Queen Mother)
in 1938. Cat. no. 532

81 For *THE NEXT VOLUME*. 1932. Sepia. Cat. no. 441

82 For *THE NEXT VOLUME*. Sepia. Cat. no. 441

84 IN A VISITOR'S BOOK. 1935. Cat. no. 291

83 For *ARMED OCTOBER*. 1932. Cat. no. 442

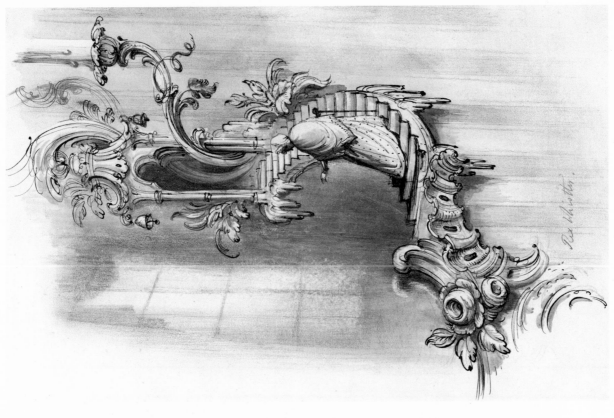

85, 86 ILLUSTRATIONS TO *THE LAST OF UPTAKE*
by Simon Harcourt-Smith. 1942.   Sepia ink and wash.   Cat. no. 499

87 BROOK HOUSE, LONDON.   Designs for panels C 7 and C 4.   1937.
Pencil and sepia wash.   Cat. no. 13

88 ILLUSTRATION TO *KONIGSMARK* by A. E. W. Mason. 1941.
Sepia ink and water–colour. Cat. no. 516

89, 90 BEFORE AND AFTER. The officers' Ante-room as it was (above) and as it might be (below). *c.* 1942. Sepia ink and wash. Cat. no. 669

91 FIDELIO.   1934. Scenery for Act II, Scene 1. Water-colour. Cat. no. 391

92   ? BALLERINA.   ? 1933.   Sepia ink and water-colour.   Cat. no. 372

93-96 THE RAKE'S PROGRESS. 1934. Costumes. Water-colour. Cat. no. 385

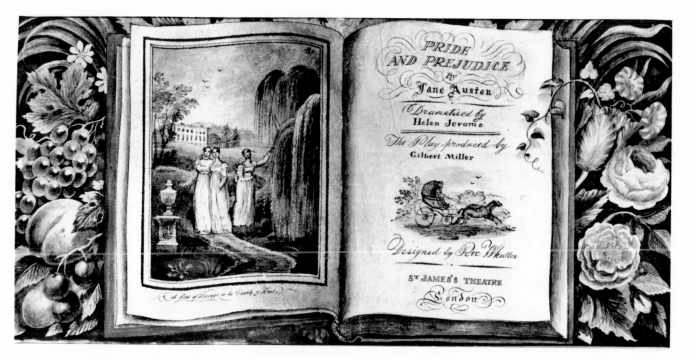

97 PRIDE AND PREJUDICE. 1936. Curtain. Water-colour. Cat. no. 376

98 THE HAPPY HYPOCRITE. 1935. Unused scene design. Water-colour. Cat. no. 408

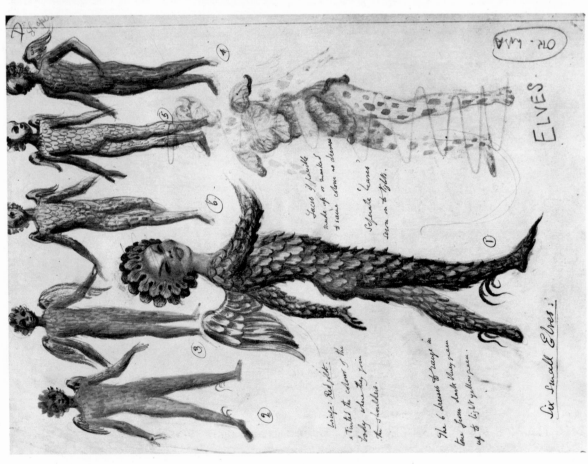

99, 100   THE TEMPEST.   1934.   Costumes for Elves and Iris.   Water-colour.   Cat. no. 374

101 LOVE FOR LOVE. 1943. Scenery for Act I, Scene 2: Sepia ink and water-colour. Cat. no. 381

102 PRIDE AND PREJUDICE. 1936. Scenery for Act II, Scene 3. Lady Catherine's drawing-room. Water-colour. Cat. no. 376

103   THE RAKE'S PROGRESS.   1942.   Curtain.   Sepia ink and wash.   Cat. no. 385

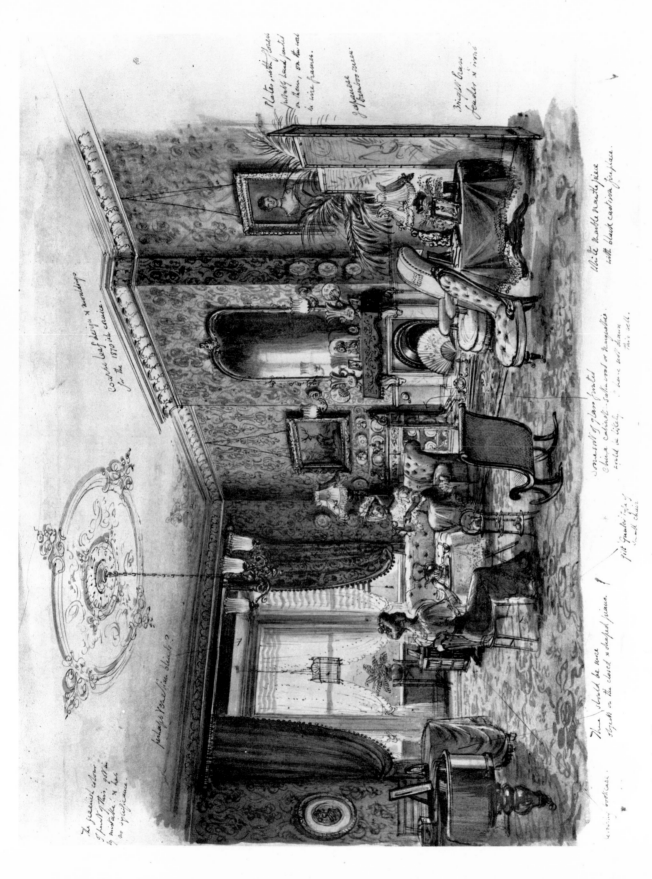

104   For the film, A PLACE OF ONE'S OWN.   1944.   Sepia ink and wash.   Cat. no. 412.   See also back end-paper

105   THE WISE VIRGINS.   1940.   Curtain.   Water-colour.   Cat. no.   387

106   VICTORIA REGINA.   1935.   Scenery for Act II, Scene 1.   Water-colour.   Cat. no. 375

107   LE SPECTRE DE LA ROSE.   1944.   Scenery.   Water-colour.   Cat. no. 390

108   AN IDEAL HUSBAND.   1943.   Scenery for Act III.   Water-colour.   Cat. no. 382

109, 110 COSTUME DESIGNS. Left—for LE SPECTRE DE LA ROSE. 1944. The girl's ball-dress. Water-colour.
Cat. no. 390. Right—for AN IDEAL HUSBAND. 1943. Lady Chiltern, Act II. Water-colour. Cat. no. 382

111   LE SPECTRE DE LA ROSE.   1944.   Curtain.   Water-colour.   Cat. no. 390

112   THE SLEEPING PRINCESS.   Programme for Royal Command
Performance, 1939.   Sepia wash on white scraper board (with embossed border
as printed).   Cat. no. 386

A Note on the Catalogue

OUR purpose has been to record all the artist's work of any consequence, and only this: not excluding, however, sketches, though slight, which have bearing on significant work.

An ADDITIONAL CATALOGUE will be placed in the Victoria and Albert Museum, London, for revision from time to time. It will contain minor sketches, decorated letters, etc., together with juvenilia (here defined as work before 1923, the year when the artist was eighteen, and a student). It will also contain corrections and additions to the printed catalogue which follows. Information will be welcome, especially information concerning works at present unknown, untraced, or unidentified.

In MEASUREMENTS, the vertical is always given first. With work on paper, the size is that of the sheet, not necessarily that of the drawing or water-colour itself.

With PORTRAITS, the description "facing half-left", like "left profile", implies the view-point of the beholder, not the sitter.

With WORK FOR THE THEATRE, all the recorded designs for each production are listed. If medium, size, and signature are not given, the whereabouts of the original drawing is not known.

Similarly, with PRINTED WORK, all known reproductions are listed; and medium and signature are only given when the original has been examined.

Original drawings for reproduction are not described when they carry their own identification in lettering (for example, dust-wrapper designs).

When a sequence of works is in single ownership, the owner's name appears after the last.

TITLES AND INSCRIPTIONS IN INVERTED COMMAS are those written by the artist himself—where another source is not named.

L W : R F

The Emperor walked under his high canopy in the midst of the Procession.

From *HANS ANDERSEN*: 'The Emperor's New Clothes'. Cat. no. 475

Murals
and Related Drawings

1   **THE HIGHWAYS CLUB,**   *1924–*
          SHADWELL   *1925*

PANELS AND PROSCENIUM ARCH IN MEMORIAL HALL
Oil on canvas and oil on board.   *Unsigned*

In the early nineteen-twenties, Professor Henry Tonks at the Slade was full of enthusiasm for mural painting. He had a small sum of money at his disposal which he was enabled to spend on an experiment at this Club, setting two of his most promising pupils to work, Rex Whistler and Miss Mary Adshead (now Mrs. Stephen Bone). Two bays were painted by the artist, and three smaller spaces by Miss Adshead. A proscenium arch was built, and this was decorated by the former alone. When the money ran out at an early stage, Sir Joseph Duveen (Lord Duveen) was approached; and he paid for the completion of the scheme. So impressed was he by the artist's work here that he suggested and willingly paid for the much larger scheme which shortly followed: in the Tate Gallery Restaurant.

(1) THE 1924 PANELS   *12 ft. × 7 ft. 5 in.*

The general theme of this pair of panels, in the words of *The Times* critic, was "people enjoying themselves in the country". In both we see music and dancing; in one, outside a half-timbered country house; in the other, near a bridge. Tonks had written to Sir Augustus Daniel, "Whistler I must set about painting the East end; he would set them dancing."

The figures in both panels are in more or less contemporary dress, which the painter afterwards avoided in his murals until the late nineteen-thirties. *The Times* critic saw the neighbourhood of Pinner in the "landscape of sandy hills" depicted—knowing perhaps of the Club's camp-site there. But the artist himself had Hampstead Heath in mind.

(2) THE 1925 PROSCENIUM ARCH WALL
Painted area: each side of arch: 10 ft. 10 in. × 6 ft. 5 in.
above arch: 4 ft. 4 in. × 18 ft. 4 in.

The themes to left and right were Comedy and Tragedy, respectively: otherwise, Summer and Winter. To the left there was song and dance against a mountainous background, which began to show Italian influence. (The artist had spent the winter abroad.) The guitar-player was to some extent a caricature of Professor Tonks. To the right there was a disconsolate group against a snowy landscape, with Death laying hands on a young man—the artist's friend and fellow-student, Stephen Tennant.

From a central cartouche, supported by a female and a male figure holding masks of Comedy and Tragedy respectively, looped swags extended above the proscenium arch to a Unicorn and a Lion at either end, each animal being teased by a couple of cherubs. These heraldic beasts might have been more appropriate if the Royal Arms had been displayed in the centre, as he originally intended; but the cartouche, though topped with the Crown, displayed the crest of "The Highways Club Incorporated". It is only in this top decoration that we see the emergence of the (first) "Rex Whistler manner".

The canvases were removed during and after the war, and have recently been presented to University College, London, in whose precincts they were mostly painted.

DESIGNS FOR THE ABOVE   *1925*

The artist's 1925 Sketch-book (no. 290) is full of ideas for the proscenium arch wall. Several studies and scale drawings also survive, as follows.

(1) PROSCENIUM ARCH WALL
Pencil, Indian ink and water-colour.   *1 ft. 4 in. × 2 ft. 7 in.*
Unsigned

The Royal Arms above (without cherubs); an early idea for the dancers on the left; a pencil sketch only of a death-scene on the right.

(2) PROSCENIUM ARCH WALL
Indian ink and water-colour.   *1 ft. × 4 in. × 2 ft. 7 in.*
Signed: Rex J. Whistler

Much as carried out.

(3) CHARCOAL STUDIES
One, 2 ft. × 4 ft. 5 in. Eight, 1 ft. 5 in. × 11 in.   *Unsigned*

Eight studies from models for the supporting figures: the cupid, the dancing boy, and the Unicorn (a Parthenon horse); and a large-scale drawing for the panel above the arch (3 in. to 1 ft.).

(4) STUDIES FOR LION, UNICORN, AND CHERUBS
Sepia ink and water-colour.   *Approx. 11 in. × 10 in.*
Owner: Laurence Whistler

2   **THE TATE GALLERY**   *1926–1927*
          RESTAURANT
"THE PURSUIT OF RARE MEATS"
Oil on canvas.   *Main walls: 8 ft. × 54 ft.*   *End walls:*
8 ft. × 32 ft.   *Signed on frieze of painted portico:* . . . Rex
Whistler fecit.   (*Plate 3*)

About 1925 Sir Joseph Duveen, as part of a scheme to help

promising British painters, offered £500 for the decoration of the Tate Gallery Restaurant, and on Professor Tonks' recommendation the commission was given to Rex Whistler. He submitted sketches in Mar. 1926 and worked continuously during the next 18 months. Even so, the mural was not quite finished on the opening day (Nov. 30th, 1927), and thus it remains. It was flooded to a depth of 8 ft. soon after completion, but escaped serious damage—on account of the wax medium employed, it was thought.

"Rex and I", says Edith Olivier, "once had the idea of writing a guide to the picture in the form of a child's story, and we made a first sketch of this, the people and places being given punning or anagrammatic names." *A Guide to the Duchy of Epicurania with some Account of the Famous Expedition In Pursuit of Rare Meats as described by Edith Olivier* was published by the Tate Gallery in 1954; with an illustrated brochure summarizing the story.

At the extreme left of the long North wall, opposite the windows, the party is shown setting forth from the portico of the Ducal Palace, below a frieze inscribed with school-boy Latin, supplied to the artist by Ronald Fuller: *Haec domus pulcherrima aedificata est anno Domini MCMXXVII Rex Whistler fecit.* They depart gaily on horseback and bicycle and in a bright red cart, to reappear by a romantic sea-shore, and pass through a small jungle crowded with wild beasts. They call at a water-mill, below which a small boy is drowning, and so reach the ruined Palace of Joisigonne (an anagram for Inigo Jones), whose Palladian Bridge is at first mistaken by one of them for that at Wilton, though ruined. At this point the landscape is interrupted by the Restaurant entrance in the East wall, which the artist has transformed into a ruined gateway with two gross caryatides symbolizing Greed. The three round-arched windows on the South wall are rather similarly treated: one becoming involved in the Great Wall of China, while another becomes a mermaids' cave. Between these are the bridges and pagodas of Cathay. On the high edge of one cliff they find a broken cross inscribed with "D.A.W." in memory of some earlier traveller who fell by the way, and this they replace with a handsome urn on a pedestal. The initials are those of the artist's elder brother Denny, who died in childhood.

The landscape between this central window and the right-hand one is the least completed, and the travellers do not appear in it. But the end wall shows the sunlit return to Epicurania. To the left of the door a park is entered through a great Corinthian arch, inspired by the arch at Stowe; and the grounds are adorned with fountains and statues. The red cart bowls along a winding road in the middle distance, now laden with spoils. In the foreground an old gardener turns his back on his posturing son, who has fallen in love with a statue of Venus. In the background we discover one of the two Boycott Pavilions at Stowe (which the artist also introduced in the background of the Tate self-portrait, no. 107). The doorway in the middle of this wall has become the entrance to a stone belvedere. Dolphins spout into the basin at its foot, and in a pair of niches there are busts—the right-hand one a likeness of Professor Tonks. And so to the right-hand corner, and the city again, where a reception awaits the travellers in front of a triumphal arch. Departure and arrival thus occupy the

same corner of the room, whose angle is ingeniously countered and concealed by the two perspectives of the painted architecture. The artist's former assistant, Victor Bowen, carried out restorations in 1949.

Photographs in *The Times*, Dec. 1st; *The Illustrated London News*, Dec. 30th; *The Queen*, Dec. 7th; *Country Life*, Dec. 10th; and *The Sphere*, Dec. 10th, 1927.

DESIGNS FOR THE ABOVE MURAL   1926

What is almost certainly the artist's earliest idea, formed during his first visit to the room, may be seen in his 1925 Sketch-book (no. 290). On one page there is a sketch-plan giving measurements; and opposite this a perspective view of the bare walls, with plain metal stanchions down the centre of the room. Above this we have a proposal for the main wall, showing separate views into a landscape, divided by architectural features containing statues in niches.

Several other sketches exist.

(1) *Sepia ink and wash, with touches of water-colour, 8 in. × 11 in. Unsigned.*
A carefully executed sketch for the departure scene, very closely agreeing with the final painting and squared out for enlargement.
Owner: Laurence Whistler

(2) *Water-colour, 1 ft. 8 in. × 2 ft. Unsigned.*
A finished drawing for the departure scene, as carried out.   *Owner: Mrs. W. H. Elliott*

(3) *Pencil and water-colour, 1 ft. 6 in. × 2 ft. 4 in. Unsigned.*
A set of four consecutive drawings, accounting for the entire main wall opposite the windows, partly squared out for enlargement and copiously annotated and altered in pencil by the artist.

(4) "WALL AT THE KITCHEN END OF REFRESHMENT ROOM." *Indian ink and water-colour, 10½ in. × 1 ft. 9½ in. Unsigned.*
Roughly as carried out, but with architectural treatment of doorway different, and scene of arrival only sketchily conceived as yet.

(5) "DESIGN FOR BUILDINGS ON LEFT." *Sepia ink, 8¼ in. × 5¼ in. Unsigned.*
Careful sketch for top of portico and cupola, etc. Reproduced in *Rex Whistler*, by Laurence Whistler, 1948 (no. 510), p. 84.

(6) "DESIGN FOR PAINTING ON COLUMNS." *Water-colour, 1 ft. 1¼ in. × 7 in. Unsigned.*
Showing chinoiserie treatment (not adopted) of the slatted wooden columns provided by the architect to conceal the central stanchions. Instead, the artist painted gilded suns round the necks of the columns.

(7) SKETCHES OF THE ENTIRE ROOM. *Sepia ink. 4 sheets: 6 in. × 2 ft. 7½ in. 1 sheet: 6 in. × 8 in. Unsigned.*
A visual memorandum, made while the artist and Edith Olivier were collaborating over the story of the murals, and covered with notes of the characters, and the features they pass.   *Owner: Laurence Whistler*

HALL AT   *1928–1929*
DORNEYWOOD, BUCKS

Oil on canvas.   6 ft. 9 in. × 6 ft. 9 in.   Signed in medallion:
Rex Whistler pinxit Anno Domini MCMXXVIII.
(*Plate 2*)

The mural is on the wall of the porch facing the hall, and consists of a landscape framed by a Corinthian portico with a square and a round column on each side. On the frieze, as though carved in gold lettering, are the words: "AVE SILVAE DORNII". The view beyond is of an imaginary formal garden, in which Flora appears barefoot, approaching the steps, crowned with flowers and holding a cornucopia. She is accompanied by a naked winged Cupid, who looks in alarm at the dog, "Spot", asleep on the terrace. Flora and Cupid have, in fact, descended from the Corinthian column in the centre of the garden, on the top of which they appear in almost exactly the same attitudes. This column and the triple-arched loggia beyond are copied from those at Wilton. The garden abounds in urns and statues, and to the left may be seen two Edwardian figures playing croquet. Beyond the garden wall and surrounding trees we catch a glimpse of Windsor Castle and the River Thames.

On the left side of the portico a red curtain is looped back to reveal a parrot's cage, and falls across a bust of Lord Courtauld-Thomson (then Sir Courtauld Thomson,) which stands on a gilt rococo bracket. On the answering square column to the right the artist has painted a medallion containing a profile self-portrait, facing left; it seems to hang from a nail by a piece of knotted string. Round the medallion is the date and signature, as above.

An early photograph proves that some repainting took place, possibly after the artist's return from Rome. Originally a different dog, on a lead, was shown leaping towards the visitors; the terrace was paved with stone, not black and white marble; there was no inscription on the frieze; and Lord Courtauld-Thomson's bust was differently conceived.

Presented to the nation by Lord Courtauld-Thomson in 1942. Photographs in *Country Life*, Dec. 7th, 1951, p. 1894.

"DESIGN FOR SIR COURTAULD *1928* THOMSON'S PANEL, DORNEYWOOD"
Pencil, ink, and water-colour.   7¾ in. × 9¾ in.   Unsigned

Very much as carried out, with sketches and notes in the margin.   *Owner: Miss K. E. Alexander*

ROUGH SKETCH   *1928*
(Approximately as carried out)
Sepia ink and wash.   7 in. × 9 in.   Unsigned

No figures. A basket of flowers where the dog would eventually be. Steps up into the view, of which the lowest step would be real.   *Owner: Laurence Whistler*

EARLY DESIGNS FOR THE   *1928*
ABOVE
Sepia ink and water-colour.   (1) 9 in. × 7½ in.
(2) 5 in. × 9½ in.   *Unsigned*

Two early designs giving the wall a more architectural treatment, with a narrow view through an archway into a romantic countryside. A pair of engaged Corinthian columns flanks the arch, with a grotesque mask for keystone. The arch would not be carried lower than dado level, beneath which there would be a real semicircular plinth painted with a medallion below swags. In one sketch the medallion contains a profile of Lord Courtauld-Thomson; in the other the letters "C.T.". On the latter there is an additional ink drawing of the plinth, showing a hat and gloves resting on it.   *Owner: Laurence Whistler*

"URNS FOR THE PEDESTALS   *1928*
IN SIR COURTAULD'S PANEL"
Pencil.   10 in. × 8 in.   Unsigned

Sketch for the balcony urns, showing how the design is formed on several circles. At the top left, a smaller sketch of the same.   *Owner: Laurence Whistler*

4   STAIRCASE HALL,   *1930–1931*
19 HILL STREET, LONDON

Oil on canvas.   11 ft. × 21 ft.   Signed: Rex Whistler *on leaf of open book.   (Plate 11)*

Painted for Captain and Mrs. Euan Wallace on the wall immediately above the staircase. The whole foreground consists of a paved terrace between two classical columns, with a romantic landscape beyond. Against the left-hand column leans a Cupid, eating an apple, his quiver and bow in the corner beside him. The right-hand column is creeper-clad. Here the artist painted a large spider, to amuse the children of the family. While they were absent, it moved a foot or two to the lower part of the shaft, where it remains to this day. A table stands to the left of the terrace, on which is a bowl of fruit and an open book. On the left-hand page the artist has written: "Rex Whistler painted this picture. Begun in June, finished in December." Near by is a canvas on an easel, with palette and brushes left on the pavement not far from a heap of dead leaves. A pair of urns marks the break in the terrace parapet. Against the right-hand one, a negro servant in crimson and gold livery leans elegantly: beside him a tray with decanter and glasses. To the left a river, flowing from a mountainous sky-line, winds past a distant town, with dome and spire reminiscent of Oxford, and so under a bridge. In the centre is a fountain with an ornamental stone basin, beyond which two figures in hunting costume are debating which direction they should take. Other horsemen gallop over a low bridge and round the base of a tree-crowned rock. Behind it stands an overgrown octagonal pavilion, and a water-mill. An old man with sciatica brings food to a dog.

The artist mentioned the mural in a letter to Lady Aberconway on Feb. 17th, 1931, when it was "almost finished. . . . It's painted in rather my old boring way with horses all like this [sketch of horses prancing] and all the trees forming the same sort of composition [sketch of crossed trees] with this *sort of foliage*. . . ." Photographs in *Decoration*, no. 32, 1932; *Country Life*, Sept. 1st, 1944.

Owner: Felix Fenston, Esq.

DESIGN FOR THE ABOVE 1930

Water-colour. 1 ft. 1½ in. × 1 ft. 9½ in. Unsigned

Very much as carried out, but lacking the dotard and other details. Probably the final drawing.

Owner: Billy Wallace, Esq.

SKETCH FOR THE ABOVE 1930

Pencil and water-colour. 10 in. × 1 ft. 2½ in. Unsigned

Roughly as carried out, but with the negro footman by the left-hand column, one very large urn beyond the right-hand column, a classical portico instead of the octagonal pavilion, and lacking many of the final details.

PROPOSAL FOR THE UPPER 1930 STAIRCASE HALL

Sepia ink and water-colour, heightened with white

A first proposal for painting all four walls and ceiling. In the event, only the Staircase Wall was painted (as above —not as here proposed).

(1) The Staircase Wall. *11 in. × 1 ft. 2½ in. Unsigned.*
Three painted arches with imposts, revealing (in pencil only) a romantic landscape beyond the terrace, with horsemen, not unlike the final conception.

(2) The East Wall opposite. *11 in. × 1 ft. 2½ in. Unsigned.*
A heavily baroque door-case with a bust in a roundel. Flanking it, and again on the extreme right, three gesturing statues on curving pedestals, labelled "Juno", "Paris", "Minerva".★ Between the last two, an answering pedestal supporting an urn full of flowers, beneath another bust in a similar roundel. Note by the artist: "The canopy above door, the two circular niches and the pedestals to be painted in *grisaille*, i.e. in tones, lighter & darker of the general colour of the wall. The sculpture: figures & busts & the rococo plaques on the pedestals painted to represent marble or light stone. Everything to be *painted*, except the Cornice (& possibly architecture of door). Door to be painted a certain green to imitate the *patina on a bronze door*. Flowers to be realistic. Vases green patina bronze, festooned with ribbon."

(3) The South Wall, the North (Window) Wall, the Ceiling. *1 ft. 9 in. × 1 ft. 3 in. Unsigned.*
On the South Wall, three arches with a central bust between medallions above them. Between the two windows the statue of Venus on a pedestal, receiving the crown from two cherubs.★ A coffered ceiling, with the letters "E.W." every way, and an ellipse of sky in the centre. For a slightly earlier use of the "Judgment

★ Reproduced in *Restoration Love Songs*, ed. John Hadfield, 1950, opp. pp. 1 and 113.

of Paris" theme, see the proposal for the bedroom of Lady Castlerosse, abandoned, at 14 Culross Street (no. 16).

Owner: Laurence Whistler

5 DINING-ROOM AT 1930–1932 PORT LYMPNE, KENT

Oil on canvas and ceiling plaster. Length: 22 ft. 1 in. Breadth: 17 ft. 2 in. Height (painted walls): 9 ft. Signed in painted medallion over entrance arch: A.D. MCMXXXI Rex Whistler pinxt. (Plates 8–10)

Commissioned by Sir Philip Sassoon in 1930. The final design beautifully accounts for the triple-curved shape of the existing ceiling, and treats the entire room as the interior of a marquee made of blue and white striped silk, through the openings of which various scenes appear. The canvas on the main wall is therefore interrupted by two actual blue and white striped tent-poles, with real tassels hanging above. We see a townscape, where a lady of quality drives in an open carriage from her country estate to visit a friend, who observes her approach from a balcony. Her black footman is knocking on the entrance gates. Beside him on the wall is a poster (Indian ink and water-colour on paper, stuck to the canvas), a miniature of that for The Four Georges Exhibition. The time, on a cupola clock, reads 4.45. Next door is a Bluecoat School, where scholars at an upper window watch the approach of their aged pedagogue. The lady has just crossed a Palladian bridge like that at Wilton. The town, here, is almost entirely English Georgian with echoes of St.-Martin-in-the-Fields, Park Lane, and the Boycott Pavilions at Stowe. Many typical figures—red-coat soldier, nurse, etc.—are about, including M. Stulik at the door of "La Tour Eiffel", a restaurant often visited by the artist, in Charlotte St.

The arched entrances at both ends of the room are treated as architectural features abutting on the marquee. One is flanked by terminal figures derived from those actually in front of the house (bought from Stowe). On each side, tent-openings reveal a landscape continuing the one already described. The river winds on past a church of un-English baroque, towards which a bishop advances at the head of a surpliced procession. It continues past a Georgian mansion (no doubt the lady of quality's home) reminiscent of Faringdon, the country house of the artist's friend, Lord Berners. In the park a lady in full mourning leans on a pedestal of an urn inscribed "In Memoriam". On this side, a lady and a little boy wait for the paddle-steamer, with a trunk lettered "B" under a coronet.

Beside the opposite entrance arch we are looking down a prodigious garden vista after Le Notre, with a canal, fountains and statuary. Between two windows on the fourth (long) wall, there is a *trompe l'œil* map, hung from real cords and tassels, and described in gilded cartouches as "An inaccurate Plan of Port Lympne. . . . Drawn but not Measured . . . MCMXXXI", "The Scale" is given, but is "Most inaccurate and Quite Useless". Beside and below each window is a trophy: in one, a Roman standard, "S.P.Q.R."—crossed by an axe bound in fasces, labelled "VIVA LENIN ANNO IX". Here, as on the ceiling, the tenting material appears to sag naturally, and it exactly agreed in texture and colour with the actual window curtains originally provided. Tassels hang from the ceiling, where, as if embroidered, there is a large cipher of "P.S.".

The house has been long unoccupied, and the mural is in a very poor state, awaiting restoration.

Photographs in *Country Life*, Feb. 4th, 1933, and Sept. 1st, 1944, and in *The Artist*, Nov. 1935.

Owner: Colonel A. C. R. Waite

SEVEN DESIGNS FOR THE ABOVE   *1930*

Water-colour. Nos. 1–4: 6 in.× 1 ft. 1¼ in.   *Unsigned*

(1) "Left-hand wall (Opposite windows)"
Very much as carried out, but lacking several figures, and some of the distant buildings. Reproduced in *The Artist*, Nov. 1935.

(2) "Dais Room end. (Facing you on entering)"
Central feature very much as carried out, but a little wider, thus reducing the landscapes. In the left-hand one, no bishop and choir. In the right-hand one, a waterfall among rocks (replaced by the Georgian house).

(3) "Entrance (from Hall)"
Central feature and right-hand view very much as carried out. But the left-hand view is of a narrow street curving beyond a classical front (replaced by the garden vista).

(4) "Window wall (Upon your Right on entering)"
Very much as carried out.

(5) "Design for the Ceiling." *9½ in.× 1 ft. 1½ in.*
Almost precisely as carried out.

(6) Design for a central lampshade. *7 in.× 8 in.*
In the same tenting material.

(7) Design for the two martial trophies below the windows. *10 in.× 11 in.*   *Owner: Laurence Whistler*

DISCARDED PROPOSALS FOR THE ABOVE

SCHEME I (involving terminal figures)

FOUR SKETCHES   *? 1930*

Sepia ink and water-colour, 11 in.× 1 ft. 1 in.   *Unsigned*

(1) Main Wall
A romantic landscape with a domed and towered town, and galloping horsemen: interrupted by four large terminal figures, painted as if supporting the ceiling of the room. The arms of the figures were originally raised to their heads, but have been expunged, as if thought too prominent in the design.

(2) a. "End Wall. Steps up to Dais room"
The archway flanked by two terminal figures on each side, supporting an entablature and broken baroque pediment. The space between each pair of figures to be filled by a plain rusticated wall or a vase of flowers on a pedestal.
b. "End wall. Entrance from Hall"
The archway flanked by Corinthian columns under baroque entablatures. Two side-arches revealing landscapes, one with a tent-like temple.

(3) Window Wall
The two windows flanked by four terminal figures almost equally spaced. In the centre space a painted niche filled by an urn on a baroque pedestal. Two cherubs supporting a medallion with a profile portrait of Sir Philip Sassoon.

This baroque scheme was probably abandoned because the twelve terminal figures would prove oppressively heavy.

SCHEME II

FIVE SKETCHES   *? 1930*
Unsigned

(1) "Side Wall. Opposite windows." *Sepia ink and wash. 11 in.× 1 ft. 3 in.*
A continuous landscape. Certain features anticipate the final design, e.g. a bridged river and a church with tower and portico.

(2) *Pencil Sketch (on Port Lympne writing-paper). 5 in.× 8 in.*
The entire end wall treated as an architectural feature—with a distant townscape through the entrance arch (presumably to be painted on the far wall of the adjoining room). A coffered ceiling, as if open to the sky in centre. A romantic landscape along the main wall.

(3) "End Wall. Arch (upstairs) into Dais room." *Sepia ink and wash. 11 in.× 1 ft. 1½ in.*
The archway supported by two terminal figures, with walls curving down from imposts to pedestals.

(4) Ceiling. *Pencil. 11 in.× 1 ft. 1½ in.*
Sketch on the reverse of *I*(2) b, "Entrance from Hall": showing centre of the ceiling as vine-clad rafters open to the sky.

(5) End Wall. *Indian ink and wash. 11 in.× 1 ft. 1½ in.*
Sketch on the reverse of *I* (2) a, "Steps up to Dais room": a central arch flanked by smaller ones. Incomplete and partly erased.   *Owner: Laurence Whistler*

6   WALL-PAPER FOR   *1932* 12 NORTH AUDLEY STREET, LONDON

Oil on canvas.   *6 ft.× 5 ft. 1 in.*   *Signed, bottom left:*
Rex Whistler 1932

Mr. Samuel Courtauld bought in Bath a chinoiserie wall-paper which did not quite cover the walls of his bedroom. The artist provided the missing section, above the chimney-piece, taking over the pattern and bringing it to a crescendo as a frame to Picasso's *L'Enfant au Pigeon*.

Owner: Christabel Lady Aberconway

DESIGNS FOR THE ABOVE   *1932*

Sepia ink and water-colour.   *Unsigned*

(1) *7¼ in.× 4¾ in.* Very much as carried out. Oriental birds flying up with looped drapery; caged birds below on each side; and above, in the centre, a cipher of "S.C.".

(2) *10 in.× 1 ft. 2 in.* With monkeys replacing the caged birds and the cipher. Showing part of the existing wall on each side.   *Owner: Laurence Whistler*

7　RESTORATION OF CEILING　*1933*
AT WILTON HOUSE, SALISBURY

In Nov. 1933 the artist restored parts of the ceiling in the Double Cube at Wilton, painted by [?] Emanuel de Critz and Edward Pierce *c.* 1653. He wrote to Lord Herbert, "I was absolutely fascinated, first by that strange and lovely *view* that one gets—from such a high platform—of that glorious room, and then by being able to examine so closely the paintings and to see to my surprise how roughly and grandly the old chaps had slapped the paint on up there—which looks so finely finished when walking in the room far below!"

8　DRAWING-ROOM AT　*1935*
90 GOWER STREET, LONDON
Oil on wall surface

The artist designed for Mr (afterwards Sir) Duff and Lady Diana Cooper seven *trompe l'œil* decorations, mainly in grisaille. These consisted of four circular plaques, painted with appropriate shadows, two apparent mezzotints, and a jug which seems to stand in a niche.

(1) FOUR CIRCULAR PLAQUES
2 ft. 2 in. diameter

Each plaque contains two or three classical figures, as if in relief. High on the wall, they seemed to hang from gold-tasselled cords: one on each side of the chimney-piece, one on the wall opposite, and one in the centre of the third wall, facing the windows, above the niche with the jug.

(2) TWO PRETENCE MEZZOTINTS
2 ft. 8 in. × 2 ft. 5 in.
Signed, bottom right on each as if by the engraver: Rex Whistler pinxit et sculpsit. MCMXXXV

These seemed to hang on the wall, opposite the fireplace, with one of the circular plaques above and between them. Each appeared to be suspended on thin cords from a pair of crossed gilded arrows, and to be held smooth by horizontal rods at top and bottom, finished with four little gilded pine-apples.

Diana provides the theme for both pictures. In the one to the left, entitled "Offrande à Diane", the artist is at his nearest to his beloved Poussin: a small altar smokes with an offering made by the chaste nymphs to their goddess; to the right is a ruinous triumphal arch, to the left graceful trees, and in the far distance a river winding among hills. The right-hand picture, entitled "Diane Chasseresse", was perhaps thought of as a Claude. The nymphs and their hounds run out from the right, with bows and spears, in front of tree-crowned rocks; on further rocks to the left stands a ruined circular temple, and a waterfall tumbles in sunlight to the stream winding at their feet. Romantic woods and mountains are glimpsed in the distance.

(3) A JUG IN A NICHE
4 ft. 6 in. × 2 ft. 2 in.

A tall Greek jug with classical figures as if carved in relief round the bowl, and a serpent handle. It is difficult to believe, except on close inspection, that the neck and lip of the jug have not been broken in several places and riveted. The artist referred to this accident in an undated letter (partly quoted in the *Sunday Times* for May 11th, 1958) to Lady Diana, who was about to return and view the work. He spoke of "the *big stone milk jug* (you will see that, most unfortunately, a housemaid knocked it over, one day, & the neck & handle got broken, but I got it well rivetted [*sic*] so I hope you won't notice it much. The silly girl tried to lift it by the handle, but of course it must *never* be lifted by that handle, its only for ornament." Photographs in the *Sunday Times*, May 4th, 1958; and in *The Light of Common Day*, by Lady Diana Cooper (1959), opp. p. 80.

The seven decorations belong to University College, and will presently be re-erected there. They were recently removed from the house, before demolition, with the plaster on which they were painted, but have been seriously damaged by cleaning.

9　DECORATED CHIMNEY-PIECE *1935*
AT 5 BELGRAVE SQUARE
Oil on wall surface.　*c. 9 ft. × 5 ft.*　*Unsigned*

A female figure in classical draperies leans on an urn above a slender pedestal, a wreathed spear in her right hand. She is framed in a *trompe l'œil* archway, through which can be seen a landscape with a river, a waterfall, and the portico of a classical temple, probably suggested by that at West Wycombe Park, which the artist had recently visited.

The wall above the chimney-piece was originally blank. The frame to the arch and the plinth below it were built out with slight projection, to the artist's design, and painted by him—the arch in marbling, to match the actual marble of the chimney-piece, the plinth with sphinxes in grisaille. The wreath on the pedestal, the decoration on the soffit of the arch, and the surrounding stars, etc., are in gold leaf. The perspective is true for someone entering the room from the left. Of the artist's murals this cool blue and green design and that of the same year for 90 Gower St. (no. 8) are the most classical: without baroque or rococo influence. This was painted for Mr. (afterwards Sir Henry) Channon, probably designed late in 1935, and completed by Mar. 1936, when Sir Henry had moved in.

Photographs in *Country Life*, Feb. 26th, 1938.
Owner: The Estate of Sir Henry Channon

TWO DESIGNS FOR THE　*1935*
ABOVE
(1) CLASSICAL FIGURE
Pencil and water-colour.　*1 ft. 4¾ in. × 11½ in.*　*Unsigned*

Much as in the final painting, but without the spear, and as if standing in a decorated niche. The arch is framed in a rectangle twisted with gold vine-leaves and showing the letters "H" and "C" in the upper corners. A drawing of the existing chimney-piece below.

(2) CLASSICAL FIGURE

Pencil and water-colour.   10 in. × 6 in.   Unsigned

Leaning the opposite way to the above, but with a distant landscape seen through arch as in the final painting. "H" and "C" completing the rectangle as above, but without the frame of vine-leaves. Chimney-piece excluded. Slightly damaged. Motifs from both these studies were therefore incorporated in the painting.

Owner: Laurence Whistler

PENCIL SKETCH FOR THE   *1935*
ABOVE
1 ft. × 9¼ in.   Unsigned

Squared out, and with notes (e.g. "Black marbled", "Gold-leaf").

Owner: Martin Battersby, Esq.

10   **DECORATIONS**   *? 1935–1936*
AT TRENT PARK, BARNET, MIDDX

A. BLUE ROOM
Oil on wood

(1) TROPHY

c. 5 ft. × 4 ft. 6 in.   Signed, on panel of Roman standard,

REX

A trophy of Roman arms in red and gold above the chimney-piece. Cipher of "P.S." on a shield.

(2) VERTICAL DECORATION

c. 9 ft. × 2 ft.   Unsigned

In red, consisting of a fountain, dolphins, shells, anchor, etc.

(3) VERTICAL DECORATION

c. 6 ft. × 2 ft.   Unsigned

In red, consisting of flags, architectural and musical instruments.

All these decorations are painted on the blue panelling of the room.

B. LIBRARY   *? 1935–1936*
Oil on wood

(1) FEMALE FIGURES

In Roman armour resting on shelves in the form of a venetian window, reclining against the arch and blowing trumpets. Grisaille on yellow. "P." and "S." on two shields.

(2) GILDED SYMMETRICAL CIPHERS OF "P.S."

Outside, over the door into the Library—one. Inside— four. And several smaller versions.

C. PRESENT LECTURE HALL
Oil on wood

(1) DOLPHINS

A pair of Dolphins above the Venetian window, fiercely squirting: grisaille, gilded, with gilded starfish in the keystone of the arch.

(2) CIPHERS

Seven small gilded, symmetrical ciphers of "P.S." on the frieze of the doorcase and tops of panels.

These decorations were carried out for Sir Philip Sassoon. The house is now occupied by the Trent Park Training College.

DESIGNS FOR THE ABOVE   *? 1935*

(1) DESIGN FOR TROPHY OF ARMS IN BLUE ROOM

Ink and body-colour.   7½ in. × 4¾ in.   Unsigned

As carried out, but in less detail. In red. A page torn from a sketch-book.

(2) DESIGN FOR VERTICAL DECORATION WITH FOUNTAIN

Body-colour, red on blue.   1 ft. 2½ in. × 10 in.   Unsigned

Roughly as carried out.   *Owner: Laurence Whistler*

11   **STAIRCASE HALL AT**   *1936*
36 HILL STREET, LONDON
Oil on canvas
EIGHT MURAL PANELS
(Plates 15–19)

In 1936 Rex Whistler was commissioned to paint eight mural panels round the upper part of the staircase hall at 36 Hill St., the home of the Baroness Porcelli. Existing 18th-century plaster-work frames were evidently designed to contain paintings, but were empty. Sir Edwin Lutyens suggested the employment of Rex Whistler to fill them. His imaginary landscape is continuous from panel to panel and is here followed in a clock-wise direction round the walls, the panels being lettered A to H in agreement with the water-colour designs (see below).

ON THE EAST WALL ABOVE THE STAIRS
8 ft. 4 in. × 3 ft. 1 in.
A. *(1 ft. 3 in. now folded in)*

In a foreground of flowers and shrubs a shepherd leans on his crook, smoking a pipe and contemplating a landscape of rocks with a cascade. Near him, sheep.

B. *7 ft. 3 in. × 5 ft. 7 in.*

In the left foreground lies a fallen tree. Beyond it four horsemen with hounds, accompanied by three running figures, ride towards a river which winds from the left towards a lake and more distant mountains. On the far bank, high on a narrow rock, and approached by a spiral pathway, stands a tower. Ships sail on the lake.

C. *8 ft. 4 in. × 3 ft. 1 in. (1 ft. 3 in. now lost)*

A lake with a distant island, on which stands a circular tower, beyond tall trees in the right foreground. In the middle distance a sailing boat, manned by two figures, is moored to a small jetty, across which two other figures carry loads. In the left-hand corner, as though resting on the frame of the panel, is a spray of roses, tied with string; the end of the string and a few leaves hang over the edge of the frame.

ON THE WEST WALL ABOVE THE LANDING
D. *4 ft. 2 in. × 3 ft. 4 in.*

A vase of flowers against mountain tops and sky, from which some rose-petals have fallen. On the wedding day of the Baroness Porcelli's daughter more rose-petals were found painted on the stairs below. These disappeared the following day.

E. *7 ft. 2 in. × 5 ft. 3½ in.*

In the foreground a road winds towards a ruined tower and a bridge over a tumbling river. On the bridge is a fisher-man with a boy. Beyond are the buildings of a town, with a dome and a tall tower: a horse and cart is entering through an arched gateway. On a distant hill-top stands what may be a baroque monastery church.

F. *8 ft. 3 in. × 3 ft. 1 in.*

Beyond a foreground of boulders and sawn trunks, with two tall trees on the right, winds a river on which a man is boating. On the far bank stands a baroque palace with elaborate coats of arms over the ends of the curving wings. The background is formed by tree-clad foot-hills, on one of which is a ruined tower, with a mountain beyond.

ON THE NORTH WALL
G. *4 ft. 2 in. × 3 ft. 4 in.*

Tree-tops and distant mountains.

H. *7 ft. 2½ in. × 6 ft.*

A plank bridge crosses a cascading stream, on whose left bank stands an all-but-dead tree, with a notice-board nailed to it:

"This Landscape and the seven neighbouring ones are strictly private and were painted specially for Mrs. Porcelli by Rex Whistler 1936."

On the right bank, sheep are grazing against a back-ground of trees and rocks, with a waterfall.

The artist's assistant was Victor Bowen. The eight canvases were removed from 36 Hill St. during the war. Photographs in *Country Life* (Mar. 25th, 1939).

Owner: The Baroness Porcelli

DESIGNS FOR THE ABOVE   *1936*
Water-colour.   Unsigned
A. *1 ft. × 4½ in.*

Much as carried out, but a skull appears to rest on the frame in the left corner. This was omitted at the Baroness Porcelli's request, and a foreground of leaves and flowering shrubs was substituted.

B. *10½ in. × 8 in.*

Much as carried out, but running figures, ships, and other details were added, in the mural; where a spiral pathway twists up the rock to the fortress.

C. *1 ft. × 4½ in.*

As yet no bunch of flowers appears on the frame. The trees to the right are comparatively few and only one figure appears on the jetty.

D. *6¼ in. × 5 in.*

A bust is painted, as if standing on the sill, against clouds and mountain tops. This would be replaced by the vase of flowers.

E. *10 in. × 7¼ in.*

The town is as yet rather simply worked out, many of the buildings being mere sketches. The figures are missing, also the church on the distant hill-top.

F. *1 ft. × 4½ in.*

Beyond trees to the right a narrow river winds, with a square, towered building rising from cliffs on the farther side. This would be replaced by the palace, and other details would be added.

G. *6¼ in. × 5 in.*

As carried out, except that a dead tree to the right does not appear in the mural.

H. *10½ in. × 8¾ in.*

The sheep are only sketched in, and in the foreground two men are sawing up a fallen trunk. The Baroness Porcelli felt they would never get through it, so they were replaced by the stream with the plank bridge. The notice-board has not yet appeared.   *Owner: Laurence Whistler*

12   DINING-ROOM AT   *1936–1938* PLAS NEWYDD, ISLE OF ANGLESEY
Main Wall: *Oil on canvas. 12 ft. 6 in. × 47 ft.*
End Walls: *12 ft. 6in. × 17 ft. 8 in.*
Ceiling and part of End Walls: *Oil direct on plaster surface*
Signed in Latin inscription (see below).   (Plates 20–24)

This is Rex Whistler's most important mural decoration, commissioned in Apr. 1936 by the late Lord Anglesey. The artist's notion was expressed to Mrs. Hamlyn, at Clovelly, about August:

"I am going to paint the walls to make it appear, as though, when dining, one is sitting on a terrace over-looking a harbour. There is going to be a stone harbour bar running out with a light at the end rather like *your* exquisite one, and a little sea girt town on a promontory, and lots of ships and rocks and islands, etc., scattered all over the sea. At either end of the room I have planned a perspective pretending to be long arcaded rooms over-looking the sea again—as though one could walk into the picture, and on into another pavillion [*sic*] above the water. . . ."

This romantic landscape is full of allusion to the ideal world of Claude and his contemporaries, to Italy and the Baroque South in general, and to Georgian England; and could be also said to answer the actual spectacular view which it faces—across the Menai Straits to the mountains of Snowdonia. To the left is a crowded town in which we can see a triumphal arch (flying Lord Anglesey's flag), the tower of St. Martin-in-the-Fields, Trajan's Column, and a baroque church. "The circular church (St. something or other *in classe* obviously) is now quite up and complete except for the statues", he wrote to Lord Anglesey. "I have based it very closely on that beautiful little round church in Rome at the corner of Trajan's Forum" (SS. Nome di Maria). The whole work contains many examples of the painter's wit, such as the wet footprints of King Neptune, who has evidently walked into the house, leaving his crown and trident propped against the vase on the parapet. From a central position in the room, the perspective is true for the whole design, including the arcades on the return walls, which then appear to lead out of the room. In the left-hand arcade the artist has painted a self-portrait as a gardener★; in the right-hand one are shown three of the family's dogs.

At each end of the room is a fireplace with an elaborate trophy above it—one martial, the other nautical—painted in grisaille directly on the wall surface between Doric pilasters. "Charles" appears in the frieze over one, "Marjorie" over the other (for Lord and Lady Anglesey). These end walls are painted to imitate stone-work, darker at the North end of the room to agree with the darker tone of that arcade. Over the doors beside each fireplace is a bull's-eye window with a grille in *trompe l'œil*. The whole ceiling is painted with imitation coffers, containing rosettes, coronets, masks, etc. The gilded cornice is of a simple coved shape, designed to strike a note of gold against the blue of the sky.

Over a triumphal arch is the following inscription (containing no less than four grammatical mistakes):

HAEC URBS IUSSU NOBILISSIMO

CAROLO PAGETIS

MARCHIONIS DE MONAE

COMITES UXBRIDGENSIS

CONDITA EST ET AEDIFICATA

A.D. MDCCCCXXXVII

REX WHISTLER INVENIT ET FINXt.

"On either side of the inscription", he told Lord Anglesey, "are two baroque females trying to blow trumpets through a flurry of drapery."

The huge single canvas for the main wall was too big for the artist's own studio, and this and the two smaller canvases for the arcades were begun in a studio rented from Alick Johnstone, the theatrical painter, at 5 Newport St., Lambeth. The mural was finished in the dining-room at Plas Newydd after the canvas had been glued to the walls. The artist's assistant was Victor Bowen.

"I must tell you", the artist wrote to Lord Anglesey, in the course of this work, "that I have been enjoying myself fantastically over the picture."

Illustrated article in *Country Life*, Feb. 22nd, 1946. Colour photographs in *Illustrated*, Aug. 15th, 1953.

Owner: The Marquis of Anglesey

★ Reproduced in *The Masque*, no. 2.

DESIGNS FOR THE ABOVE 1936
(1) MAIN WALL

Water-colour. 9½ in. × 2 ft. 11 in. *Unsigned*

At a glance, very similar to the final painting, but many details are lacking: e.g. the urn supporting Neptune's trident and crown, the distant fortified island, the bottle and bowl of fruit on the parapet, and the gondola. Also the schooner riding at anchor in this sketch would disappear. (It was at first included in the mural, where the ghost of it may still be seen.) It was replaced by a circular ruined tower leading to a mole and a distant township, where, in the sketch, there is only a rock with a light-house. In general it is the right-hand half of the composition which was afterwards greatly enriched.

(2) ARCADE ON NORTH WALL
Water-colour. 9½ in. × 4 in. *Unsigned*

In the main as carried out, though the distant architecture in the mural is more detailed and various. Doubtless figures were always intended, but are barely suggested as yet. The main addition will be the charming self-portrait with a broom.

(3) ARCADE ON SOUTH WALL
Water-colour. 9½ in. × 4 in. *Unsigned*

Very much as finally painted, though there would be busts added to the imposts of the arches, a third dog, a dolphin, fountain, etc. The lute would be replaced by a 'cello. *Owner: Laurence Whistler*

(4 and 5) TROPHIES
Pen and Indian ink, with ribbons and tassels gilded.
Each 9½ in. × 5 in. *Unsigned*

Almost exactly as carried out over North and South fireplaces, but with the indication of looped wreaths above.
Owner: Laurence Whistler

13 SITTING-ROOM AT BROOK 1937 HOUSE, PARK LANE, LONDON
Oil on canvas, wood, and ceiling plaster
Wall A: 8 ft. 9 in. × 23 ft. 5 in.
Wall B: 8 ft. 9 in. × 14 ft. 7 in.
Wall C: 8 ft. 9 in. × 17 ft. 2 in.

Signed in C4 cartouche: Rex Whistler. (*Plates 12 and 87*)

When old Brook House was replaced in the nineteen-thirties by a modern block of flats, Lord and Lady Louis Mountbatten retained a pent-house on the roof. Here the artist entirely decorated a moderate-sized room for Lady Louis. It was rectangular: one of the shorter walls being filled with windows giving a spectacular view of Kensington, and the distant hills, across the tree-tops of Hyde Park. It is therefore three walls and the ceiling that are painted. The scheme was to cover the walls with grisaille panels framed in rectangles on a pale-blue ground, there being three panels (or sometimes two) in each vertical group. The taffeta curtains were striped in two greys, with yellow fringes and ropes. The three walls are here lettered as follows: (A) the fireplace wall; (B) the shorter wall (opposite the main windows); (C) the wall with an additional window, opposite (A). And the vertical groups of panels are numbered from left to right along each wall.

WALL A

1. *Top panel*, a Corinthian arch; *centre*, a gardening trophy; *bottom*, a triple-arched bridge with tower.
2. *Top*, Time and a sleeping Venus, supporting a clock—the face of Venus a likeness of Lady Louis Mountbatten; *bottom*, the river front of "Broadlands in the County of Hampshire", with Lord and Lady Louis in a canoe.
3. *Top*, China; *centre*, a musical trophy; *bottom*, Egypt.
4. *Top*, a sleeping Cupid; *centre*, Africa; *bottom*, a cartouche with a cipher "E.M." (for Edwina Mountbatten).
5. *Top*, Schloss Heiligenberg, a family home of Lord Louis; *centre*, a nautical trophy; *bottom*, a battle between classical troops.
6. *Top*, a festive trophy; *centre*, the Mountbatten arms over a baroque arch; *bottom*, a different cipher of "E.M.".
7. *Top*, a shepherd and shepherdess under a tree; *centre*, a painter's trophy; *bottom*, Don Quixote and Sancho Panza passing through an archway, with windmills in the background.

WALL B

1. *Top*, a bust of Inigo Jones; *centre*, a fishing trophy; *bottom*, crossed dolphins.
2. *Top*, Adsdean, a family home at this period; Lord Louis on horseback with a polo stick; *centre*, Ceres in a shell-topped niche; *bottom*, a circular folly at the end of a vista.
3. *Top*, a bust of Sir Christopher Wren; *centre*, a hunting trophy; *bottom*, a tragic mask.
4. *Top*, Lady Louis Mountbatten's lion-cub, "Sabi"; *centre*, a martial trophy, with a cipher of "E.M."; *bottom*, a harbour with a tower and sailing ships.
5. *Top*, a bust of Sir John Vanbrugh; *bottom*, an amorous trophy.
6. *Top*, "Brook House 1870" on a flying ribbon (i.e., as it appeared before re-building) with figures in Victorian dress; *centre*, Ceres in a shell-topped niche. The face (as also that in B2) is a likeness of Lady Caroline Paget. *Bottom*, two men sawing a tree-trunk.
7. *Top*, a bust of Robert Adam; *centre*, a marine trophy; *bottom*, an heraldic eagle.

WALL C

1. *Top*, an obelisk with rocks and a waterfall; *bottom*, an oval plaque of Venus bending over a sleeping Cupid.
2. *Top*, a cascade below a Corinthian temple; *bottom*, a martial trophy.
3. *Top*, a vertical swag; *bottom*, an oval plaque of Venus examining Cupid's tongue.
4. *Top*, flowers, trophy, and cartouche hanging vertically from a lion's mask. On a shield the letter "E". On the cartouche, "This room was painted in 1937 by Rex Whistler." *Bottom*, Venus on a unicorn led by Cupid.
5. *Top*, a similar panel to C4, but with "M" on the shield; and on the cartouche: "Begun in June and finished on the last day of December." *Bottom*, fishermen on a lake among trees.
6. *Top*, similar to C3; *bottom*, a naked boy and girl, armed, with Hymen holding a torch.

7. *Top*, naked Venus in a shell-topped niche pouring water from a jug, with Cupid; *bottom*, an arrangement of instruments, sword, ink-pot, quills, etc.
8. *Top*, similar to C7, but Venus and Cupid are both with jugs; *bottom*, a jewel-box, skull and bones.

Venus and Cupid were used as code-words by Lord and Lady Louis in a privately printed *Addendum to Everybody's Pocket Code*, 1927.

The artist designed the circular clock set in *rocaille* in A2 top panel. Along the simple coved cornice he painted a pattern of diamonds and stars in silver, with the letters "E" and "M" alternating throughout. In the centre of the ceiling a rich cipher of "E.M." appeared in a cartouche ringed by flowers; centrally at each end was painted a trophy of flags, with a trident and dolphin; and in the four corners were vine-wreathed swans with coronets. This ceiling decoration was chiefly in white on a grey and blue ground, the remainder of the area being scattered with painted roses. A grille, composed of the cipher "EM" and made of wood, silvered, was designed for the radiators below the book-cases on wall (C), and for the space below the window between them.

The artist had wished to paint on the actual walls (as afterwards at Mottisfont). Lady Louis, with admirable foresight, insisted on canvas. At the outbreak of war this was cut into vertical strips and removed; and within a year the pent-house had been bombed, with severe damage to the immovable painted ceiling. Traces of the ceiling decoration can, however, be detected under the paintwork still—the room is now an office. The artist's assistant was Victor Bowen. Photograph in *Decoration*, 1939, no. 32.

Owner: The Estate of the Countess Mountbatten of Burma

DESIGNS FOR THE ABOVE   *1936*
Unsigned
I. PANELS

A1. Grisaille wash-drawing on pale blue background, 1 ft. 1 in. × 6¼ in. The three panels virtually as carried out.

A2. Pencil, sepia ink and water-colour, 1 ft. 4 in. × 7½ in. *Top*, sketch for two figures and a clock; *bottom*, proposal for a mirror in the form of a flower-fringed shell—an idea abandoned in favour of the picture of Broadlands, which is sketched below in the space left for the fireplace.

A3. Water-colour, 6½ in. × 5½ in. The trophy as carried out.

A4 and A5. Ink and water-colour, 1 ft. 4 in. × 8¾ in. A4 *top*, half A4 *bottom*, and A5 *centre*, as carried out.

A6. Sepia ink and wash, 1 ft. 4 in. × 5¼ in. *Top*, the trophy almost as carried out; *bottom*, half the cartouche as carried out.

B1. Ink and wash, 1 ft. 2¾ in. × 2¾ in. *Centre*, the trophy as carried out.

B2. Water-colour, 6¾ in. × 4¼ in. *Centre*, the statue as carried out, but with consoles to the plinth.

B3, 4, 5. Pencil, 5 in. × 8½ in. *Top panels only*: B3, a bust on bracket, but of Lady Louis Mountbatten; B4, a dog in a wreath; B5, a bust on bracket, but of Lord Louis Mountbatten.

B3. Pencil and ink, 10½ in. × 7 in. Top right corner missing. *Centre*, almost as carried out; *bottom*, an eagle (transferred to B7, bottom panel).

B3. Another version. Pencil and ink, 10¾ in. × 6½ in. Top right corner missing. *Centre*, sketch for a trophy (transferred to B7); *bottom*, a mask as carried out.

B4. Pencil and Indian ink, 6½ in. × 4¼ in. *Centre*, virtually as carried out.

B5. Pencil and Indian ink, 10¾ in. × 2 in. *Centre and bottom*, as carried out.

B6. Sepia ink and wash, 5 in. × 9 in. *Top*, as carried out, with a flying ribbon: "Old Brook House".

B6. Pencil and wash, 6½ in. × 4 in. *Centre*, the statue as carried out.

C5 and C7. Pencil and sepia ink, 10¾ in. × 9¼ in. Top left corner missing. C5 *bottom*, crossed dolphins (transferred to B1 *bottom*). C7 *top*, an old-fashioned bee-hive; *bottom*, a sheaf of corn. A note by the artist says that these were for C4 and C5; but they were not adopted.

C7 and C4. Pencil and sepia wash, 1 ft. 2 in. × 7 in. C7 *top*, much as carried out, but in the niche a masked head spouting water (not the subsequent Venus and Cupid). C5 *top*, much as carried out, but with no inscription. (*Plate 87*.)

A1 (the top and centre panels), B2 (centre), and B6 (centre) were reproduced in *Rex Whistler*, by Laurence Whistler, 1948, pp. 86–87; A3 (centre), A6 (top), and C7 (part of top) in *Restoration Love Songs*, ed. John Hadfield, 1950, opp. pp. 8, 73, and 80; A6 (top) in *The Masque* dust-wrapper device.

II. FULL-SIZE DESIGN FOR THE CLOCK
(A2 Top Panel)
Pencil.   *1 ft. 8 in. × 1 ft. 11 in.*   *Unsigned*

Annotated by the artist: "Carved wood (or composition?) frame, representing rocks and drapery, to join on to the surrounding painting." "The section of frame (and whole clock) to be as *low in relief* as the carver can properly make it." "The figures about ¼″ tall. Very fine Roman numerals in burnished silver. The clock face to be made the pale grey of the curtains (that exact shade) with one or two rings in deeper grey and silver painted round the centre. (I will paint a wreath of flowers in pale yellow to match the fringe round the hands.)." "The hands: some rich flowery pierced design in silver." "Diameter of Dial 6 in.". The clock was made by Messrs. Gent and Company in 1937.

III. FULL-SIZE DESIGN FOR THE CORNICE
Pencil and water-colour.   *9 in. × 1 ft. 8 in.*

Two of the diamonds showing a specimen "E" and "M". Here the intended colour-scheme, however, appears to have been blue, grey, and black on a white ground, without silver.

IV. DESIGN FOR THE CEILING
Pencil, ink, and water-colour.   *1 ft. × 1 ft. 2 in.*

Half the area painted as it was carried out.

V. FULL-SIZE DRAWING FOR THE GRILLES
(on Wall C)
Pencil.   *1 ft. 10 in. × 2 ft. 6 in.*

Probably drawn by his assistant from a lost original scale-drawing.   *Owner: Laurence Whistler*

ALTERNATIVE DESIGNS FOR THE ABOVE   *1936*
Water-colour.   *9 in. × 1 ft.*   *Unsigned*

One shows the upper part of the walls as if hung with blue drapery, on which white trophies and medallions would appear (an idea clearly derived from his room at Port Lympne). Where the drapery fell short, above the doors, and everywhere below the dado, grisaille panels would be painted, as if on the wall behind.

(1) Wall A and Wall C according to the above proposal.

(2) Wall A with a sketch of Wall C according to the final proposal, but in brown on very pale green. Note in the artist's hand: "You approved of this *kind of arrangement* of the panels, I think, but painted in the manner of the pale-blue–grisaille-&-white design in the other paper."
    Owner: Laurence Whistler

14   DRAWING-ROOM   *1938–1939* AT MOTTISFONT ABBEY, HANTS
Oil on wall-surface and wood.   *46 ft. × 24 ft. 9 in. × 15 ft. 6 in. high.*   *Signed on spine of book in painted niche:*
Rex Whistler.   (*Plates 26–29*)

An entire room decorated for Mrs. Gilbert Russell. It was remodelled to the artist's design with a coved ceiling, and painted pink, and he began working on it in December. He treated the room (his last major work) in the manner of the 18th-century Gothic Revival, and it contains at least his most notable achievement in *trompe l'œil*. The main decorations are in grisaille on the pale pink ground. A painted cornice (of pointed machicolations with tracery) encircles the room, supported on painted columns and pedestals. Between these hang large trophies, all twined with leaves, or there are panels of Gothic tracery; and the dado is painted with similar tracery. The South wall opposite the entrance doors contains a large bay window, to left and right of which are trophies of music and the chase, the musical instruments being antique or mediaeval. In the traceried arches above the three bay windows there are pelmets, apparently of ermine with crimson fringes. These pelmets are painted on wood like the falling drapery below. For many years the fringes remained cut out of paper; but in 1950 these were replaced in canvas by Percy Willats (who retains the paper prototypes). Below them are actual crimson curtains, lined with material partly spotted, to represent ermine, so that real and sham were indistinguishable, apart from fading. Over the centre window a cipher of "M.R." was painted.

On the West wall, crosier, candle, censer, etc., are involved in a trophy of priest-craft. Between the windows, here, which are similarly treated with sham ermine, a painted niche contains a work in *trompe l'œil*. Clouds of incense float up to the ceiling itself from a large urn draped in ermine. Its pedestal bears the inscription, as if incised, "Magna est veritas et praevalebit", under a flaming heart ringed by an ouroboros in relief. A black glove appears to have been left lying on this pedestal. To the right is a lute and a roll of music. To the left, a packet of letters rests on books, of which two have the following titles on the spine: "REX WHISTLER INVt. ET PINXt." and "BEGUN DEC. 19th. 1938. FINISHED OCTOBER 31st. 1939."

In the centre of the North wall are rich double doors. They are painted with blank tracery, rising to a coat of arms, riotously mantled above a twisted ribbon with the motto: *Che sará, sará*. The trophies on each side of these doors are martial, and suggestive of Crusaders and Saracens.

In the centre of the East wall is a chimney-piece, which appears to be of green and white marble, though in fact painted on wood. The mirror above it, of gilt rococo, is the one major feature of the room which the artist did not design; it came from Wardour Castle. The trophies on each side are martial. The artist designed the ten wall-lights of gilded metal, in the form of urns topped with obelisks and branching into four candles. These were made by Messrs. Dernier & Hamlyn. He also designed the Gothic radiator grilles below the windows.

The coving above the cornice is painted to look like diminishing diamond-shaped coffers, filled with rosettes. The ceiling, in parchment colour, is painted as if in very low relief: a large Gothic design, twisted with vine-leaves and containing a formal sun in the centre.

On the cornice to the left of the bay window it seems as though the painter had carelessly left a little pot with a brush in it, and a box of matches. The illusion is perfect.

In the first months of the war (Oct. 21st, 1939) he wrote from Mottisfont to Lord Uxbridge: "I am *just* finishing this wretched room—in about four or five more days. Well there will be no more which will be a pleasant relief. . . ." On top of the bay-window cornice he had inscribed these words, unseen by anyone for many years: "I was painting this Ermine curtain when Britain declared war on the Nazi tyrants. Sunday September 3rd. R.W." His assistants were Victor Bowen and Percy Willatts.

Photographs in *Country Life*, May 6th, 1954, and *The Ideal Home*, Apr. 1958.   *Owner: The National Trust*

DESIGNS AND SKETCHES   *1938*
FOR THE ABOVE

(1) PROPOSAL FOR THE SOUTH (FIREPLACE) WALL
Pencil, Indian ink, water-colour, and gold.
9 in. × 1 ft. 8 in.   Unsigned

The paired columns and coving much as carried out. In the space to the left (instead of the ultimate trophy) a romantic landscape in grisaille under lifted curtains. The alternative proposal of a trophy in the corresponding space to the right, but all in gold, hanging from antlers. *Trompe l'œil* statues in niches each side of the chimney-piece.

(2) ANOTHER PROPOSAL FOR THE ABOVE
Pencil, Indian ink, and water-colour.   9½ in. × 1 ft. 8½ in.
Unsigned

The spaces each side of the fireplace are treated as three-light Perpendicular windows: that to the left is a sham window with a wall-light in the centre: that to the right reveals a landscape seen behind the two mullions.

(3) PROPOSAL FOR THE WEST BAY-WINDOW WALL
Pencil, Indian ink, water-colour, and gold.
9¾ in. × 1 ft. 3 in.   Unsigned

Painted looped pelmets, much as carried out, but not ermine. To the left of the bay (instead of the ultimate trophy) a vignette of a Gothic landscape suggested.

(4) ANOTHER PROPOSAL FOR THE ABOVE
Pencil, Indian ink, and water-colour.   9 in. × 1 ft. 3 in.
Unsigned

Incipient idea for the looped pelmets. Wall-lamps in panels each side of the bay (instead of trophies).

(5) PROPOSAL FOR THE WEST (TWO-WINDOWED) WALL
Pencil, Indian ink, water-colour, and gold.
10 in. × 1 ft. 8½ in.   Unsigned

A pencil sketch of the wall, with a finished idea for the niche—holding a great standing trophy of arms, all in gold.

(6) ALTERNATIVE PROPOSAL FOR THE ABOVE
Pencil, Indian ink, water-colour, and gold.
10 in. × 1 ft. 8½in.   Unsigned

Showing a slightly narrower niche, and standing trophy, all in gold.

(7) EARLY PROPOSAL FOR THE NORTH WALL
(WITH DOUBLE DOORS)
Pencil.   10¼ in. × 1 ft. 3 in.   Unsigned

Each side of the doors, narrow niches between Gothic columns, containing statues. A ruled architectural drawing, worked over by the artist.

(8) ANOTHER PROPOSAL FOR THE ABOVE
Pencil and water-colour.   10¾ in. × 1 ft. 2½ in.   Unsigned

Nearer to the final solution. A small trophy to the right of the doors. A ruled architectural drawing, worked over by the artist.

(9) DESIGN FOR THE TROPHY TO THE LEFT OF THE
BAY-WINDOW (SOUTH WALL)
Water-colour.   10½ in. × 5½ in.   Unsigned

More musical instruments would be added.

(10) DESIGN FOR THE TROPHY TO THE RIGHT OF THE
BAY-WINDOW (SOUTH WALL)
Water-colour.   1 ft. ½ in. × 6 in.   Unsigned

Most of the ingredients would be altered or switched elsewhere.

(11) DESIGN FOR THE TROPHY AT THE SOUTH END OF
THE WEST WALL

Water-colour.   1 ft. ½ in. × 6 in.   Unsigned

Priestcraft. Much as executed. At one stage the artist inserted the chalice and patten, but was persuaded with some difficulty that they were better left out.

(12) DESIGN FOR THE URN NICHE

Water-colour.   1 ft. 1¾ in. × 9¾ in.   Unsigned

Much as carried out, but without the billowing incense and many other delights. The letters "M.R." alone on the plinth.

(13) DESIGN FOR THE TROPHY TO THE LEFT OF THE
FIREPLACE

Water-colour and gold.   1 ft. 1¾ in. × 9¾ in.   Unsigned

Much as carried out.

(14) DESIGN FOR THE TROPHY TO THE RIGHT OF THE
FIREPLACE

Water-colour and gold.   1 ft. 1¾ in. × 9¾ in.   Unsigned

Much as carried out.

In addition, there are ten rough pencil sketches of details by the artist, on large paper.   *Owner: Mrs. Gilbert Russell*

15   ROOM AT 39 PRESTON PARK *1944* AVENUE, BRIGHTON

Oil on wall-paper

(1) "ALLEGORY."   *5 ft. 2 in. × 8 ft. 1 in.*

Signed, bottom right: Rex Whistler June 5th–7th 1944

(*Plate 31*)

(2) "GEORGE IV."   *4 ft. 3 in. × 3 ft. 1 in.*

Inscribed above the head: Georgius IV REX

(*Plate 30*)

The house in which the artist was billeted with his fellow-officers immediately before the invasion contained an unlovely chamber, which they had to use as their sitting-room. He provided a chinoiserie wall-paper for the dreary brown walls by painting on them flowering trees, ferns, caged and flying birds, in pink and blue and green—all as a background to more notable paintings. Over the fire-place, in a sham plaster medallion wreathed in leaves, was a head of George IV in left profile. On another wall was the Welsh Guards crest as if modelled in white plaster, with a gold and blue motto and with a gilded leek, to which he had given a flourish felt by him to be lacking in the official version. On a third wall appeared "Allegory. H.R.H. The Prince Regent awakening the Spirit of Brighton." The corpulent Prince, almost naked but for the Garter, bends over a lovely nymph, stark naked but for the ribbon reading "Brighthelmstone". With lifted finger and sidelong leer at the beholder, enjoining silence, he plucks the drapery from her. Behind is the sea, with sailing ships. The colouring is warm and Titianesque. The artist is thought to have spent no more than a few hours over the painting in very brief periods, and the battalion left before it could be finished, with embarkation in the offing.

"Allegory" and the portrait of George IV are now in the Royal Pavilion, Brighton. The Welsh Guards crest is the property of the Regiment (reproduced on the dust-wrapper of *The Welsh Guards at War*, 1946). The painted wall-paper passed to the owner of the house when it was derequisitioned: Mrs. Norman Dalrymple.

Unused Designs for Murals

16   BEDROOM AT   *c. 1927* 14 CULROSS ST., LONDON

Indian ink and water-colour.   10 in. × 1 ft. 3 in.

Unsigned

Three designs—for three walls of a small first-floor room. (The drawing for the fourth wall is missing.) Corinthian columns and pilasters on a high base with intervening scenes and niches. The theme is the judgment of Paris, who himself appears in a niche between the two windows in the South wall, plainly worried, with Cupid whispering in his ear. On the East wall "Athene" is seated on a balustrade, looking coyly round, with a seascape beyond (this figure has been crossed out). On the West wall, "Juno" is similarly seated in front of a landscape and between two floral urns in niches. On the North wall (missing) the figure would have been "Venus". Evidently for Lady Castlerosse's bedroom.

Owner: Laurence Whistler

17   UNIDENTIFIED DESIGN   *c. 1927* FOR A MURAL

Indian ink.   7 in. × 9 in.   Signed: R.W. *at the top of left-hand cartouche*

A sketch for a fireplace wall, showing Ionic columns on a very high base, with an archway above the chimney-piece containing a standing female and two seated males. Each side, a square-headed arch, with a cartouche above. Probably fanciful, though possibly connected with the Culross St. designs above.

Inscribed by the artist: "*All painted,* except mantelpiece and scurting" [*sic*].   *Owner: Laurence Whistler*

18   UNIDENTIFIED DESIGN   *? c. 1927* FOR A BEDROOM

Pencil, sepia ink, and wash.   8 in. × 9¾ in.   Unsigned

A perspective sketch showing the painted treatment

proposed. An order of Corinthian pilasters rising from the floor; a painted niche and statue above the chimney-piece; the chimney-breast flanked by two painted arches, showing, to the left, a classical corridor, to the right a landscape. Two windows are visible on the wall to the left.

Owner: Laurence Whistler

19 DESIGNS FOR A BEDROOM *1929* AT BULBRIDGE HOUSE, WILTON, WILTS

Mentioned by Edith Olivier in her unpublished Journal for Mar. 4th, but without description. The proposal is said to have involved painting the coved ceiling like a tent. For Lady Juliet Duff. *Whereabouts unknown*

20 SKETCH FOR MURAL *1931* DECORATION
Ink and wash. 5 in. × 8 in.
Signed, bottom right: Rex Whistler 1931

To the left a baroque palace invaded by a surging revolutionary crowd, under slanting flags and clouds of smoke. The inhabitants, mostly very young or very old, fleeing unsuccessfully for their lives. Squared out in light pencil as if for enlargement.

This drawing was reproduced in *The Artist* for Nov. 1935, in an article on Rex Whistler, where it is described as a "Sketch for Mural Decoration", doubtless at the suggestion of the artist. It very closely resembles his headpiece to *Suppose*—, Max Beerbohm's contribution to *The New Keepsake*, 1931 (no. 435), p. 76, and is evidently connected with it. Rex Whistler is known to have provided his own theme for Max Beerbohm to describe, not to have illustrated a text already written. *Owner: Laurence Whistler*

21 SKETCH FOR A CLASSROOM *1932* AT PORT REGIS, KENT
Pencil, sepia ink, and water-colour. 5½ in. × 9¼ in.
Unsigned

Mr. Howard Evans, the Headmaster of Port Regis Preparatory School, proposed to employ the artist to paint panels appropriate to four classrooms: Classics, French, English, and History and Geography. Probably the artist himself chose to begin on the Classics room. There is a sheet giving measurements for eight panels, each 7 ft. × 3 ft. 6 in.: four to be Greek, and four Roman, on opposite walls. The plan was abandoned but his sketch for the Roman wall survives, showing scenes of Sport, Warfare, Authority (a litter-borne emperor), and Religion, with rich architectural backgrounds. The four panels are divided by painted Doric pilasters, and have small panels with trophies below them. *Owner: Laurence Whistler*

22 DESIGN FOR A MURAL *pre-1935*
Sepia ink and water-colour. 11 in. × 1 ft. 2 in.
Unsigned

One wall of a room treated as the interior of a tent, with a pelmet indented like that at Port Lympne, but with a flat ceiling. Looped back curtains reveal a formal garden with a baroque sculptured rape on a pedestal, and a distant palace. Victorian figures in the garden. Each side, in front of the curtains, black busts on pedestals. Described by the artist in a list of works sent to the Whitechapel Art Gallery as "Design for a room. (Black busts, curtains, Versailles.)".

Owner: Michael Renshaw, Esq.

23 DESIGN FOR A MURAL PANEL *n.d.*
Sepia ink and water-colour with gold. 1 ft. 2 in. × 10 in.
Unsigned

A rectangular panel, with a gilded acanthus border re-entrant at the corners to admit small square panels containing flowers. In the centre an elliptical panel—possibly to be a painted mirror—in a gold wreath supported by cherubs. Trophies above and below, the upper one containing crossed "C"s. Probably for Lady Diana Cooper. A pencilled suggestion of bracket lights with candles each side of the oval, as an alternative.

Owner: Laurence Whistler

From *THE NEW KEEPSAKE*. Cat. no. 435

Easel Paintings and Panels in Oils
and Related Drawings

(Excluding Portraits)

24   **"SUMMER"**   *1923*

Oil on canvas.   *2 ft. 6 in. × 3 ft. 4 in.*   *Unsigned*

In the foreground a group of revellers with goblets, singing to the music of a lute-player, bottom left, opposite whom an old man huddles himself in his cloak. Behind them is a background of thick trees, to the left a glimpse of a stream with bathers. Awarded 2nd Prize for a Summer Competition at the Slade School, 1935, £5.

Owner: The Royal Drawing Society

25   **"2nd PRIZE.**   *1923*
PAINTING FROM LIFE (FIGURE). £2"

From the artist's list of prizes won at the Slade School.

Whereabouts unknown

26   **NUDE MALE STUDY**   *1924*

Oil on canvas.   *c. 2 ft. 3 in. × 1 ft. 6 in.*   *Unsigned*

Standing, with *cache sexe*. Probably mentioned in the artist's list of prizes won at the Slade School, as "2nd Prize. Painting from Life (Figure). £2."

Owner: Laurence Whistler

27   **NUDE FEMALE STUDY**   *1924*

Oil on canvas.   *2 ft. 6 in. × 1 ft. 8 in.*   *Unsigned*

Seated on model's throne, facing left, head in profile looking down; left arm resting on left knee. "First Prize, Painting from the Life, at the Slade School. £5."

Owner: University College, London

28   **"2nd PRIZE.**   *1924*
PAINTING FROM LIFE (HEAD). £4"

Oil on canvas

From the artist's list of prizes won at the Slade School.

Whereabouts unknown

29   **"A SMALL AND VERY POOR**   *1924*
**DECORATION WHICH I DID FOR THE
ROCKEFELLER GIFT FUND"**

Letter from the artist to Ronald Fuller, June 13th.

Whereabouts unknown

30   **TRIAL SCENE FROM THE**   *1925*
      MERCHANT OF VENICE

Oil on canvas.   *3 ft. × 4 ft. 1 in.*   *Signed on plaque above door*, This house was built by R. J. Whistler

The trial is taking place on the terrace of a brick and stone building, seen in perspective on the right. In front of a numerous company, on the terrace and above in the galleries, Antonio stands stripped, with Shylock demanding, and Portia dilating on the quality of mercy. To the left, trees, horsemen, and a remote idea of Venice.

Owner: University College, London

TWO SKETCHES FOR THE   *1925*
ABOVE

(1) *Sepia ink and wash. 11 in. × 1 ft. 3 in. Signed, bottom left:* Rex J. Whistler.
Very much as carried out.

(2) *Ink and water-colour. 6¾ in. × 9 in. Unsigned.*
A discarded proposal, showing the principal figures only, on a terrace colonnaded on the right, against an Italian landscape.
For another sketch, see no. 218.

Owner: Laurence Whistler

UNTRACED OIL PAINTINGS   *1928*

A few of the untraced items in the artist's Rome Diary for this year are likely to have been in oils. See no. 240.

31   **"THE STORY OF JONAH"**   *1928*

Oil on canvas.   *1 ft. 3 in. × 3 ft. 2 in.*   *Signed on obelisk pedestal to left:* Rex Whistler pinxit. AD. 1928

Mr. and Mrs. Alastair Wedderburn commissioned a panel for a chimney-piece at Rathmore Lodge, South Bolton Gardens, London. Edith Olivier records in her unpublished Journal for Feb. 6th: "He has got to work on the Wedderburns' little panel, and on Sir Courtauld Thompson's Hall partition—has sketched the landscapes, though he hasn't decided on his Subjects." Then on Feb. 13th: "He sketched at lightning speed a Jonah scene into his picture." The picture was completed at the British School at Rome in July and August.

To the left are wooded cliffs and mountains, fading into the distance, beside a sea on which appears, far off, the ship that cast away Jonah. In the centre the whale has just "vomited out Jonah upon the dry land": we see him running forward, to be greeted by a dog. In the right foreground we see him again (with the dog now attached to him), striding out, undistracted by a beckoning mermaid, towards the classical town, which is Nineveh. Today the picture hangs, framed, at Parsonage Farm, East Hagbourne, Berks.   *Owners: Mr. and Mrs. Wedderburn*

SKETCH FOR THE ABOVE   *1928*
Pencil and water-colour.   1 ft. 3 in. × 3 ft. 2 in.   Unsigned

Squared out for enlargement, but the landscape as yet at an early stage of invention. To the right, ruin-crowned rocks (instead of a town); to the left, crossed trees, much as carried out. A whale and a ship have been roughly pencilled in, later.   *Owner: Laurence Whistler*

32   THE BATHS OF CARACALLA   *1928*
Oil on canvas.   9½ in. × 1 ft.   Signed, bottom left:
Rex Whistler

Ruinous walls in sunlight with two figures to the right, beneath a group of trees, and a boy seated on a wall. On the back: "Baths of Caracalla, Rome. June 8th 1928."
Owner: Laurence Whistler

33   "THE TEMPLE OF REMUS   *1928*
FROM THE PALATINE"
Oil on canvas.   11 in. × 1 ft. 2¼ in.   Signed, bottom
right: Rex Whistler June 1928.   (Plate 6)

In the left foreground is the so-called Temple of Divus Romulus, with modern priests pacing before it. In the background on the extreme right a portion of the Basilica of Constantine. Begun on June 11th (Rome Diary). Artist's title on label at back. Exhibited in the Imperial Gallery of Art, Mar. 11th, 1930.
Owner: Dr. L. R. Simpson

34   GLAUCUS AND SCYLLA   *1929*
Oil on canvas.   3 ft. 3 in. × 4 ft. 6 in.   Signed, bottom
left: Rex Whistler 1929

Mr. Carrier, in America, commissioned a panel to be fixed above a fireplace at 642 Willet Street, Memphis, Tennessee, and left the subject to the artist. On Apr. 5th the artist wrote: "Your panel is about *half done* now, & I send you a *rough* sketch of the design which I hope you will like. It represents the sea-god *Glaucus* wooing *Scylla*. As he wasn't very successful, he appealed to Circe to make Scylla return his love, but Circe out of jealousy turned poor Scylla into a monster."
The painting now hangs framed at Oxford, Mississippi.
Owner: Mrs. Robert M. Carrier

SKETCHES FOR THE ABOVE   *1929*
(1) *Sepia ink and water-colour. 6¾ in. × 9¼ in. Signed, bottom right (almost cut away): Rex Whistler.*

Sketch sent on Apr. 5th (see above). Much as carried out, but Glaucus is not yet offering Scylla a handful of

pearls and coral; nor, as yet, is his shell-chariot seen waiting in the distance, drawn by sea-horses, with a merman in attendance. The great arch of rock could have been suggested by the caves which pierce the promontory at Gli Scafari, Lerici, or by the Window-Rock at Clovelly.   *Owner: Mrs. Robert M. Carrier*

(2) *Pencil. 1 ft. 6 in. × 1 ft. 4 in. Unsigned*

Squared-out drawing, intermediate between the sketch above and the final painting: nearer in detail to the former. On the back, pencil notes by the artist on the mythology.   *Owner: Laurence Whistler*

35   "ROME"   *1929*
Oil on canvas.   6¼ in. × 10¼ in.   Signed, on stone block
in foreground: Rex .W. MCMXXIX

Described as:—a symbolic picture, showing the nude figure of a woman reclining on red drapery above a sarcophagus. To the right, an urn with figures in relief, and behind it a ruined triumphal arch. In the distance the dome of St. Peter's. Exhibited at the Imperial Gallery of Art, Apr. 1929.
Owner: Mrs. Herbert Graham

36   THE ARCH OF CONSTANTINE *1929*
AND THE FORUM
Oil on canvas.   9 in. × 1 ft.   Signed, bottom right:
Rex Whistler 1929

To the left the side of the Arch of Constantine, with a priest and another figure in the foreground; in the middle distance the Arch of Titus, etc. On the back: "Arch of Constantine ~~& Titus~~ begun Monday morning June 24th–25th–26th–27th. Finished 28th." The artist himself erased the words "& Titus".
Owner: The Earl and Countess of Iddesleigh

37   "TIVOLI FROM THE ROAD"   *1929*
Oil on canvas.   10 in. × 1 ft. 2 in.   Signed, bottom right:
Rex Whistler 1929.   *(Plate 7)*

Houses silhouetted on the skyline to the left. To the right, an olive-clad slope with a distant view of the Campagna in evening light. On the back: "Tivoli from the road, seen through arch of the viaduct. Begun Mon: afternoon July 1st–2nd–3rd, Finished. 1929." And in a letter to Edith Olivier of July 2nd: ". . . a very lovely view from there of Tivoli, jutting high up in silhouette against the blue-grey haze of the distant Campagna . . . looking almost exactly like the sea, as it lies far below, stretching away in gentle rolling planes to the horizon." Exhibited at the Imperial Gallery of Art, Mar. 1930.   *Owner: Laurence Whistler*

38   STILL LIFE   *1929*
Oil on canvas.   10 in. × 1 ft. 2 in.   Unsigned

A wicker basket of peaches, with bottles and an open book, on a table in front of a dark tapestry. On the back: "Peaches & tapestry. In the dining room, no 3 Foro Romano Sat: July 6th & 7th, finished. 1929."
Painted in Lord Berners' house in Rome.
Owner: Laurence Whistler

39 "ST. GREGORIO NEAR *1929*
PALATINE"

Oil on wood. *9 in. × 1 ft.* *Unsigned*

To the left, steps in hot sunlight leading up to the church, with figures at the foot. A big tree to the right. On the back: "Started Mon. morning July 8th, 9th, Finished July 15th." *Owner: Kenneth Rae, Esq.*

40 THE PIAZZA OF ST. PETER'S *1929*

Oil on canvas. *11 in. × 1 ft. 2 in.* *Signed, bottom right:*
Rex Whistler, 1929

View across the Piazza from the end of the North colonnade, in shadow, to the sunlit South colonnade. The Obelisk to the right. A priest mounting steps in the foreground. *Owner: Sir Eardley Holland*

41 AN URN WITH FLOWERS *? 1929*

Oil on canvas. *1 ft. 7 in. × 1 ft. 1¼ in.* *Unsigned*

Filled with flowers on a window-sill of Lord Berners' house, No. 3 Foro Romano, in Rome, with a view beyond of a part of the Capitol. Background unfinished.
Owner: Laurence Whistler

42 "IN THE SALONE, AULLA" *1929*

Oil on canvas. *9 in. × 1 ft.* *Unsigned*

An interior with a vaulted ceiling and large chimney-piece to the left. A figure in shorts, seated at a long table. Beyond the window another figure painting at an easel. "Berners painting self having tea."
Owner: Robert Heber-Percy, Esq.

43 CHARTRES: THE NORTH *1929*
PORCH AND OLD BISHOP'S PALACE

Oil on canvas. *11 in. × 1 ft. 3 in.* *Signed, bottom right:*
Rex Whistler July 29th 1929

To the right, the porch; in the centre background the wrought-iron gates of the Palace. In the foreground, two nuns, and Lord Berners painting.
Owner: Michael Renshaw, Esq.

44 CAUDEBEC, FRANCE *1929*

Oil on canvas. *10 in. × 1 ft. 2 in.* *Signed, bottom right:*
Rex Whistler 1929

View of a jetty on the River Seine with a steam ferry in the middle distance, figures on the bank and a group of trees to the left. Painted while returning to England on a motoring tour. On the back: "Caudebec July 1929. Rex Whistler." Exhibited at the Goupil Gallery, Nov. 1930.
Owner: Laurence Whistler

45 THE SQUARE AT CAUDEBEC *1929*

Oil on canvas. *11 in. × 1 ft. 2 in.* *Signed, bottom left:*
Rex Whistler 1929

Part of the Square with shuttered windows, the spire rising behind red roofs in a cloudy sky. To the right, two figures in conversation and a woman at an upper window. A small dog. On the back, "Cau de Bec. View of the spire from the Square, July 30th 1929". A wedding present from the artist. *Owner: Mrs. Hilary Bray*

46 WESTON HALL, TOWCESTER, *1929*
NORTHANTS

Oil on canvas. *9 in. × 1 ft.* *Unsigned.* *(Plate 4)*

"From the kitchen garden. Oct. 1929." To the left the gabled house in perspective over a wall. Mr. Sitwell walking towards it, axe on shoulder. Pencil lines show that it was sketched on to the canvas direct, and probably finished in London: certain small details of the architecture are incorrect. Exhibited at the Leicester Galleries, Oct. 1936.
Owner: Sacheverell Sitwell, Esq.

47 "THE ELDERS" *c. 1930*

Oil on canvas. *8¾ in. × 1 ft. 4 in.* *Signed, bottom right:*
Rex Whistler

A pair of grotesque aged heads, among leaves, relishing Susanna, who does not appear. On the reverse a label: "Rex Whistler, 20 Fitzroy St., W.1."
Owner: Laurence Whistler

48 THE JUDGMENT OF PARIS *? c. 1930*

Oil on canvas. *Approx. 3 ft. × 2 ft. 3 in.*
Signed, bottom right: Rex Whistler

The three naked goddesses, Juno, Venus, and Minerva, standing. *Whereabouts unknown*

49 HADDON HALL, DERBYSHIRE *1932*

Oil on canvas

A preliminary oil painting for the panel (no. 50, below). Explained in a letter to the artist's mother on Sept. 12th. "I sat out on the hillside and did a painting of the scene on Sunday afternoon, so all the *outdoor* work is already done and this morning I walked about with a notebook and pencil and drew certain bits of the house in detail and the bridges etc which were indistinct or hidden by trees from a distance. Now I can start on the small panel and hope to have it done in a few days. This afternoon I finished the imitation of the original strip of painting on my panel so shall be ready to begin the rest tomorrow morning. A bit of the summer house and some branches; that is all that remains of the original painting . . . but I have also copied it much smaller on my little panel to scale."
Owner: The Duke of Rutland

SKETCH FOR THE ABOVE *1932*

Sepia ink and wash. *9 in. × 1 ft.* *Unsigned*

His outdoor "painting of the scene", as described to his mother above, showing the house and river alone, without the fanciful framework of trees and shelter.
Owner: Laurence Whistler

50 PANEL AT HADDON HALL, *1933*
DERBYSHIRE

Oil on wood. 6 ft. × 8 ft. 6 in. Signed, bottom left:
Rex Whistler March 1933. *(Plate 13)*

The house seen from above in the middle distance, with the river winding in front and a wooded hill behind it. In the left foreground a group of trees; in the right foreground the late Duke of Rutland and Lord Granby (the present Duke) with dogs, beside a dead tree. This panel replaced an old one, in the Long Gallery, representing a scene from classical history, of which only a narrow strip down the right-hand side remained, showing the fragment of a curious shelter. To preserve this, the new panel was shaped and glued to it, and the shelter completed. Photograph in *Country Life*, Dec. 23rd, 1949.

Owner: The Duke of Rutland

51 HADDON HALL, DERBYSHIRE *? 1933*

Oil on canvas. 1 ft. 3 in. × 1 ft. 8 in. Unsigned

A view of the Castle from the North East, showing the old entrance under Peverel's Tower and the valley beyond, in misty sunlight. *Owner: Laurence Whistler*

52 ULYSSES' FAREWELL *1932–*
TO PENELOPE *1933*

Oil on canvas. 4 ft. 2 in. × 5 ft. Signed, bottom right:
Rex Whistler. 1932–3. *(Plate 25)*

To the right in perspective, sumptuous baroque architecture along the quay; to the left in the middle distance, Ulysses' ship. The farewell is taking place above the water-steps, watched by the silent suitors. In the left foreground a naked madman reads the future in cards. The baroque clouds swarm with Immortals; and the whole painting is more full of figures than any other by the artist. Reproduced in *The Radio Times*, Jan. 31st, 1947.

Owner: Sir Malcolm Bullock, Bt.

SKETCH FOR THE ABOVE *1932*
Pencil and water-colour. 1 ft. 8½ in. × 1 ft. 3½ in.
Unsigned

A similar conception roughly sketched, but with a twisted tree in the left foreground, instead of steps and a circular tower. Squared out. Evidently intermediate between the original design (undiscovered) and the painting.

Owner: Laurence Whistler

53 TRENT PARK, MIDDLESEX: *1934*
THE TERRACE

Oil on canvas. 10½ in. × 1 ft. 2 in. Signed, bottom right:
Rex Whistler 1934

On the back: "Sunday May 20th 1934 and Monday." The house appears in perspective to the left, with trees in the distance, and an urn, large, in the foreground. Sir Philip Sassoon and Mrs. Gubbay on a seat, with the lurcher "Blazer". Exhibited at the Leicester Galleries, Oct. 1936.

Owner: The Marchioness of Cholmondeley

54 LONG CROSS HOUSE, *1934*
CHERTSEY, SURREY

Oil on canvas. 2 ft. 4 in. × 4 ft. 6 in. Signed, bottom
right: Rex Whistler 1934

To the left in perspective a red-brick neo-Georgian house with two bay windows. In the distance beyond the lawn, great clumps of trees with a river glimpsed between. Figures in front of the house, including a boy on a bicycle, and in the foreground a little girl with a wheelbarrow.

The late Mr. Micklem commissioned this picture as a stranger. The artist went down, made a sketch, painted the canvas in his studio and returned to add the finishing touches. He allowed himself some licence in transforming a string of ponds into a river and in clumping the timber in the Capability Brown manner. *Owner: Mrs. Micklem*

TWO SKETCHES FOR THE *1934*
ABOVE

(1) *Water-colour. 8½ in. × 1 ft. Signed, bottom right:* Rex
Whistler 1934.
As carried out, but with differences of detail.
Owner: Mrs. Micklem

(2) *Pencil. 8¼ in. × 11 in. Unsigned.*
As painted, but without figures.
Owner: Laurence Whistler

55 HOT NIGHT *? 1934*
Oil on canvas. 10 in. × 1 ft.

Sold by Arthur Tooth in Jan. 1935 to Mrs. Blane Robinson.
Whereabouts unknown

56 NUDE *c. 1934*
Oil on canvas. 8 in. × 10½ in. Unsigned

Reclining nude with right leg raised and right arm above head. Beside her a dish of fruit. Remembered as painted hastily for an exhibition. *Owner: Lady Reed*

57 FAGIN AND *? c. 1934*
MRS. CORNEY IN "OLIVER TWIST"

Oil on canvas. 7 in. × 9¼ in. Signed, bottom right:
Rex Whistler

Two heads. The man lean, with a hooked nose and chin; the woman fat-faced. This and the following picture were painted for Miss Elizabeth Wellesley as a child (Lady Elizabeth Clyde) one rainy afternoon at Penns in the Rocks, Sussex. *Owner: The Lady Elizabeth Clyde*

58 GIRL'S HEAD BESIDE *? c. 1934*
A SKULL

Oil on canvas. 8½ in. × 9½ in. Signed, bottom right:
Rex Whistler

The head of a beautiful girl, rather like the recipient of the picture. The eyes, from which tears fall, are turned slightly to the left and away from a grinning skull, close beside her to the right, which looks at her in profile. The artist described it as "a girl thinking of her dead lover".

Owner: The Lady Elizabeth Clyde

59 **WILTON HOUSE, WILTS**   *1935*
AND THE PALLADIAN BRIDGE
Oil on canvas.   1 ft. 6 in. × 2 ft.
Signed: Rex Whistler

The South front of Wilton House, with, to the left, the North end of the Palladian Bridge. A dog on the opposite bank of the river.

Painted on July 26th–29th, for immediate showing in the Country Seats and Manor Houses Exhibition at the Leicester Galleries. The artist was very dissatisfied with this painting, about which he wrote to Edith Olivier: ". . . The painting was such a failure. . . . It *is* very poor. It's a very carefully and quite well *drawn* view of Wilton, but it can't possibly pretend to be a painting and it is almost entirely colourless." Photograph in *Country Life*, Sept. 1st, 1944.

Owner: Mrs. Ionides

60 **CRANBORNE MANOR,**   *? 1935*
DORSET
Oil on canvas.   1 ft. 5½ in. × 1 ft. 2 in.   Signed, bottom left: Rex Whistler.   (Plate 14)

A romantic picture of the old house, seen, in light, beyond the dark piers of the gateway. The right half of the iron gates is open, and a gardener is sweeping by the wall to the left. Shown at the Country Seats and Manor Houses Exhibition at the Leicester Galleries, in October.

Owner: Miss K. Robinson

61 **FARINGDON HOUSE, BERKS** *? 1935*
Oil on canvas.   9 in. × 1 ft.   Signed, bottom left: Rex Whistler

The house in the middle distance on rising ground, right centre. In the foreground the lake. Two trees to the left; one to the right. Shown at the Country Seats and Manor Houses Exhibition at the Leicester Galleries in October.

Owner: The Lord Astor of Hever

62 **FARINGDON HOUSE, BERKS** *c. 1935*
Oil on canvas.   1 ft. × 1 ft. 4 in.   Unsigned

The country house of Lord Berners. On the left, part of the house with the portico; on the right, a view across the Park. A pair to the picture following.

Owner: Laurence Whistler

63 **FARINGDON HOUSE, BERKS** *c. 1935*
Oil on canvas.   1 ft. × 1 ft. 4 in.   Unsigned

A lamplit interior. A further room seen through an open doorway. In the foreground, a Cupid and Psyche in china.

Owner: Laurence Whistler

64 **RUSHBROOKE HALL,**   *? 1935*
SUFFOLK
Oil on canvas.   10 in. × 1 ft. 2 in.   Signed, bottom left: Rex Whistler

A view along the moat to the bridge, with the house to the right and high trees beyond. Two figures stand on the bridge. Shown at the Country Seats and Manor Houses Exhibition at the Leicester Galleries in October.

Owner: Laurence Whistler

65 **CRESLOW HALL, BUCKS**   *? 1935*
Oil on canvas.   1 ft. 1 in. × 1 ft. 2¼ in.   Signed, bottom left: Rex Whistler

In the centre a farmhouse, with a large tree in the background to the right. In the foreground a wall with a cartwheel leaning against it. Shown at the Country Seats and Manor Houses Exhibition at the Leicester Galleries in October. Now at Ascott Hall, Bucks.

Owner: Anthony de Rothschild, Esq.

66 **"THE FOREIGN BLOKE"**   *? 1935*
Oil on canvas.   1 ft. 2 in. × 10 in.   Signed, bottom left: Rex Whistler

A stolid bowler-hatted Englishman listening to a voluble companion, intended to look foreign: the one with beer, the other with wine. Through the window, sunlight on a Georgian Soho street. Exhibited in the Festival of Contemporary Arts, Bath, 1935, and presented to the Art Gallery by the Bath Society of Artists in that year.

67 **PILGRIM'S HALL, ESSEX**   *1936*
Oil on canvas.   1 ft. 4 in. × 1 ft. 10½ in.   Signed, bottom right: Rex Whistler 1936

Two sides of the house, with a pergola extending to the right, seen across the lawn. Tall trees to the left, and in the distance to the right. Two vases in the left foreground.

Owner: Mrs. J. F. N. Lawrence

SKETCH FOR THE ABOVE   *1936*
Pencil.   8 in. × 1 ft. 1 in.   Unsigned
With colour notes, and details of windows and pergola.

Owner: Laurence Whistler

68 **QUENDON HALL, ESSEX**   *1936*
Oil on canvas.   1 ft. 2 in. × 1 ft. 8¼ in.   Signed, bottom left: Rex Whistler 1936

The front of the late 17th-century red-brick house, with round-topped windows between stuccoed Doric pilasters. Large trees behind. In the foreground, a girl on horse-back. The artist spent three or four hours making a sketch on the site, and finished the painting in his studio.

Owner: Lady Ellis

SKETCH FOR THE ABOVE   *1936*
Pencil.   7 in. × 9 in.   Unsigned
The house as painted. With notes of details.

Owner: Laurence Whistler

69   **ASHCOMBE, WILTS**   *1936*

Oil on canvas.   *8½ in.× 1 ft. 4 in.*   *Signed, bottom left:*
Rex Whistler 1936

The Georgian house to the right; the studio to the left;
a group of dark trees in the centre, and the distant hillside.
    Reproduced as the jacket of *Ashcombe* by Cecil Beaton
(Batsford, 1949).   *Owner: Cecil Beaton, Esq.*

70   **THE STUDIO, ASHCOMBE,**   *c. 1936*
WILTS

Oil on canvas.   *1 ft. 8 in.× 2 ft.*   *Unsigned*

A cool grey interior, with sunlight across the carpet from
three windows to the right. Two tables in the form of
drums.
    Reproduced in *Ashcombe* by Cecil Beaton (1949) opposite
p. 13.   *Owner: Mrs. Hambro*

71   **THE BUCKINGHAM ROAD**   *? 1936*
IN THE RAIN

Oil on canvas.   *8 in.× 10 in.*   *Unsigned.*   *(Plate 5)*

The road runs under telegraph wires from the left foreground to a clump of trees on the right. In driving rain two
figures huddle beneath an umbrella, followed by a third.
Rain blurs the distant hedgerows. The place is just north
of Whitchurch, Bucks., the artist's village at the time.
    Exhibited at the French Gallery, 11 Berkeley Sq., W.1,
June 1936.   *Owner: Lady Mander*

72   **EROS AND PSYCHE**   *? 1937*

? c. 4 in.× 5 in.   *Probably unsigned*

Description from memory. To the left, the naked
Psyche kneeling, her face lifted to the winged Cupid who
bends above her. Background mysterious. Given to the
artist's brother for his flat in Charlotte St. Darkened by
fire in 1942. Returned to the artist in camp for touching up.
And by him lost. "I am *so* distressed about Eros and
Psyche", he wrote that autumn. "I was well aware that
you valued it, which you made clear in your letter when
you sent it, and I was absolutely certain I had it here. I
cannot understand its disappearance." Unretrieved.
    Owner: Laurence Whistler

73   **NUDE**   *c. 1937*

Oil on canvas.   *7¼ in.× 8¾ in.*   *Unsigned*

With head to the left, reclining on a bed. Lying on the
right side with arms forward. In the background, furniture
of the artist's studio.   *Owner: Laurence Whistler*

74   **FLOWER DECORATION**   *c. 1937*

Oil on canvas.   *8¾ in.× 7 in.*   *Unsigned*

Flowers in a vase. A decoration made for one of a pair of
oval Victorian frames.   *Owner: Laurence Whistler*

75   **HATLEY PARK, CAMBS**   *1938*

Oil on canvas.   *2 ft. 6 in.× 4 ft. 11 in.*   *Signed, below
right-hand balustrade:* Rex Whistler 1938

The front of the house seen almost in elevation between
two urns in the foreground; a large tree to the right. In
the lower centre a cartouche with flowers and ribbons,
reading "Hatley Park in the County of Cambridgeshire".
This cartouche was substituted for a wheelbarrow with
scattered tools, because Sir Herman Lebus was a tidy and
keen gardener. A wedding present from his wife.
    Owner: Lady Lebus

ROUGH SKETCH OF THE ABOVE

Pencil.   *10 in.× 1 ft. 2 in.*   *Unsigned*
    Owner: Laurence Whistler

76   **KNEBWORTH HOUSE, HERTS**   *1938*

Oil on canvas.   *11¾ in.× 1 ft. 4 in.*   *Signed, bottom left:*
Rex Whistler July 3d. 1938

The turreted house to the right of centre, seen over
pleached trees, with Lady Caroline Paget standing on the
path in the foreground. To the left a distant landscape under
a shower.   *Owner: Pamela Countess of Lytton*

77   **GODMERSHAM PARK, KENT**   *1938*

Oil on canvas.   *2 ft. 5½ in.× 4 ft. 2 in.*   *Unsigned*

In the left foreground Mr. and Mrs. Tritton under a walnut
tree, beside a table with a tea urn and a plate of cherries, etc.
Mrs. Tritton is looking at a book; to the right is the Sealy-
ham "Val", and in the middle distance a footman in
livery with a tray. In the background the south front of
Godmersham Park.   *Owner: Mrs. Tritton*

78   **TRIPTYCH AT**   *1938*
BROMPTON ORATORY, LONDON

Oil on canvas

Side panels: *approx. 5 ft.× 1 ft. 6 in.*
Centre panel: *approx. 5 ft.× 3 ft.*

Unsigned

In 1937 Mrs. R. H. Twining commissioned the artist to
paint an altar-piece, commemorating the English Roman
Catholic Martyrs in the Chapel of the Martyrs at the
Oratory; and in memory of her parents.
    The centre panel shows in the middle distance a general
scene of execution at Tyburn, with several figures being
hanged on the gibbet and the smoke of a bonfire in the
distance. In the foreground, a cartouche supported by two
cherubs, one looking at a skull, the other pointing heavenwards. On it, in gilded lettering:

Omnes Sancti et beati
Martyres Angliae
Qui pro tuenda fide Catholica
tormenta passi estis et mortem
Orate pro nobis.

Ribbons across the shoulders of the cherubs read, "Pretiosa in conspectu Domini" and "Mors sanctorum eius".

In the left-hand panel appears St. Thomas More beside the executioner's block, against a background of mediaeval architecture. He is named in an oval cartouche supported on the clouds by two cherubs. In the right-hand panel is St. John Fisher in Cardinal's robes, holding the Hat, with a background of trees; and similarly named. The crowds and scenery continue from panel to panel, giving unity to the whole.

The artist was far from content with the snowy marble frame provided for the triptych, but he evidently designed the gilded Martyrs' Crown and palms seen in relief above the centre panel, and the similar devices each side and below. He received £300 for this work on Oct. 6th, 1938. His assistant was Victor Bowen.

DESIGNS FOR THE   1937–1938
ABOVE

(1) *Water-colour, now cut into three pieces. 5¼ in. × 10 in. Unsigned.*
> Very much as carried out, but in the centre both cherubs point heavenwards, and the cartouche is topped by a skull, to be replaced by a crown. In the sky a gilded crown on palm-leaves. This was omitted in favour of the same device on the marble frame in relief. In the side panels the executioner's block and the haloes do not yet appear.

(2) *Pencil, pen-and-ink, and water-colour. 10 in. × 8 in. Unsigned.*
> Unfinished enlargement of the above drawing, squared out.   *Owner: Laurence Whistler*

79   PLAS NEWYDD, ISLE OF   1939
ANGLESEY, FROM THE NORTH-WEST

Oil on canvas.   1 ft. 8 in. × 1 ft. 4 in.   Unsigned

The house seen from high ground with the mountains of Snowdonia rising beyond. To the right, the Menai Straits, glimpsed beyond evergreen trees. Tall trees to the left. In the foreground the artist himself, lying on the grass (unfinished). Lord Uxbridge appears on a bicycle in the middle distance. The wall designed by the artist can be seen projecting from the house. Painted on Apr. 11th and 12th, 1939.   *Owner: The Marquis of Anglesey*

80   IN THE WILDERNESS   1939

Oil on canvas.   1 ft. 4 in. × 1 ft. 8 in.   Unsigned.

(*Plate 49*)

St. John the Baptist is shown as a naked boy leaning on a parapet contemplating a skull, with a Roman ruin in the background against a stormy sunset. The artist also had in mind the text, " As I was in the days of my youth, when the secret of God was upon my tabernacle" (*Job* xxix, 4).

The model was "Jim", an evacuee from Portsmouth, billeted at the artist's house, 69 The Close, Salisbury. The picture was painted for charity and sold at the Red Cross Sale at Christie's on July 8th, 1940, to the late Mr. David Grieg, whose son, Mr. David Grieg, presented it to the

present owner. Reproduced in *The Queen's Book of the Red Cross* (Hodder and Stoughton, 1939) as a full plate in colour, opposite p. 176, and in *The Evening News*, Feb. 14th, 1953.   *Owner: Laurence Whistler*

81   AMOROUS PAINTING ON   1940
GLASS

Oil on glass.   3 ft. 3½ in. × 2 ft. 7½ in.   Unsigned

A winged Eros passionately embracing a naked Psyche, who yields to him, leaning back on one knee. Painted impromptu on a sheet of glass as a mural decoration for a dinner-party given by the owner: Lady Elizabeth von Hofmannsthal.

82   BIERTON VICARAGE, BUCKS   1940

Oil on canvas.   1 ft. × 1 ft. 4 in.   Unsigned

The back of the Vicarage, with two bay windows and two figures sketched in on the lawn. To the right a buttress of the church. Painted in May 1940, with no. 83, and given to the artist's mother.   *Owner: Mrs. Frederick Turner*

83   BIERTON CHURCH AND   1940
VICARAGE, BUCKS

Oil on canvas.   1 ft. × 1 ft. 4 in.   Unsigned

To the right, part of the church, rising large above the garden wall; to the left, the back of the more distant vicarage; in the foreground the artist's uncle, Canon W. H. Elliott, shouldering a rake.

Owner: Mrs. Frederick Turner

84   THE ENTRANCE GATES TO   1940
THE DAYE HOUSE, WILTON, WILTS

Oil on canvas.   10 in. × 1 ft. 2 in.   Unsigned

(*Plate 34*)

Deep shadow under the yew-trees fills the picture, with the sunlit roadway glimpsed beyond the open carriage-gates. Edith Olivier seated to the left. Flecks and patches of sunlight in the gloom. Painted on May 19th.

Owner: Miss Rosemary Olivier

85   THE PARK SCHOOL,   1940
WILTON, WILTS

Oil on canvas.   Approx. 1 ft. × 1 ft. 5 in.

Signed: Rex Whistler May 20th 1940

To the right the rich front of the building against a background of trees in full leaf. In front, Mr. David Herbert on sunlit grass with a poodle.

Owner: Beatrice, Countess of Pembroke

86   LANDSCAPE TARGET   1940

Oil on board.   3 ft. 1 in. × 8 ft. 9½ in.   Unsigned

Painted for the Welsh Guards Training Bn. Three street vistas radiating from a statue, the right-hand street adjoining a canal. It was thought too good to be shot to pieces by recruits on the range, and is preserved by the regiment. No one appears in these battle-deserted streets, except, as the artist wrote to his mother on Aug. 19th: "A mysterious figure with a gun at one of the windows and another on a roof." He told her, "today the King came to inspect our battalion here, but of course I was away at Pirbright. . . . The King much admired a target which I had painted for the miniature range here . . . and left a message for me to say that I ought to put a great many more Quislings in the picture."   *Owner: The Welsh Guards*

87 · **CLAREMONT, SURREY**   *1940*
*Oil on canvas.   1 ft. 4 in.× 1 ft. 8 in.   Signed, bottom
left: Rex Whistler. Aug. 1940.   (Plate 33)*
The front of the Palladian house, with the sunlit right-hand side just visible. To the right, trees. To the left, cedars beyond the house. Beyond a low ha-ha running straight across, a self-portrait of the artist on a camp-stool painting the house at his easel: seen in uniform, with a bicycle on the grass just beside him. Blue sky and sun-splashed grass.
Owner: H.R.H. Princess Alice, Countess of Athlone

88   **THE PALLADIAN BRIDGE**   *1942*
AND RIVER, WILTON, WILTS
Oil on canvas.   1 ft. 2 in.× 1 ft. 6 in.   Unsigned
Painted in the centre of the bridge near Edith Olivier's house, the parapet forming the foreground. The Palladian Bridge far off down the tree-lined vista of the river, under a pure blue sky. Two swans on the water.
It is possible that this picture began as a moonlight scene; for Edith Olivier records in her unpublished Journal for June 21st: "All morning, the loveliest landscape he has ever done, the stretch of the river from my bridge to the Palladian—in silvery moonlight, and with two swans on it. It is quite exquisite. . . ."
On the back the artist has written (perhaps by mistake —perhaps referring to an earlier picture, painted out) "Heytesbury. May 2nd 1942."
Owner: Miss Rosemary Olivier

89   **THE HALL AND STAIRCASE,**   *1942*
MELLS, SOMERSET
*Oil on canvas.   10¼ in.× 1 ft. 1¾ in.   Signed, bottom right:
Katharine from Rex May 23rd*
To the left a passage, with a gilded angel on a pedestal and a hanging blue overall; to the right the stairs rising, with John Jolliffe, aged 10, seated half-way up. Painted during a wet week-end, on leave from an Army course at Weston-super-Mare.   *Owner: Mrs. Raymond Asquith*

90   **THE DAYE HOUSE, WILTON,**   *1942*
**WILTS, FROM NEAR THE ENTRANCE
GATES**
*Oil on canvas.   1 ft. 2 in.× 1 ft. 8 in.   Signed, bottom right:
Rex Whistler June 21st 1942*
To the right the Daye House in the middle distance; to the left, closer, under trees, the back of the artist's Hudson

Terraplane car. To the right again, a little nearer, Edith Olivier standing on the grass.
Owner: Miss Rosemary Olivier

91   **WILTON RECTORY, WILTS**   *1942*
Oil on canvas.   10 in.× 1 ft. 2 in.   Unsigned
A first attempt at a picture to be presented to Mr. and Mrs. Campbell for the 30th anniversary of their coming to the Rectory at Wilton. Unfinished. Dark cedars to the left, with the house partly hidden by them, the window-frames unpainted. Edith Olivier records in her unpublished Journal for Dec. 12th:
"After luncheon we went to the Rectory garden where he began a picture to be given to the Campbells. The garden completely flooded. We sat on the path behind the water-fall and there was no way to get to the lawn and garden as deep water was everywhere. . . ."
Owner: Miss Rosemary Olivier

92   **WILTON RECTORY, WILTS**   *1942*
*Oil on canvas.   9¼ in.× 1 ft. 7½ in.
Signed: Rex Whistler Dec 12th 1942*
The artist was dissatisfied with his first sketch (above), and painted on the following day a new version on a long-shaped canvas, showing on the left the campanile of the Italianate church of Wilton, on the right the Rectory, and in the centre a group of dark trees dividing the composition into two halves.
Edith Olivier records on Dec. 13th: "He began a lovely composition—house, lawn, Campanile, with cedars and ilex. It is full of imagination. Painted in great discomfort— deluges of rain and very cold."   *Owner: Mrs. Campbell*

93   **THE DAYE HOUSE,**   *c. 1942*
WILTON, FROM THE RIVER-SIDE
Oil on canvas.   1 ft. 2 in.× 1 ft. 8 in.   Unsigned
(Plate 32)
The bay-windowed end of the house in the middle distance, surrounded by trees. Edith Olivier standing to the right. Tousled grass in sun and shadow.
Owner: Miss Rosemary Olivier

94   **BACKGROUND TO**   *1942–1943*
**PORTRAIT OF MISS BARBARA
TOWNSEND (Unfinished)**
Oil on canvas
A half-length portrait, by an unknown painter, of Miss Townsend as a young woman with folded arms, given to her friend Miss Edith Olivier after her death. It was un-finished. Rex Whistler provided the background of blue sky and clouds; with Mompesson House (Miss Townsend's home for 97 years) and the adjoining buildings in the Close at Salisbury.   *Owner: Miss Rosemary Olivier*

Erratum before going to press:—
HEYTESBURY HOUSE, WILTSHIRE *1943*
Wrongly described to the authors as a water-colour, and so catalogued. See no. 275.

95 **LANDSCAPE NEAR** *1943*
THETFORD, NORFOLK

Oil on canvas. 10¾ in. × 1 ft. 2 in.   *Unsigned*

(Plate 35)

In the left foreground a self-portrait of the artist in shirt-sleeves on a camp-stool, painting at a paint-box easel. The scene before him is of a little house and untidy out-houses, with the back of an old pale-blue charabanc. Beyond are the tower and roof of a country church, and great trees under a clear sky. High summer, with brilliant sunlight.

In a letter to Lady Juliet Duff of May 29th, 1943, written at Thetford, where the artist was stationed with his battalion, he mentions that he has been painting landscapes in the district.   *Owner: Simon Fleet, Esq.*

96 **BINDERTON,** *1944*
nr. CHICHESTER, SUSSEX

Oil on canvas. 1 ft. × 1 ft. 3½ in.   *Unsigned*

The house, with a central bay, in perspective to the right, the main block partly framed by a tree in the left foreground. Painted while the artist was visiting Mr. and Mrs. Anthony Eden on leave, shortly before embarking for Normandy.   *Owner: Sir Anthony Eden*

97 **RIVER SCENE IN ROME** *n.d.*

Oil on canvas. 1 ft. 4 in. × 2 ft.   *Unsigned*

Unfinished. So listed by the artist's mother.

Whereabouts unknown

98 **HACKWOOD PARK, HANTS** *n.d.*

Oil on canvas. 10¼ in. × 1 ft. 4 in.   *Unsigned*

View of the Terrace at Hackwood Park with part of the house to the right and the swimming-pool to left. In the foreground a chaise-longue with two figures, one of them Lady Pamela Berry. Unfinished.

Owner: Laurence Whistler

99 **"DRAWING-ROOM, MERTON** *n.d.*
HALL, CAMBRIDGE"

Oil on canvas. 1 ft. × 1 ft. 3½ in.   *Unsigned*

Back-view of Lord Rothschild seated at a piano, on which stands a very tall vase of flowers. Nearer, to the right, a desk.   *Owner: Laurence Whistler*

100 **A CHIMNEY-PIECE PANEL** *n.d.*

Oil on wood. Approx. 2 ft. × 2 ft. 7 in.   *Unsigned*

A small oval panel above the chimney-piece mirror at 12 Kensington Palace Gardens. Backed by crimson and gold drapery, a cipher of "S.C." on a shell, from which hangs a small circular medallion containing a portrait of "Brownie", Lady Cholmondeley's dachshund.

Owner: The Marchioness of Cholmondeley

DISCARDED IDEA FOR THE *n.d.*
ABOVE

Pencil, sepia ink, and water-colour. 7½ in. × 9¾ in.

Unsigned

An ellipse of the same size, containing a cipher of "S.C." between sprays of flowers, with "Brownie" tied by a blue bow to the crossing of the "C's".

Owner: Laurence Whistler

101 **MUSICAL TROPHY** *n.d.*

Oil on canvas. 3 ft. 4 in. × 3 ft. 8 in.   *Unsigned*

In rosaille and green: trumpets, flags, a lute, and grapes. At the top, a female bust facing left. A painted, ruled border.   *Owner: Michael Renshaw, Esq.*

DESIGN FOR THE ABOVE *n.d.*

Sepia ink and water-colour. 4¾ in. × 4 in.

Signed, bottom right: R.W.

Trumpets, flags, lute, drum, and grapes. The bust, male and bearded. Plum-coloured. In a ruled border.

Owner: Nicolas Furse, Esq.

Portraits in Oils
and Related Drawings

102   **SELF-PORTRAIT**   *1924*

Oil on canvas.   *1 ft. 7½ in.× 1 ft. 4 in.*   *Unsigned*

Head and shoulders facing half-right, in oblique light from that side, with a striped shirt and green tie.

Possibly the earliest attempt at portraiture in oils, and certainly the first self-portrait in the medium. Probably the painting referred to in a letter to Ronald Fuller of Jan. 28th, 1924: "I am at present at work on a painting of myself; with a mirror beside my canvas. I find my sitter always most obliging, &, unlike some others, always ready to pose for me when I wish!"   *Owner: Laurence Whistler*

103   **DAME EDITH SITWELL**   *c. 1929*

Oil on canvas.   *1 ft. 5 in.× 1 ft. 2 in.*   *Unsigned*

Facing half left, seated in a high-backed gilt rococo chair upholstered in red. Background a flat, dark greenish-grey.

Owner: Sir Osbert Sitwell

? SKETCH FOR THE ABOVE

In the 1929A Sketch-book, p. 31 (no. 298). Head only, facing half-right; with a similar sketch beside it. "Edith. Jan:".

104   **LORD BERNERS**   *1929*

Oil on canvas.   *1 ft. 4 in.× 1 ft. 1 in.*   *Unsigned*

Lord Berners seated at an easel facing half-right, in shirt-sleeves, his right hand raised in the act of painting. On the back: "Lord Berners. Started afternoon July 12th 1929, 13th, finished 14th."   *Owner: Laurence Whistler*

105   **CONVERSATION PIECE**   *1932–*
AT PENNS IN THE ROCKS,   *1934*
WITHYHAM, SUSSEX

Oil on canvas.   *3 ft.× 4 ft.*   *Signed, bottom left:*
Rex Whistler 1932–4.   (*Plate 39*)

Mr. Valerian Wellesley (Lord Douro) as a boy, standing leaning against a rock, facing half-right, with a gun under his arm. Miss Elizabeth Wellesley (Lady Elizabeth Clyde) seated facing half-right and leaning on her right arm. To the right a huge dog below a rock. Between rocks in the middle distance, part of the house is seen, with their mother, Lady Gerald Wellesley (the poetess, Dorothy Wellesley), at an upper window.

Owner: The Marquis Douro

STUDIES FOR THE ABOVE   *c. 1932*

(1) VALERIAN WELLESLEY, ESQ. *Oil on canvas. 1 ft. 6 in.× 1 ft. 2 in. Unsigned.*

Half-length in front of a rock, with the house to the right; in a blue shirt, facing half-left. Much as in the final painting, but folded arms are indicated.

Owner: The Marquis Douro

(2) MISS ELIZABETH WELLESLEY. *Oil on canvas. 1 ft. 1 in.× 10 in. Signed on the back:* Rex Whistler 20 Fitzroy Street. Head and shoulders of Lady Elizabeth as a girl, in an open-necked shirt and blue overall, the head slightly turned to the left; background of uneven tone.

Owner: The Lady Elizabeth Clyde

(3) MISS WELLESLEY. *Pencil and water-colour. 1 ft. 2 in.× 10 in. Unsigned.*

Full-face in an open-necked shirt, sitting with legs folded, supported on her right hand. "April 30th, 1933."

(4) MISS WELLESLEY. *Pencil. 8 in.× 1 ft. ½ in. Unsigned.*

In the above pose, wearing shorts. On the reverse: sketch for a drawing, "What is the Junior Book Club?": a youth reading aloud to a girl under a tree, near a waterfall. Pencil. "Will you kindly lend me this page again, as I did not know there was a drawing on the back? I will copy it out when you return it as I need the sketch of the child. R.W."

(5) 3 PENCIL SKETCHES. *Average size 1 ft. 1½ in.× 9¼ in. Unsigned.*

Sketch of the whole, as carried out, but with the butt of the gun resting on the ground, and without the dog.

A closer view of the house, at the chosen angle between rocks. (In the final picture he would paint it as more remote than it actually is.)

A sketch for Mr. Wellesley's pose, with the gun butt resting on the ground.

(6) 2 STUDIES. *Sepia ink and wash. 11 in.× 7 in. Unsigned.*

One of rocks and one of trees: both on Penns in the Rocks writing-paper, the former torn at top and bottom. On the reverse of the latter there is a pencil note "to R.H." (Ronald Horton, his assistant at 19 Hill St.) concerning the roughing out of that mural.

Owner: Laurence Whistler

106   **DAVID HORNER, ESQ.**   *1933*

Oil on canvas.   *1 ft. 2 in.× 10 in.*   *Unsigned*

Head and shoulders, facing half-right, wearing a green scarf. To the right, a pagoda in the distance—because the sitter was soon leaving for China with Sir Osbert Sitwell. *Owner: David Horner, Esq.*

107 SELF-PORTRAIT *1933*
Oil on canvas. 1 ft. 3½ in. × 1 ft. 2 in. Unsigned

Three-quarter-length, in a dark overcoat with turned-up collar and red scarf. On the right, in a romantic landscape under a cloudy sky, one of the twin Boycott Pavilions at Stowe.

Bequeathed to the Trustees of the Tate Gallery by Miss Edith Olivier. The inscription on the placard beneath was composed by Sir Osbert Sitwell. It is now on permanent exhibition in the Tate Gallery Restaurant.

108 MISS EDITH OLIVIER *1933*
Oil on canvas. 1 ft. 2 in. × 10 in. Signed, bottom right:
Edith with best love from Rex. Christmas, 1933

Head and shoulders, facing half-left, with folded arms. In an easy chair, wearing a dark-green, open-necked blouse, the head resting against a yellow-brown cushion.
Owner: The Marquis of Anglesey

109 MISS PENELOPE DUDLEY *c. 1933*
WARD (Lady Reed)
Oil on canvas. 11 in. × 9 in. Unsigned

Head and shoulders, with head turned half-left. As Penelope, with Ulysses' ship small in the background, departing at night over wine-dark sea. Rolling clouds and scattered stars, one star above her head. *Owner: Lady Reed*

110 SELF-PORTRAIT *? c. 1933*
Oil on canvas. 1 ft. × 9 in. Unsigned

Profile, seated at a table, in a roll-top sweater, facing left. Rejected by the artist, and rescued by the present owner from a waste-paper basket. No likeness.
Owner: Lady Reed

111 MISS PENELOPE AND *1933–1934*
MISS ANGELA DUDLEY WARD
(Lady Reed and Lady Laycock)
Oil on canvas. 3 ft. 1½ in. × 4 ft.
Signed below the fountain mask: Rex W pinxt Anno Domini MCMXXXIII–IV. (Plate 40)

The two Miss Dudley Wards, in white dresses with black-edged collars, are standing (Miss Angela to the left) by a fountain into which water pours from a stone mask—a self-portrait of the artist with satyr horns. A top-hatted negro page stoops to lay out fruit and chicken on the steps, from a picnic basket. In the distance a river winds away into romantic mountains. Exhibited at the Royal Academy, 1934. *Owner: The Marquesa de Casa Maury*

SKETCHES FOR THE ABOVE
(1) *c. 1933*
Oil on canvas. 9 in. × 1 ft. Unsigned
Much as carried out, but without the self-portrait mask.
Owner: Lady Reed

(2) *c. 1933*
Water-colour. 7¾ in. × 8¼ in. Unsigned
Roughly as carried out, but with the faces afterwards erased; a dog in place of the negro; a cherub pouring water in place of the self-portrait mask; and, to the left, a hurrying crone. *Owner: Laurence Whistler*

112 VALERIAN WELLESLEY, ESQ. *1934*
(The Marquis Douro)
Oil on canvas. Approx. 9 in. × 6 in.

A semi-humorous sketch of Mr. Wellesley as a young man, in bed after sunstroke, in a high vaulted room at the Fortezza della Brunella, Aulla. Painting mislaid.
Owner: The Marquis Douro

113 THE VISCOUNTESS *1934*
HAMBLEDEN
(The Dowager Viscountess Hambleden)
Oil on canvas. 2 ft. 3 in. × 1 ft. 10 in. Signed, bottom left:
REX

Three-quarter length, facing half-left, with arms folded. Landscape background. Unfinished.
Owner: The Dowager Viscountess Hambleden

114 MRS. GUBBAY *1934*
Oil on canvas. 1 ft. 5 in. × 1 ft. 9 in. Unsigned

An unfinished portrait of Mrs. Gubbay, seated sewing on a chaise-longue in the drawing-room at 44 Hertford St., with a dachshund to the left. The face unfinished. Much of the interior carefully painted: a high green-panelled room with windows to the right, behind the sitter.

SKETCH FOR THE ABOVE *1934*
Sepia ink and water-colour. 5½ in. × 6 in. Unsigned

A moderately finished sketch of sitter and room, as carried out, but without the dog.

FIVE PENCIL DRAWINGS FOR *1934*
THE ABOVE
8¾ in. × 7 in.
Careful notes of furniture in the room.
Owner: Laurence Whistler

115 MRS. GUBBAY *? c. 1934*
Oil on canvas. 11½ in. × 9 in. Unsigned
Head and shoulders, wearing a red blouse.
Owner: Mrs. Gubbay

116 **SELF-PORTRAIT** *? 1934*
Oil on canvas. *1 ft. 4¼ in. × 1 ft. ½ in.* *Unsigned.*
(Frontispiece)

Head and shoulders, facing half-left, lit from the right; in an open-necked pink-checked shirt against a curtain. Sold by Arthur Tooth to Mr. G. H. Hynes in Jan. 1935. Sold by Christie on Nov. 6th, 1959, to the National Portrait Gallery.

117 **"SAINT TOUGHIE"** *c. 1934*
Miss Angela Dudley Ward (Lady Laycock)
Oil on canvas. *Approx. 1 ft. 3 in. × 10 in.* *Unsigned*

Portrait of Lady Laycock as a girl. Head and shoulders, looking half-left; in armour, with a gloved right hand raised on the shaft of a spear or banner; and with a halo.
Owner: Lady Laycock

118 **MRS. HENRY WHISTLER** *1935*
(The Artist's Mother)
Oil on canvas. *1 ft. × 10 in.* *Unsigned*

Seated in a winged chair, facing half-left, reading a book held high in both hands; in a mauve jersey, leaning against a green-striped cushion. In pencil on the back: "M. Whitchurch. 1935, 11th of May."
Owner: Laurence Whistler

119 **THE LADY CAROLINE PAGET** *1935*
(The Lady Caroline Duff)
Oil on canvas. *1 ft. 4 in. × 1 ft.* *Unsigned*

On the back: "Caroline in the tent at Knebworth. July 3rd 1935." She is sitting in a wicker chair in coat and skirt, facing right, reading a newspaper. Furniture in the background.
Owner: The Lady Caroline Duff

120 **GIRL WITH A RED ROSE** *1935*
Oil on canvas. *1 ft. 6 in. × 1 ft. 2 in.* *Signed, bottom right:*
Rex Whistler 1935. *(Plate 47)*

Seated in front of a mirror facing half-right; in a yellow dress off the shoulders, and black gloves, with left hand raised to her hair, and her right hand holding a red rose in front of her bodice. Painted during one week-end at the Park School, Wilton: Lady Caroline Paget (Lady Caroline Duff) being the model.
  Exhibited at Tooth's Gallery, Dec. 1935. Reproduced in colour by Messrs. Pulman, a small number of copies being signed by the artist. Also in *The Artist*, Sept. 1937.
Owner: Mrs. Harriet O'Cock

121 **THE LORD IVOR GUEST** *1935*
(The Viscount Wimborne)
Oil on canvas. *1 ft. 8 in. × 1 ft. 4 in.* *Unsigned*

Half-length, facing half-left, with face turned towards the beholder. Arms folded. In a black tail-coat and white stock.

A landscape background, including to the left a view of Ashby St. Ledgers. *Owner: The Viscount Wimborne*

122 **DOROTHY WELLESLEY** *c. 1935*
(The late Duchess of Wellington)
Oil on canvas. *1 ft. 8 in. × 1 ft. 4 in.* *Unsigned*

Head and shoulders, full face, the left shoulder draped in red, the right shoulder bare: in a sketched oval. A painting in the Restoration manner. Unfinished.
Owner: Laurence Whistler

123 **CECIL BEATON, ESQ.** *? c. 1935*
Oil on canvas. *1 ft. 3 in. × 1 ft. 10 in.* *Unsigned*

Painted in the artist's studio at 20 Fitzroy St. Mr. Beaton is reclining on the bed, with one knee raised and a cigarette in his left hand, his head propped on the other hand.
Owner: Cecil Beaton, Esq.

124 **SELF-PORTRAIT** *1936*
Oil on canvas. *1 ft. 6 in. × 1 ft. 2 in.* *Unsigned*

The artist in *lederhosen*, seated facing half-right, at work at a drawing on his knees. The face unfinished. In the distance, the house and lake beyond a field of stooks. Painted while staying with Mr. Raimond von Hofmannsthal at Schloss Kammer am Attersee, Austria. *Owner: Laurence Whistler*

125 **"SONNY GRANT"** *1936*
Oil on canvas. *1 ft. 3¼ in. × 11¼ in.* *Signed, bottom left:*
Rex Whistler 1936

A negro boy: head and shoulders, full-face, in a grey coat. Tone background. Shown at the Leicester Galleries, Summer, 1940, and reproduced in *The Connoisseur*, Sept. 1940. *Owner: Laurence Whistler*

126 **MRS. HAMLYN** *1936*
Oil on canvas. *8¾ in. × 10½ in.* *Unsigned*

Seated in an open carriage, facing half-left. Background (sketched only): part of the front of Clovelly Court, Devon, with a glimpse of the sea. Only the figure of Mrs. Hamlyn is finished. *Owner: Laurence Whistler*

127 **MRS. HAMLYN** *c. 1936*
Oil on canvas. *11¾ in. × 9¼ in.* *Unsigned*

Mrs. Hamlyn in old age, seated in an arm-chair at Clovelly Court, Devon, facing half-left; with a paper in her right hand, her left hand resting on a folding table.
Owner: Laurence Whistler

128 **THE EARL OF UXBRIDGE** *1937*
(The seventh Marquis of Anglesey)
Oil on wood. *1 ft. 4 in. × 1 ft. 1 in.* *Unsigned*

Half-length portrait of Lord Anglesey as a boy. His left arm rests on a pile of books. From one a paper projects with the inscription: "Henry, Earl of Uxbridge"; from another a slip, with "Aetate sui XIV." Bookshelves compose the entire background.

Owner: The Lady Katharine Farrell

129 THE LADY PATRICIA *c. 1937* DOUGLAS (The Lady Patricia Hornak)

Oil on canvas.   6¼ in. × 4¾ in.   Unsigned.

Head only, full-face; in a grey shirt, buttoned at the neck. Tone background.   *Owner: Laurence Whistler*

130 THE LADY CAROLINE PAGET *? 1937* (The Lady Caroline Duff)

Oil on canvas.   1 ft. 1½ in. × 10 in.   Unsigned.
(Plate 48)

Head and shoulders: the head turned half-left, resting against a green quilted cushion, and with a black-striped open collar to the dress. Probably the portrait sold by Arthur Tooth in Feb. 1937. *Owner: The Lady Juliet Duff*

131 THE HON. ROSANAGH *1938* CRICHTON

Oil on canvas.   1 ft. 2½ in. × 1 ft.   Signed, on blackboard:
Rex Whistler July 21st 1938.   (Plate 50)

A commissioned portrait of Miss Crichton at the age of six, sitting up in bed, after tonsillitis, doing paper cut-outs. Full-face, looking down. On a blackboard in the background there is a childish outline of a man in chalk, with the inscription given above—as if the sitter had portrayed the artist in return. *Owner: The Lady Davina Woodhouse*

132 THE LADY CAROLINE PAGET *? c. 1938* (The Lady Caroline Duff)

Oil on canvas.   2 ft. 1 in. × 1 ft. 10½ in.

Leaning sideways, her head resting on her right hand, in a brown shirt. Half-length. *Owner: The Lady Diana Cooper*

133 CONVERSATION PIECE: *1938–* THE FAMILY OF THE SIXTH *1939* MARQUIS OF ANGLESEY

Oil on canvas.   2 ft. 6 in. × 2 ft. 1 in.   Unsigned.

A view through the open doorway into the Gothic Hall at Plas Newydd. Lady Caroline Paget (face unfinished) leans against the left door-post. Within the room, Lord Uxbridge is standing painting at an easel; Lady Rose is seated in a red chair reading a magazine; Lord Anglesey is seated full-face in an arm-chair. On the far side, Lady Anglesey sits at the piano, facing right, with Lady Katharine and Lady Mary beside her.

Owner: The Marquis of Anglesey

134 THE SIXTH MARQUIS OF *1939* ANGLESEY

Oil on canvas.   1 ft. 8 in. × 1 ft. 2 in.   Unsigned.

The Marquis of Anglesey seated in the Library at Plas Newydd, facing half-right, with a yellow book and two envelopes on the floor beside him. The wall behind is hung with red toile, and a marble fireplace forms the right background.

The portrait was given by the present Lord Anglesey to the University College of North Wales, to commemorate his father's term of office as President. Exhibited at the Leicester Galleries, July 1940.

Owner: The University College of North Wales, Bangor

135 THE LADY PAMELA BERRY *1939*

Oil on canvas.   3 ft. 6 in. × 1 ft. 5½ in.   Signed, left, as if inscribed on temple: Rex Whistler pinxit Anno Domini
MCMXXXIX

Reclining in a great formal garden, facing half-left; her son Adrian, aged about 2, in the foreground, playing with a caged bird. In the background, left, a temple derived from the Boycott Pavilions at Stowe. Photographs in *Country Life*, Nov. 27th, 1958.   *Owner: The Lady Pamela Berry*

SKETCH FOR THE ABOVE *1939*

Pencil.   10 in. × 1 ft. 2 in.   Unsigned

Adrian Berry, in the same attitude as in the oil painting, seated with legs folded; to the right a larger study of the head and shoulders only.

Reproduced in *Rex Whistler* by Laurence Whistler, 1948, p. 88.   *Owner: Laurence Whistler*

136 EDITH OLIVIER *1939*

Oil on canvas.   2 ft. 3 in. × 1 ft. 8 in.   Unsigned

In a striped suit, seated nearly full-face in a winged arm-chair, with hands holding a book on her lap. In the background the panelled walls of the artist's studio at 29 Fitzroy Square, with the unfinished portrait of Miss Elizabeth Maugham (Lady John Hope) on an easel.

On the back: "Miss Edith Olivier Mayor of Wilton." Below are the names of the friends who gave the picture to her after the artist's death. *Owner: Miss Rosemary Olivier*

137 MISS ELIZABETH MAUGHAM *1939* (The Lady John Hope)

Oil on canvas.   2 ft. 4 in. × 1 ft. 9 in.
Signed, bottom left: Rex Whistler

Unfinished portrait in a snow scene, with a tall-crowned hat. In the distance one of the Boycott Pavilions at Stowe.

Owner: The Lady John Hope

138 MISS LAURA RIDLEY *1940* (Mrs. Adrian Carrick)

Oil on canvas.   1 ft. 8 in. × 1 ft. 4 in.   Unsigned.
(Plate 42)

Miss Ridley at a tender age in the uniform of the Northumberland Hussars: a little girl dressed as a drummer-boy, with side-cap and striped trousers, beating a drum. In the background, bell tents, and a distant view of the garden front of Blagdon, Northumberland.

The artist wrote from Blagdon to Lady Aberconway in January: "I am just finishing the best portrait I have yet done—only quite a small one of little Laura Ridley. . . . Can I come to Bodnant soon to try and do a better one of Anne? I do so long to, as I feel very much in the mood and encouraged by *this* one and it will be very cheap because nowadays it's so wonderful to have a commission at all."

Reproduced in *Country Life*, Aug. 8th, 1952, p. 399.

Owner: The Viscountess Ridley

139   **MISS LAURA RIDLEY**   *1940*
(Mrs. Adrian Carrick)

Oil on canvas.   1 ft. 1 in. × 10 in.   Unsigned

Miss Ridley as a little girl standing at a table covered with small paint-pots. Left profile. Background, a marble chimney-piece at Blagdon. *Owner: The Viscountess Ridley*

140   **THE HON. ANNE McLAREN**   *1940*

Oil on canvas.   2 ft. 5½ in. × 1 ft. 11 in.   Signed, bottom left:
Rex Whistler Feb 1940.   (*Plate 51*)

As a child aged 12, in a long dress: seated on a wall, facing left, holding up a "Jacob's Ladder" toy. In the right background The Pin Mill at Bodnant, North Wales.

Owner: Dr. Anne McLaren

141   **THE HON. ANNE McLAREN**   *1940*

Oil on canvas.   1 ft. 7½ in. × 1 ft. 3¼ in.   Signed, bottom right:
Rex Whistler Feb. 1940

As a child aged 12, lying on a sofa in a pink tunic, facing half-right, with head supported on her right hand.

Owner: Christabel Lady Aberconway

142   **THE HON. ANNE McLAREN**   *1940*

Oil on canvas.   1 ft. 4 in. × 1 ft. 6 in.   Unsigned

As a child aged 12, seated on the end of a sofa, in a beret, with head turned nearly full-face, and left leg folded under right. *Owner: Christabel Lady Aberconway*

143   **THE VISCOUNTESS RIDLEY**   *1940*

Oil on canvas.   1 ft. 6 in. × 1 ft. 2 in.   Unsigned

Head and shoulders, facing half-left, looking down. With a large bow at the neck. Painted shortly before the artist joined up in May. *Owner: The Viscountess Ridley*

144   **THE LADY ELIZABETH VON**   *1940*
HOFMANNSTHAL

Oil on canvas.   1 ft. 8 in. × 2 ft. 1 in.   Signed, bottom
right: Rex Whistler 1940

Seated facing left, reading a letter, at 27 York Terrace, London. In the background to the left, a writing-table between pink curtains; to the right, behind the head, a window on to Regent's Park. Reflections in a mirror beneath the writing-table. Reproduced as "The Letter" in *The Studio*, 1944.

Owner: The Lady Elizabeth von Hofmannsthal

145   **THE LADY ELIZABETH VON**   *1940*
HOFMANNSTHAL

Oil on canvas.   2 ft. 6 in. × 3 ft. 4 in.   Unsigned

In a long yellow dress, reclining on a sofa; a small Bible, closed, in the hand: meditating.

Owner: The Lady Elizabeth von Hofmannsthal

146   **THE HON. JOHN McLAREN**   *1940*

Oil on canvas.   2 ft. 3 in. × 1 ft. 8 in.   Signed, bottom
right: Rex Whistler

Seated in the wings of a theatre, almost full-face, looking down at his watch; in the background, Lady Rose McLaren on stage, dancing.

A wedding present, inscribed on the back: "For darling Rose and John with love from Rex. April 3rd 1940."

Owner: The Lady Rose McLaren

147   **SELF-PORTRAIT IN**   *1940*
UNIFORM

Oil on canvas.   2 ft. 4 in. × 1 ft. 11 in.   Unsigned.
(*Plate 1*)

The artist is seated on the balustrade outside his temporary first-floor studio at 27 York Terrace, Regent's Park (the home of Lady Elizabeth von Hofmannsthal). In his left hand is a glass, in front of him a tray of bottles and glasses and a bundle of brushes. To the right, a chair with his Welsh Guards cap and belt, etc. In the background, Regent's Park in sunlight.

Painted in May 1940, just before entering the Regiment. Mentioned by Edith Olivier in her unpublished Journal for June 10th, 1941: "An enchanting portrait of himself on balcony at York Terrace, done the day his uniform came."

Painted over an unfinished portrait of Cecil Beaton in Moroccan dress, referred to incorrectly as a "Conversation Piece" on p. 78 of *Ashcombe* by Cecil Beaton, 1949. Canvases were scarce during the war.

Owner: Laurence Whistler

148   **PORTRAIT GROUP AT**   *1940*
COLCHESTER

Oil on canvas.   1 ft. 1¼ in. × 1 ft. 5 in.   Unsigned

The Young Officers' "Dormitory" at Roman Way Camp, Colchester. Mr. Adrian Pryce-Jones reading on a bed in the foreground. Beyond, the artist seated on a bed attending to his shoe. Another figure to the right.

Given to the Welsh Guards
by the artist's mother and brother in 1944

149   **PORTRAIT GROUP AT**   *1940*
SANDOWN PARK

Oil on canvas.   1 ft. 7½ in. × 1 ft. 11¼ in.   Unsigned

Inside the Royal Box at Sandown Park, then occupied by the Welsh Guards Training Battalion. To the left, Mr. Adrian Pryce-Jones in an arm-chair; right centre, Mr. Francis Egerton with feet up, on a sofa. Over the balcony a view of the race-course and neighbourhood. The right half is unfinished.

Given to the Welsh Guards
by the artist's mother and brother in 1944

150 MAJOR JOHN STEEL LEWES *1940*
(Jock Lewes)

Oil on canvas.   *1 ft. 8 in. × 1 ft. 4 in.*   *Unsigned.*
(Plate 52)

Sitting in the stand at Sandown Park, then occupied by the Welsh Guards, with a view of the race-course in sunlight beyond. Facing half-right, looking down at a Bren gun across his knees, with a box of ammunition sketched in to the left. The artist was at first dissatisfied with this portrait of a friend who afterwards won fame with the Special Air Service in the African desert; but it is described by his brother as a revealing likeness.   *Owner: A. H. Lewes, Esq.*

151 DAVID VAUGHAN, ESQ.   *1940*

Oil on canvas.   *2 ft. 6 in. × 1 ft. 8 in.*   *Unsigned*

Standing nearly full-face, in knickerbockers, with a gun under the right arm, watched by his black Labrador, "Duke". Painted in the Royal Box at Sandown Park, where their battalion of the Welsh Guards was stationed. A fanciful background of trees and a field gate.

Owner: David Vaughan, Esq.

152 GILBERT RYLE, ESQ. *1940–1941*

Oil on canvas.   *1 ft. 4 in. × 1 ft. 1 in.*   *Unsigned*

Head and shoulders in uniform, the head slightly right of centre, against a dull tone background. Facing half-left, with grey-blue eyes and a stern expression.

Owner: Professor Gilbert Ryle

153 THE MASTER-COOK   *? 1941*
(Sergeant Isaacs of the 1st Bn. and Training Bn. The Welsh Guards)

Oil on canvas.   *1 ft. 3½ in. × 1 ft.*   *Unsigned.*
(Plate 53)

Seated with knees apart and hands on knees, in white jacket and trousers and regimental cap, facing half-right. Through a door, in the background to the right, a figure is dish-washing.   *Owner: The Welsh Guards*

154 THE HON. ROBERT CECIL   *1942*
(The Viscount Cranborne)

Oil on canvas.   *1 ft. 2 in. × 10 in.*   *Unsigned*

Painted during a visit to the Hospital, where the sitter was recovering from an accident on Salisbury Plain, when he and other officers were fired at in error by a British aeroplane. Head and shoulders, facing half-left, in white pyjamas, propped against a pillow. Unfinished.

Owner: Laurence Whistler

155 LIEUT. RICHARD WHISKARD *1942*

Oil on canvas.   *2 ft. × 1 ft. 8 in.*   *Unsigned*

Half-length, in the beret and dark-blue overalls worn during training. Full-face. Under his left arm a map case. In the left background a Cromwell tank. Painted when the 2nd Bn. the Welsh Guards was stationed at Codford St. Mary, Wilts.

Richard Whiskard records in his Diary for June 29th, 1942: "In the Mess this evening Rex suddenly said 'Let me paint you', so we moved to his room and he made a beginning for about an hour of what may be rather a pleasant portrait in beret and denims. . . . It has been very hot all day." Reproduced in *The Welsh Guards at War*, by Major L. F. Ellis (Gale and Polden, 1946), opp. p. 38.

The artist was the first officer of his battalion to fall in Normandy—his subject was the second. A poem on this picture by the artist's brother, entitled *A Portrait in the Guards* was published in *The Listener* for Nov. 30th, 1958.

Owner: John Whiskard, Esq.

156 LADY STUDHOLME   *1942*

Oil on canvas.   *1 ft. 4 in. × 1 ft.*   *Signed, bottom right:*
Rex Whistler 1942

The sitter in an arm-chair facing right, with needlework. Behind, in the corner of the green, panelled room, a folded red wigwam. Painted at Norton Bavant Manor, Wilts, while the artist was stationed at Codford. He suggested that, if exhibited, it should be described as "Lady with a Wigwam".   *Owner: Lady Studholme*

157 THE HON. ALEXANDER   *1942*
THYNNE

Oil on canvas.   *Unsigned*

The schoolboy son of Lord and Lady Bath (Mrs. Fielding). Head and shoulders in right profile, looking down at the sporting gun which he holds. A background of hedgerow trees.   *Owner: Mrs. A. W. Fielding*

158 EDITH OLIVIER ON A DAY-BED *1942*

Oil on canvas.   *1 ft. × 1 ft. 6 in.*   *Unsigned*

Reclining in the garden of the Daye House with the round-topped windows of the house behind her. On the back: "Edith O. September 12, 1942".

She says in her unpublished Journal: "After luncheon he began a painting of me in the paved garden with Nasturtium bed behind. The sun blazed on us and I had to get my huge muslin hat, which looked very funny and turned the picture—with its blazing light—into a mid-19th-century 'Plein-air' Impressionist. The sun chased us about, and we had to move again and again. . . ." On the next day: "The weather has completely changed and is quite cold and sunless. Sat to Rex all afternoon, but the light has gone, and the picture quite different. But nothing stopped the artist, who spent all day on this completely altered scene."

Owner: Miss Rosemary Olivier

159 **PORTRAIT GROUP** ? *1942*
Oil on canvas. 11¾ *in.* × 1 *ft.* 6 *in.* *Unsigned*
Labelled on the frame: "Officers' Mess Tent." Possibly at Codford St. Mary. The interior of a tent with a table to the right and Lord Lloyd reading in a deck chair. Beyond, to the left, another figure in a deck chair. Through the tent opening other tents against a hill-side.
Given to the Welsh Guards
by the artist's mother and brother in 1944

160 **THE FIFTEENTH EARL AND** *1943*
COUNTESS OF PEMBROKE
Oil on canvas. 2 *ft.* 3 *in.* × 1 *ft.* 10 *in.* *Unsigned*
The late Lord Pembroke seated playing Patience. Lady Pembroke in riding habit, standing facing a window to the right, with a golden Labrador asleep at her feet. Unfinished.
Owner: Beatrice Countess of Pembroke

161 **MISS JULIET HENLEY** *1943*
Oil on canvas. 1 *ft.* 3½ *in.* × 1 *ft.* *Signed, bottom right:*
Rex Whistler 1943
A half-length portrait of Miss Juliet Henley, turned half-left and seated at a table with plate and cups. Shelves of books compose the background.

Painted at Breccles Hall, the home of Mrs. Edwin Montagu. The foreground unfinished.
Owner: The Hon. Mrs. A. Henley

162 **SELF PORTRAIT** *n.d.*
Oil on canvas. 1 *ft.* 2 *in.* × 10 *in.* *Signed, bottom right:*
Rex Whistler
Head and shoulders, facing half-left, lit from the right; in an early 19th-century dark coat and white stock.
Owner: Felix Fenston, Esq.

163 **IVAN MOFFAT, ESQ.** *n.d.*
Oil on canvas. c. 2 *ft.* × 1 *ft.* 6 *in.* ? *1939*
As a young man, half-length, full-face. In a soft shirt and grey sports jacket. *Whereabouts unknown*

164 **LOUIS XVIII AS A CHILD** *n.d.*
Oil on canvas. 1 *ft.* 6 *in.* × 1 *ft.* 2 *in.* *Unsigned*
Half-length, full-face, wearing a pink coat with a blue Order ribbon and a Star, in an oval frame. The portrait is taken from Latour's *Dauphin*. Left unfinished by the artist, the coat was finished by Miss Joan Hassall.
Owner: Siegfried Sassoon, Esq.

From *HANS ANDERSEN*: 'The Old Street Lamp'. Cat. no. 475

Portraits in Drawings and Water-colours

165 **LAURENCE WHISTLER** *c. 1915*
Indian ink. 4¼ *in.* × 3 *in.* *Unsigned*
Head and shoulders in silhouette, left profile. At about the age of 3, the artist being 9 or 10.
Owner: Mrs. Laurence Whistler

166 **LAURENCE WHISTLER** *1928*
Pencil. 6½ *in.* × 5¾ *in.* *Unsigned*
"Laurie. Easter Day, 1928." Head and shoulders, in right profile: at the age of 16. *Owner: Mrs. Laurence Whistler*

167 **MARK BONHAM CARTER, ESQ.** *1928*
Pencil and water-colour. 11 *in.* × 9 *in.*
Signed: Rex Whistler 1928 April
At the age of 6. Drawn at the suggestion of the artist, who sought experience in portraiture at this time.
Owner: The Lady Violet Bonham Carter

168 **MISS SUSAN LOWNDES** *1928*
(D. Susan Lowndes Marques)
Pencil and water-colour. 11 *in.* × 8 *in.* *Signed, bottom right:*
April 1928, Rex Whistler
Full-length, seated in a painted French chair, three-quarter face, with hands in lap: wearing a pale blue jersey.
Owner: D. Susan Lowndes Marques

169 **SELF-PORTRAIT** *1928*
Sepia ink. 11 *in.* × 9¼ *in.* *Unsigned*
Head and shoulders in an open-necked shirt and pullover, facing half-right. A poorish likeness drawn at the British School, "Rome / May 10th 1928".
Owner: Laurence Whistler

170 **THE LORD PAKENHAM** *1929*
Pencil. 7¾ *in.* × 5¾ *in.* *Unsigned*
A page from the 1929A Sketch-book (cat. no. 298). A sketch of the left profile. "Frank Pakenham." Probably drawn at Pakenham Hall, Ireland, in January.
Owner: Laurence Whistler

171 **EDMUND BLUNDEN, ESQ.** *1929*
Pencil. 1 *ft.* 2 *in.* × 10 *in.* *Unsigned*
Head only, facing left. Inscribed by the artist: "London. At Siegfried's. February 28th."
Owner: Siegfried Sassoon, Esq.

172 **WILLIAM WALTON, ESQ.** *1929*
(Sir William Walton)
Pencil. *c.* 9½ *in.* × 10¾ *in.* *Signed, bottom right:*
Rex Whistler. *(Plate 46)*
Head and shoulders in left profile, with soft collar. "Willie —Haus Hirth / AN 27 1929." The drawing was damaged during an air-raid in 1940. It was presented to the National Portrait Gallery by Sir Osbert Sitwell.

173 **MRS. G. A. MARTELLI** *1929*
Pencil. 8 *in.* × 6 *in.* *Unsigned*
Head and shoulders of Mrs. Martelli as a girl, holding a book. *Owner: Mrs. G. A. Martelli*

174 **AN OLD LADY, IN DEATH** *? 1929*
Pencil. 8¼ *in.* × 7¾ *in.* *Unsigned.* *(Plate 44)*
Pillowed head in drapery, facing half-left. "Thursday evening, Aug. 15th." If the artist was accurate, the year can only be 1929 or 1935. There is a resemblance to Nanny Trusler, the childhood nurse of Mr. Stephen Tennant and a dear friend of the artist, who died about the middle of August, 1929. *Owner: Laurence Whistler*

175 **MISS PEGGY MORRISON** *1930*
(Mrs. Egerton)
Pencil. 11 *in.* × 9 *in.* *Signed:* Rex Whistler, 1930.
(Plate 41)
Seated at the piano, the head turned full-face, the right hand on the keyboard. *Owner: Mrs. Egerton*

176 **MRS. BELLOC LOWNDES** *1930*
Pencil. 1 *ft.* 2 *in.* × 10 *in.* *Unsigned*
Seated facing half-right with both hands on a portable writing-desk. Unfinished.
Owner: The Countess of Iddesleigh

177 **MRS. BELLOC LOWNDES** *1930*
Pencil. 1 *ft.* 2 *in.* × 10 *in.* *Unsigned*
Seated at a portable writing-desk with her left hand raised to her chin. *Owner: The Countess of Iddesleigh*

178 **LAURENCE WHISTLER** *c. 1931*
Pencil. 1 *ft.* × 10 *in.* *Unsigned.* *(Plate 43)*
Head and shoulders in left profile, the head slightly inclined, reading. A book indicated. At about the age of 19.
Owner: Laurence Whistler

179 DAVID HORNER, ESQ. *1933*
Water-colour. 1 ft. × 8½ in. Unsigned

Half-length, seated leaning against a tree facing half-left, with arms crossed. In the distance Renishaw Hall, very faint. Unfinished. Parts of the painted surface are half erased, as if to reduce the tone.
Owner: David Horner, Esq.

180 THE MARQUIS OF GRANBY *1933*
(The tenth Duke of Rutland)
Pencil. 7¼ in. × 7 in. Unsigned

Profile of Lord Granby as a child, facing left. "April 4th 1933." A sketch for this is in the 1929C Sketch-book (cat. no. 300). *Owner: Laurence Whistler*

181 DOROTHY WELLESLEY *1933*
(The late Duchess of Wellington)
Pencil with faint touches of water-colour. 1 ft. 2 in. × 10 in.
Unsigned

Half-length of the poetess, seated facing half-right in an open-necked shirt. "D.W. May 1st 1933."
Owner: Laurence Whistler

182 CECIL BEATON, ESQ. *c. 1933*
Pencil. 1 ft. × 9 in. Unsigned

Head and shoulders, the head slightly inclined to the left, eyes looking right. *Owner: Cecil Beaton, Esq.*

183 GROUP, WITH A PORTRAIT *? c. 1933*
Sepia ink and wash. 7¼ in. × 6½ in. Unsigned

Miss Penelope Dudley Ward, looking down from a box at the Opera, lit as from the stage. To the left a caricature of Lady Cunard. Behind, three unprepossessing male opera-goers, unidentified. *Owner: Lady Reed*

184 MISS ANGELA DUDLEY WARD *c. 1934*
(Lady Laycock)
Water-colour. 5¼ in. × 7 in. Unsigned

Sleeping out in the garden on a slung bed: her pillowed head, asleep, nearly full-face. On a sheet of Penns in the Rocks writing-paper. *Owner: Lady Laycock*

185 MISS ANGELA DUDLEY WARD *c. 1934*
(Lady Laycock)
Pencil and water-colour. 1 ft. 4 in. × 10¼ in. Unsigned

In shorts, facing half-left, seated fishing from an arm-chair, one knee over the arm—queasy after strawberries and cream (half-eaten). At the back, a sailor at a port-hole remarking behind his hand: "Kid thinks she knows how to fish!" *Owner: Lady Laycock*

186 MISS PENELOPE AND *c. 1934*
MISS ANGELA DUDLEY WARD
(Lady Reed and Lady Laycock)
Water-colour. 4 in. × 5 in. Unsigned

The artist's notion of what they looked like as little girls, sitting on the sands in bathing dresses.
Owner: Lady Laycock

187 MISS JUDY MONTAGU *c. 1934–1935*
Pencil. Approx. 9 in. × 6 in. Signed: Judy with love
from Rex

Head of Miss Montagu as a child, in right profile. Reproduced in *Vogue*, Sept. 1957. *Owner: Miss Judy Montagu*

188 SIR OSBERT SITWELL, Bt.: *1935*
A MEDALLION
Pencil and water-colour. 6 in. × 6 in. Unsigned

The head in right profile, as if in relief on a circular medallion or plaque, with the Christian name on one side and the surname on the other, in Roman capitals. On a green arabesque background, resembling wallpaper.
Owner: Laurence Whistler

189 SIR OSBERT SITWELL, Bt.: *1935*
A BUST
Pencil and water-colour. 1 ft. 2 in. × 10 in. Unsigned

A classical bust, the head facing half-left, unfinished. Framed in an oval with a blue-green background. "August 1st, 1935." Evidently contemporary with no. 188.
Owner: Laurence Whistler

190 THE LADY CAROLINE PAGET *c. 1935*
(The Lady Caroline Duff)
Pencil. 7 in. × 6 in. Unsigned

Head only, looking down, half-right.
Owner: Miss Audrey Carten

191 THE LADY CAROLINE PAGET *c. 1935*
(The Lady Caroline Duff)
Pencil. 6¼ in. × 4¾ in. Unsigned

Head only, looking down, half-right.
Owner: Miss Audrey Carten

192 CONVERSATION PIECE AT *1937*
THE DAYE HOUSE
Water-colour on pencil, with touches of white
8¼ in. × 1 ft. 1¼ in. Unsigned. (Plate 36)

The interior of the Long Room at the Daye House, near Wilton, Wilts, the home of Edith Olivier. Figures from left to right: reclining on the day-bed, Edith Olivier; seated on the end of the day-bed, Lord David Cecil; in an arm-chair, Lady Ottoline Morrell; standing with his back to the fireplace, a cigarette in his hand, the artist. The three guests are all facing Miss Olivier, who is reading from a manuscript.

As a likeness, this is one of the artist's best self-portraits. He wrote to Edith Olivier from Plas Newydd:

"About March 8th 1937

Here at last is your picture. I *do* hope you will like it & also that it has not held up your book too long.

I'm afraid all the likenesses are rather characatures [*sic*], & *please* don't show it to David before publication! or he will take out a writ to restrain you.

He won't mind when it's in the book, as then all the faces will be *so* small that it will not matter. But I *could* not remember much about his looks—particularly his hair— & *does* he wear clothes like this? In my mind's eye I have kept seeing him dressed like this, but perhaps its completely wrong. Oddly enough the best likeness *I* think is Lady O. whom I have not seen for about 3 yrs!

You will find a thousand points wrong in the room I'm *certain*, but most of it has been done *from memory* as I only had a very slight pencil sketch to go by, & that had practically vanished by handling on its innumerable journeys up & down here. It always travelled with me, *in case* there would be time to do it. I think I have been lucky, however, in getting the *right size* of the room conveyed, which is very difficult, & drawings of interiors almost always make the room seem too big. & mirabile dictu, the perspective is pretty fairly accurate I believe. Darling Edith, if you die before me, will you leave this picture to me, as I shall love it as a 'Long Room' souvenir. If I die first, please bring it with you when you come.

Much love
Rex."

Painted for Edith Olivier's autobiography, *Without Knowing Mr. Walkley* (Faber, 1938), and reproduced as the frontispiece. Also in *Mercury*, a Review of the Arts (Bournemouth, Autumn, 1948).

Owner: Laurence Whistler

ROUGH SKETCH FOR THE ABOVE
Pencil.   6¼ in. × 8¼ in.   Unsigned

The "Long Room", probably the "very slight pencil sketch" from which the artist worked, showing the position of the furniture without the figures. Edith Olivier sent the artist detailed colour notes of the room.

Owner: Laurence Whistler

193   **CONVERSATION PIECE:**   *1937*
THE ROYAL FAMILY
Pencil.   1 ft. 1 in. × 10 in.   Unsigned

The King and Queen, with Princess Elizabeth and Princess Margaret as children, on an imaginary terrace under trees. The King seated on the balustrade, the Queen in a chair. Two dogs.

Owner: H.M. Queen Elizabeth the Queen Mother

194   **THE HON. ANNE McLAREN**   *1937*
Pencil.   6¾ in. × 5¼ in.   Signed, bottom right:
Anne with love from Rex. Aug. 2nd.

Head and shoulders, facing half-right, a hair-ribbon on right side of head. Aged 10.   *Owner: Dr. Anne McLaren*

195   **MISS PEGGY MORRISON**   *c. 1937*
(Mrs. Egerton)
Pencil.   11 in. × 9 in.   Unsigned

Head and shoulders, facing half-right, with pearl ear-rings. Requested to alter his earlier pencil portrait of Miss Morrison (no. 175), the artist preferred to make a new drawing.   *Owner: Mrs. Egerton*

196   **NURSE EILEEN KELLY**   *c. 1937*
Pencil.   Each approx. 8 in. × 5¼ in.   Unsigned

(1) Head only, looking half-right, with a nurse's cap indicated.
(2) Head only, in right profile. Cap and uniform indicated. Sketches on Plas Newydd writing paper.

Owner: Nurse Kelly

197   **ARTHUR WALEY, ESQ.**   *n.d.*
(pre-*1938*)
Pencil.   1 ft. × 9½ in.   Unsigned

Head only, in right profile; with a bow tie.

Owner: Laurence Whistler

198   **MISS ROSEMARY SALMOND**   *1939*
Pencil.   5½ in. × 4¼ in.   Unsigned.
(*Bottom left:* R.W. in another hand.)   (*Plate 45*)

In Jan. 1939, Miss Salmond (aged 9) was recovering from an illness at Panshanger. This portrait-sketch was drawn for her in her bedroom, in the company of Walter de la Mare, who was writing a poem, in a minute hand, in a small pocket-book she had been given for Christmas. Head and shoulders, lying in bed; right profile, with the left arm raised, supporting the chin.

Owner: The Hon. Lady Salmond

199   **THE HON. ANNE McLAREN**   *? 1940*
Pencil.   1 ft. × 8½ in.   Unsigned

Full-length, seated in an arm-chair with a book resting on her knees and wearing the artist's hat. Left profile. "Anne wearing my hat." Aged thirteen.

Owner: Christabel Lady Aberconway

200   **THE ARTIST'S FATHER,**   *1940*
HENRY WHISTLER, AFTER DEATH
Pencil.   7 in. × 9 in.   Unsigned

The head in left profile, resting on a pillow. Drawn at Bierton, Bucks, the day after his father died. "October 7th, 1940." This refers to the day of death.

Owner: Laurence Whistler

201 **BILLY WALLACE, ESQ.** *1941*
Charcoal.   1 ft. 2 in. × 10 in.   Signed, bottom right:
For darling Barbie with love from Rex, Aug. 8, 1941
As a boy of 14, facing half-right, in an open-necked shirt.
Owner: Mrs. Herbert Agar

202 **PETER WALLACE, ESQ.** *1941*
Charcoal.   1 ft. 2 in. × 10 in.   Unsigned
Half-length, full-face, leaning on his right arm. Aged 18.
Turned into a joke with the addition of eye-glass, moustache
and diplomatic uniform. At the bottom: "Je t'adore!"—
"Shut it yourself!"   *Owner: Mrs. Herbert Agar*

203 **GEORGE SASSOON** *1941*
Charcoal on grey paper.   1 ft. 6 in. × 11 in.
Signed, bottom right: R.W.
As a child, head and shoulders, seated facing half-left,
looking down. Inscribed by the artist "George sewing.
Dec. 21st 1941."   *Owner: Mrs. Siegfried Sassoon*

204 **BRIGADIER WINDSOR LEWIS** *1942*
Black chalk.   1 ft. 3½ in. × 1 ft. 6 in.   Unsigned
Described as: head in left profile, as if carved in relief in a
circular medallion.   *Owner: Brigadier Windsor Lewis*

205 **LIEUT. RICHARD WHISKARD** *c. 1942*
Pencil and charcoal on grey paper.   1 ft. ¼ in. × 9¼ in.
Unsigned
Head and shoulders in battle-dress, facing half-left.
Owner: Laurence Whistler

206 **THE LADY CAROLINE PAGET** *c. 1942*
(The Lady Caroline Duff)
Pencil.   3½ in. × 2½ in.   Unsigned
Head and shoulders, in left profile, looking down.
Owner: Miss Audrey Carten

207 **RICHARD SAWREY-COOKSON,** *1943*
ESQ.
Pencil.   1 ft. 2 in. × 10 in.   Signed, bottom right: Richard
from Rex with many thanks for all those coupons.
April 28. '43
Head and shoulders, facing half-left.
Owner: Richard Sawrey-Cookson, Esq.

208 **MRS. SACHEVERELL SITWELL** *1944*
Pencil.   c. 9 in. × 7 in.   Unsigned
Head nearly full-face, above a cartouche intended for
wording (a bookplate), but left empty. "May 1944."
Owner: Reresby Sitwell, Esq.

209 **SELF-PORTRAIT** *n.d.*
Pencil.   8 in. × 8 in.   Unsigned
Head only, in left profile. Bottom left, a small unidentified
head in left profile.
Reproduced in *Rex Whistler*, by Laurence Whistler,
p. 15.   *Owner: Laurence Whistler*

210 **THE LADY CAROLINE PAGET** *n.d.*
(The Lady Caroline Duff)
Pencil.   8 in. × 6 in.   Unsigned
Head and shoulders, facing half-right with eyes on the
beholder, wearing an open-necked shirt. An indication of
the left elbow supported, and forearm folded towards the
body.   *Owner: Laurence Whistler*

211 **A. CROOKES RIPLEY, ESQ.** *n.d.*
Pencil.   Signed, bottom right: Rex Whistler
Half-length, facing half-right, hands folded over knees.
Mislaid.   *Owner: A. Crookes Ripley, Esq.*

212 **CONVERSATION PIECE** *n.d.*
Water-colour.   6½ in. × 4¾ in.   Unsigned
Sketch for an unidentified painting of two girls, one seated
at an ormolu table with head turned full-face, the other
standing just behind her. Looped curtains on left. Background: an open door to a farther room and window.
Owner: Laurence Whistler

From *THE NEW KEEPSAKE*. Cat. no. 435

Miscellaneous Drawings and Water-colours

(Excluding Sketches for Oil Paintings)

---

213 A GEORGIAN CONGREGATION *1923*
LEAVING CHURCH

Indian ink and water-colour. $7\frac{1}{2}$ *in.* × $5\frac{1}{4}$ *in.*

Signed: Rex J. Whistler pinxit

A procession out of a churchyard in 18th-century clothes, regarded mockingly by topers to the right. Picturesque houses.   *Owner: Mrs. Henzell Case*

214   "REVOLUTION"   1923
Pen and Indian ink.   11 in. × *1 ft. 1 in.   Signed, bottom left:* Rex J. Whistler 1923; *also bottom right, on mount:* Rex J. Whistler Sculpsit! 1923

A street crowded with people fighting violently; in the background a church spire; on the right a house in flames; to the left a corpse hanging from the sign of a public house, which reads "Rose & Crown, 1995". In the right foreground is a group of three with their backs turned to the slaughter: an old man appears to be telling his horrified small son what his world will be like in 1995. The mother stands serenely beside them. *Owner: Arthur Fanshawe, Esq.*

215   "A HAPPIE CHRISTMAS"   1923
Indian ink and water-colour. $8\frac{1}{2}$ in. × *6 in.   Signed, bottom left:* Rex Whistler pinxit, 1923

A Georgian street-scene. A figure in 18th-century dress with a lute, serenading a lady, who appears dimly at an upper window. To the right, round a corner, a masked rival with drawn sword. The title is ironical; though the drawing may have formed a Christmas present.
Owner: W. Gooderson, Esq.

216   NUDE STUDY   *c. 1923*
Pencil.   1 ft. 1 in. × *7 in.   Unsigned*
Back of standing male model.   *Owner: Isaac Scher, Esq.*

217   THREE UNTRACED   *1923–1924*
DRAWINGS
"Senile Decay", "Sinister Street", and "The Red Flag". Sent to an Exhibition at Haileybury College in Nov. 1924. "Revolution" (no. 214) was shown with them.
Whereabouts unknown.

218   A ROMANTIC SHORESCAPE   *1924*
Water-colour. $6\frac{1}{2}$ in. × *10 in.   Unsigned*
Under misty, moonlit cliffs a small cloaked figure on the sands gestures to a high-pooped sailing ship. Possibly suggested by Ronald Fuller's poem, *Wanderlust*, which the artist illustrated in *An Anthology of Mine* (no. 288) at about this date. Dated July 28th, 1924. On the reverse a sketch in water-colour for the Slade Summer Composition, 1925 (no. 30).   *Owner: Mrs. Laurence Whistler*

219   "HENRY BROCKEN MEETS   *1924*
ANNABEL LEE"

Water-colour.   10 in. × $7\frac{1}{4}$ *in.   Signed, bottom right:* 1924. Rex Whistler

A scene from *Henry Brocken* by Walter de la Mare. The hero, walking on the windy shore of the "kingdom by the sea", bends towards the lost child of Poe's poem.
Owner: Ronald Fuller

220   THE SLEEPING BEAUTY   *c. 1924*
IN VICTORIAN DRESS
Indian ink and water-colour.   1 ft. 5 in. × *11 in.*
Unsigned

Apparently a reception room in a small residential hotel, crowded with grotesque characters, all asleep, sitting, or lying on the floor. Beauty on the sofa. The dago-Prince with clasped hands bursting in through the open window.
Owner: The Hon. Stephen Tennant

221   SEVEN UNTRACED   *1924–1925*
DRAWINGS
In a pocket diary for 1924 the artist wrote out, in the following year, under a heading "1925", a list of recent drawings and paintings, adding the initials of purchasers or recipients. Those untraced are listed below. "A.B." is Mr. Archie Balfour, "S.T." is Mr. Stephen Tennant, "M" is the artist's mother, "A.T.D." is possibly Mr. Tudor Davies of Abbotts Langley, Herts.

"A.B.   A Warf [*sic*]. Ink drawing and w. colour."

"A.T.D.   Porta S. Giusseppe [*sic*]. Ink drawing and water colour."

"A.T.D.   The Mother. Ink drawing and w. colour."

"S.T.   Henry Brocken. Ink drawing and w. colour." ★

"M.   Fisherman and his soul. Ink drawing and w. colour."

★ This appears to be an earlier drawing than no. 233.

"M.   Cathedral from P. Mercato, S. Remo. Ink drawing".
"M.   C. Porch, Bairdo. Ink drawing."

222   "2nd PRIZE.   *1925*
FIGURE DRAWING. £3"

From the artist's list of prizes won at the Slade School. A
note, written this year, in his 1924 pocket diary, gives
"Figure drawing. Prize and Purchase. £4-0-0". It was
probably bought by a member of the Staff for £1.

Whereabouts unknown

223   Illustration to THE SLEEPING   *1925*
BEAUTY   by Edith Sitwell
? Approx. 8 in. × 5 in.

Edith Olivier records in her unpublished Journal for
Easter, Apr. 12th, 1925, writing at San Remo, where she
had just met the artist for the first time: "Rex gave me a
picture he has painted—of the gardener telling the story in
Edith Sitwell's Sleeping Beauty—a lovely little water-
colour." It was his first present to her. Below the aged
gardener talking to the girl there was a quotation from the
poem, beginning, "The gardener was old as tongues of
nightingales . . ."—a line he delighted in. Mislaid.

Owner: Miss Rosemary Olivier

224   "GREEN DUSK FOR DREAMS" *1925*
Indian ink and water-colour.   10½ in. × 8 in.
Signed, bottom left: Rex J. Whistler pinxit A.D. 1925

An ilex wood, with a ruined portico in perspective to the
right. To the left of centre, a girl in a blue dress is seated
under a tree, her right hand raised to the left hand of a man
in 18th-century dress, who bends above her. The greenish-
light of early twilight. The title on the ruled mount is
flourished. It alludes to *The Song of the Mad Prince* by
Walter de la Mare; but the picture is not an illustration of
the poem.   *Owner: Archie Balfour, Esq.*

225   "THE OLD CITY—SAN REMO" *1925*
Indian ink and water-colour.   11 in. × 8 in.
Signed, bottom right: Rex J. Whistler pinxit 1925

The old bridge across the stony bed of a narrow stream.
Old houses beyond, and each side. One figure on the
bridge, another looking over a parapet to the left. Blue sky,
faintly clouded.   *Owner: Archie Balfour, Esq.*

226   "TERROR"   *1925*
Signed, bottom right: Rex J. Whistler, 1925 A.D. pinxit.

The dark interior of a dungeon. A crowd of figures to the
left, shrinking in theatrical horror from an opening door,
on which a hand appears.   *Owner: Miss Coralie Portal*

227   "BUSSANA VECCHIA   *1925*
DEYSTROYED BY AN EARTHQUAKE
IN 1887" [*sic*]

Indian ink and water-colour.   1 ft. 1 in. × 9½ in.   Signed,
bottom right: Rex J. Whistler pinxit, A.D. 1925.

In the right background the deserted town on a hill-top.
In the foreground a man and boy on the road. A man
asleep under a tree to the left.   *Owner: Miss Coralie Portal*

228   Two Illustrations to   *1925*
HENRY BROCKEN   by Walter de la Mare
Indian ink and water-colour.   Approx. 1 ft. × 9 in.
Signed, bottom right: Rex J. Whistler pinxt 1925

(1)   "Henry Brocken comes to Ferndean Manor"
Brocken on Rosinante. Jane Rochester at the gate with
a dog. A romantic house in the background.
(2)   "Henry Brocken flees from Prince Ennui"
Brocken tiptoeing out of a great portal below an oriel
window.   *Owner: The Countess of Iddesleigh*

229   "MEDUSA"   *1925*
Water-colour.   9 in. × 6 in.   Signed, bottom right:
Rex Whistler 1925

Head and shoulders, full-face, the face almost entirely
framed in writhing serpents. A background of sea and rocks.
Owner: A. W. Wrigglesworth, Esq.

230   "SALOME"   *? 1925*

"A small picture"—so described by the artist in a letter to
Ronald Fuller, on May 10th, 1925, reporting its sale in
Oxford [to Mr. Robert Shaw].   *Whereabouts unknown*

231   THE LAST SUPPER   *1926*
Indian ink and water-colour.   8 in. × 10 in.   Unsigned

A high, shadowy, classical interior, which seems to have
interested the artist more than the occasion portrayed.
Our Lord, seen from behind, seated at a table with hand
raised, silhouetted against the light radiating from him
upon the disciples, round-faced and surprised in 18th-
century dress. The picture won a prize at the Slade Sketch
Club competition in March, and was bought by Sir
Augustus Daniel, who referred to it as a "Hunt Breakfast".
Owner: Lady Daniel

SKETCH FOR THE ABOVE   *1926*
Indian ink and water-colour.   3½ in. × 4 in.   Unsigned
A rapid study of the scene, without detail.
Owner: Laurence Whistler

232   DANCE   *1926*
Water-colour.   10¼ in. × 1 ft. 1½ in.   Signed, bottom right:
Rex Whistler 1925 [*sic*]

To the right a group of dancers in front of a ruined
Corinthian temple, with an old man reclining to watch

them. In the centre a man sits, playing pipes. To the left a high group of ilexes, below which are two lovers seated on a broken column. Painted on March 21st, "a small classical landscape"; and sold to Col. E. Armstrong on the 24th. "1925" in the signature appears to be a mistake of the artist's. The title, Dance, appears on an exhibition-label at the back. *Owner: Miss Stella MacDonald*

SKETCH FOR THE ABOVE *1926*
Water-colour. 3½ in. × 4¾ in. Unsigned

Inscribed on the back by the artist: "Pastoral Scene. 1st sketch, 1925 [*sic*]. Finished water-colour sold to Col. Armstrong." Also on the back, a pencil sketch of a paddle steamer. *Owner: Victor Bowen, Esq.*

233 "HENRY BROCKEN AND *1926*
PRINCE ENNUI"
Indian ink and water-colour

"My [Easter] present to S was a little painting of 'Henry Brocken and Prince Ennui'." The artist's diary for April 3rd. Mislaid. *Owner: The Hon. Stephen Tennant*

234 "FEAST OF HYMEN" *1926*

April 12th. "Drew and painted 'Feast of Hymen'." Artist's diary. *Whereabouts unknown*

235 AN ORIENTAL *? c. 1927*
QUAYSIDE SCENE
Pen and Indian ink. 10½ in. × 1 ft. 2 in. Signed as if stencilled on bale: R.W.

A gesturing Englishman directs the loading of a wagon with barrels by native workmen. In the right background, a sailing ship. For reproduction at the size of "21½ in. × 16 in." For a poster? *Owner: Laurence Whistler*

236 "THE HONEYMOON" *? c. 1927*

"Water-colour. Sir Cyril Butler." Entry in a list by the artist, showing work sold before 1930.
Whereabouts unknown

237 SKETCH FOR A PAINTING *? c. 1927*
Pencil. 1 ft. 1¼ in. × 1 ft. 9½ in. Unsigned

To the right, in a rectangle a huge urn and pedestal. To the left, a male and female figure approaching from a classical archway. Also sketches of furniture, keystone masks, and a window in the Tate Gallery Refreshment Room. *Owner: Laurence Whistler*

238 SAMSON DESTROYING THE *1928*
PHILISTINES IN THE TEMPLE OF
DAGON
Pen and sepia ink heightened with Indian ink. 11¾ in. × 7½ in.
Signed, bottom left: Rex Whistler 1928. (Plate 54)

Grappling a pair of columns, Samson brings down the crowded gallery. Tumbling architecture and contorted bodies, above. Terror-stricken Philistines fleeing, below. Edith Olivier records in her unpublished Journal for Mar. 31st that "he did it all in one night". On the reverse is an unsigned pen and ink study of a Corinthian capital. Exhibited at the Imperial Gallery of Art.
Owner: The University of Oxford, Ashmolean Museum
(Weldon Bequest, 1937)

SKETCHES FOR THE ABOVE *1928*
Pencil. 1 ft. 4¾ in. × 10 in. Unsigned

Both are pages from the "1926B 1927" Sketch-book.
(1) Very rough sketch, on the same page as "Proposed Architect's Nightmare". On the reverse (pen and sepia ink), a man drawing a scimitar.
(2) The tottering columns rise to the top of the drawn rectangle and only the floor of the gallery is shown. To the right another study of Samson. On the reverse, three pencil designs for a garden pavilion, seen in aerial perspective. *Owner: Laurence Whistler*

239 HOUSES IN THE CLOSE, *1928*
SALISBURY

"Mar. 3rd. To the Close, where he drew Mompesson and the adjoining houses for Country Life." (Edith Olivier's unpublished Journal.) Apparently not used.
Whereabouts unknown

240 THIRTEEN UNTRACED *1928*
DRAWINGS OR PAINTINGS

While at the British School at Rome between Apr. 22nd and Aug. 7th, 1928, the artist kept a brief diary. Untraced works mentioned in it are listed below. Most of them are likely to be leaves from his 1928 Rome Sketch-book (no. 296). Some may be very slight. He also refers to his "Baroque Note Book" (no. 297), containing detail drawings, partly from books. (Whereabouts unknown.)

May 25th. Capri. "Up to M. Tiberio, afternoon. Drew 5 drawings among ruins. 3 not painted." Two of the latter, very light pencil outlines (1 ft. × 1 ft. 3 in.), are the property of Laurence Whistler.

June 7th. "Painted rocks for Connell's Capri plan." I.e. decorations to a measured drawing by one of the architectural students who accompanied him.

June 12th. "Painting after [lunch]. Doing scene in the P[assaggiata] Archiologico [*sic*]. Berners sitting sketching under tree." Possibly an oil painting.

June 22nd. "Painted after [lunch]. Different view in the Passagiato [*sic*] A. Looking down road to the Palatine in distance." Possibly an oil painting.

June 27th. "Took tram along Tiber side, and got down on to the banks to draw the new Ponte del Littorio, which is in the middle of being built. The centering is being put up. Deep shade from embankment wall."

June 28th. "Did pen drawing of distant view of St. Peter's from the Bosco [Sacro]."

July 2nd. "Ruined castle of P[assarano]. Did painting of one of the towers etc."

July 8th. "Drew pencil and w. colour of S. Vito [near Palestrina] from near the little church across valley."

37

July 14th. "Did a painting in the moat of a tower of the Fortezza [at Aulla] in *Tempora* [*sic*] for first time, not finished.

August 5th. "Bathed and drew" in fields near Lake Bracciano.

August 7th. "To the Forum and drew Berners' house." A water-colour on a leaf from the Rome Sketch-book (no. 296), formerly in the possession of the artist's brother.

241   **CAVES AT THE VILLA**   *1928*
BRANCACCIO
Water-colour.   9 in. × 11 in.   Unsigned

Bottom left in the artist's writing, "Mon. May 14th. Caves in the Garden. Villa Brancaccio." In his Diary he records that he spent the day there with Nan West, "Water-colour painting. Took lunch with us. Very hot and quite deserted. Masses of poppies and roses." The dark caves are shown looming through masses of soft foliage, and crowned with trees.   *Owner: Miss Rosemary Olivier*

242   **DECORATIONS TO AN**   *1928*
ARCHITECTURAL DRAWING
Sepia ink and wash.   2 ft. 1 in. × 3 ft. 8 in.   Unsigned

While at the British School at Rome, the artist was asked by Mr. Herbert Thearle, then a fellow student studying architecture, to decorate his measured drawing of the 2nd century B.C. Italic Temple Signia, at Segni, Central Italy. It consists of four sectional elevations on a single sheet. The artist lavishly decorated three of them, with an imaginary townscape, trees and precipices, together with a fictitious baroque Assumption of the Virgin on one of the interior walls revealed by the section.

On May 20th he wrote to Edith Olivier about the Rome Scholars' Annual Exhibition: "I, of course, was not an exhibitor, but nevertheless, was just as busily engaged during the 3 or 4 days before the exhibition opened as any of the scholars. For I was roped in to putting little figures, trees & mountains in some of the huge measured drawings of the architects!! I also helped to colour such things as 'Romanesque mosaic pavements' & to stick down or mount some of their enormous sheets. *So much* had to be done before the quickly approaching exhibition that few of us went to bed before 3 in the morning for several nights. . . ." See also no. 240, June 7th.
      Owner: Herbert Thearle, Esq.

243   **A HEAD ON A STAKE**   *1928*
Pencil.   Unsigned

Held aloft, bleeding, by two hands. Drawn on the corner of a sheet of architectural notes by the owner, a fellow student of the British School at Rome.
      Owner: Robert Cummings, Esq.

244   **"IN GARDEN OF VILLA**   *1928*
BRANCACCIO"
Indian ink and water-colour.   10 in. × 10¼ in.

Unsigned, but inscribed bottom left by the artist as above. "Rome, Tuesday: May 22nd." To the right, a group of tall trees; in the centre behind a line of trees, a great ruin. The foreground in shadow.   *Owner: Laurence Whistler*

245   **"FROM LORD BERNERS'**   *1928*
WINDOW"
Pen and sepia ink.   6¾ in. × 10½ in.   Unsigned

The top of the Arch of Septimius Severus to the left, with the domed church of SS. Luca e Martina in the centre, and the Roman Curia to the right. Inscribed by the artist, "Sat. June 9th. From Lord Berners' window. 3 Foro Romano." This and nos. 246, 248, and 250 are pages from the Rome Sketch-book (no. 296).
      Owner: Laurence Whistler

246   **"BOSCO SACRO"**   *1928*
Sepia ink and water-colour.   6¾ in. × 10½ in.   Unsigned

To the left a distant landscape; to the right Lord Berners, far off under the trees of the Bosco. Inscribed by the artist, "June 29th. Bosco Sacro (G.B. sketching)."
      Owner: Laurence Whistler

247   **"CASTEL GANDOLFO AND**   *1928*
LAKE ALBANO"
Sepia ink and water-colour.   7 in. × 10¼ in.
Signed, bottom left: July 3rd 1928. Rex Whistler

The Pope's Palace in the middle distance to the left, with the lake below and the Campagna far off. Trees in the right foreground.

The artist's Diary records that this was painted in the company of Lord Berners. "Did sepia ink and water-colour drawing of Castel Gandolfo & Lake of Albano. Hackneyed composition. Painted till dusk. Dined on the little balcony of the Hotel Pagnagnelli above the lake. This our last day's painting together." (Rome Diary.) Framed with a ruled mount drawn by the artist, and labelled at the back with the title and his address, 20 Fitzroy St., W.1.
      Owner: Laurence Whistler

248   **"VIEW OF ROCCA DI CAVE"**   *1928*
Sepia wash.   6¾ in. × 10½ in.   Unsigned

On the extreme left a peasant woman and boy following a cow, beneath olive trees. In the distance to the right "the ruined castle and town of Rocca di Cave. I did a horrible little sketch in sepia water-colour." (Rome Diary.) Inscribed by the artist, "July 9th. View of Rocca di Cave. Painted about 6.30 a.m." See note to no. 245.
      Owner: Laurence Whistler

249   **"DRAWN IN TRAIN TO AULLA,**   *1928*
MIDNIGHT"
Pencil.   1 ft. 2 in. × 10 in.   Unsigned.   (Plate 38)

A double sheet, folded. In the railway compartment, three sprawling figures abandoned to sleep: one, a little boy. "Drawn in train to Aulla, midnight." (July 10th–11th, 1928). On the reverse a little pencil and wash sketch of an

Italian town in the middle distance. "San Vito. July 8th, Sunday." On the opposite sheet an unfinished sketch in Indian ink of "Porta Maggiore. Wed. June 27." (1928).

Owner: Laurence Whistler

250   **"THE CARRARAS FROM**   *1928*
BOCCA DI MAGRA"

Water-colour.   *6¾ in. × 10½ in.*   *Unsigned*

The blue mountain range across the blue waters of the estuary. To the left a tower-crowned promontory. In the foreground a rock with a seated figure, and another figure in a rowing-boat. "Wed. July 17th." See note to no. 245.

Owner: Mrs. Huskinson

251   **A CONGREGATION**   *? c. 1928*
SHOCKED BY A DOG

Sepia pen and ink.   *8 in. × 6 in.*   *Signed, bottom left:*
Rex Whistler

An 18th-century parson and congregation shocked by a dog, which lies on the church floor. ? An illustration to an unidentified story.   *Owner: Kenneth Rae, Esq.*

ROUGH SKETCH FOR THE ABOVE

Pencil.   *6¼ in. × 4½ in.*   *Unsigned*

Owner: Laurence Whistler

252   **THE EXODUS**   *1929*

Water-colour.   *7¼ in. × 1 ft.*   *Signed: Rex W. 1929*

In the left foreground a shepherd guards his sheep on a rocky height beside an archway, under which surges a cascade. In the middle distance innumerable Israelites cross from left to right, marshalled by a few men mounted on camels and horses. Far off are seen the pyramids and towers of a distant town. Edith Olivier records in her unpublished Journal for Mar. 4th that he thought of using it "for the Carrier panel" (no. 34).

Owner: Mrs. Barrington Haynes

SKETCHES FOR THE ABOVE   *1929*

(1) *Sepia ink and water-colour. 9½ in. × 1 ft. 1¾ in. Unsigned.*
It may have been this sketch which Edith Olivier saw.
(2) *Pencil. 10¾ in. × 1 ft. 2¾ in. Unsigned*
An early rough sketch.   *Owner: Laurence Whistler*

253   **FARINGDON HOUSE**   *1929*

Sepia ink and wash.   *4¾ in. × 7¾ in.*   *Unsigned*

To the right the entrance front in perspective, with pediment and Doric porch. Trees in the left distance. Inscribed "Faringdon". Evidently torn from the 1929B Sketch-book (no. 299).   *Owner: Laurence Whistler*

254   **"HIS MAJESTY'S BATH-CHAIR"**   *1929*

Sepia ink and wash.   *1 ft. × 1 ft. 3 in.*

Signed: Rex Whistler 1929.   *(Plate 59)*

On the back the artist has given an alternative title: "Corridor in a Palace". It shows a huge baroque vaulted loggia in perspective to the right, reminiscent of the entrance vestibule to St. Peter's. From a grand door on the left the King emerges in a bath-chair among bowing courtiers. Exhibited at the Goupil Gallery, Jan. 1930.

Owner: Kenneth Rae, Esq.

255   **THE ABATED FLOOD**   *1930*

Sepia ink and wash on grey paper, heightened with white.

11 in. × 7¾ in.   *Signed, bottom left: Rex Whistler 1930*

The artist's title reads: "and at the end of one hundred and fifty days the waters were abated". The broken Doric portico of a ruined palace. Stripped and weed-hung trees. Emaciated corpses hang from windows and branches, and are scattered about among the diminishing waters.

Owner: Laurence Whistler

256   **A BUNCH OF FLOWERS**   *1930*

Sepia ink and water-colour.   *5¼ in. × 3¾ in.*

In a rococo frame a bunch of flowers, tied with a blue bow and a label reading: "With sincerest Apologies from Rex Whistler." This was to atone for having arrived at lunch-time for a sitting at 11 o'clock. See no. 175.

Owner: Mrs. Egerton

257   **THE LAST SUPPER**   *1931*

Sepia ink and water-colour.   *5 in. × 7 in.*   *Signed, bottom*
right: Rex Whistler 1931

Our Lord with his back to us at the centre of the table; the disciples opposite in the light issuing from his face; Judas slinking away with face buried in hands. A ruled and marbled border by the artist. Somewhat similar in conception to no. 231, but with more sentiment. A note on the back, by another hand, records that it was done in two or three hours, one evening at Cheddington Rectory, Bucks.

Owner: Canon W. H. Elliott

258 **"AT THE FRENCH EXHIBITION"** *1932*

Sepia ink and wash.   *7½ in. × 6 in.*   *Signed, bottom left:*
Rex Whistler 1932

Top-hatted vulgarian and wife, protuberant at belly and bosom respectively, reacting with different emotions to *La Source* by Ingres.   *Owner: Laurence Whistler*

259   **LADY BLESSINGTON**   *? c. 1933*

Indian ink and wash.   *9½ in. × 7½ in.*   *Unsigned*

Lady Blessington reclining, on a bed framed by swan's head and foot, with a writing-desk on her lap and pen held aloft.   *Owner: Lady Reed*

260   **DRAWING FOR ALFREDO'S**   *1934*
RESTAURANT, ROME

Formerly in the Visitors' Book: a decorated page, probably with the signatures "Rex Whistler" and "Kenneth Rae", and a March or April date. Subsequently removed by a hand unknown.

261 **TWO FIGURES IN AN** *1934*
ARCHITECTURAL SETTING
Sepia ink and wash.   *10 in.× 7½ in.*   *Signed, bottom right:*
To Baba with love. Rex Whistler 1934

A fanciful drawing of a baroque colonnade to the right. An obelisk to the left, in front of a distant palace. A male and female figure in the foreground. A wedding present from the artist.   *Owner: Mrs. Hambro*

262 **THE MERMAID** *c. 1935*
Water-colour.   *6 in.× 9 in.*   *Signed on back:* For Mary with love and best wishes from Rex. 19 July 1935.
(Plate 60)

A wedding present from the artist to Lady Mary Dunn (Lady Mary Campbell). A wrecked ship and distant town seen through the mouth of a shaggy cave. On the rocks in the left foreground a reclining mermaid.
Owner: Derrick Morley, Esq.

263 **SYMBOLIC DRAWING** *? c. 1935*
FOR LORD ASHFIELD
Given by Lady Diana Cooper and composed of emblems appropriate to him. In an undated letter to her, the artist's sketch shows two flanking, female, terminal figures (representing daughters); in the centre, Piccadilly Eros, a Tube

tunnel, a horse-bus, the *Aquitania's* funnels, etc. Whereabouts of the finished drawing unknown.

264 **"PAGODA WINKY"** *1935–6*
Two drawings of a particoloured Pekinese
Water-colour.   *11 in.× 9 in.*

(1) In a Chinese hat and dress pouring out tea at a little table. In the background, a pagoda. Signed, bottom right: "With love from Rex 1935." (*Reverse of title-page of this book.*)
(2) Facing right, holding a parasol. Signed, bottom right: "With love from Rex 1936."
A complete screen of pictures of Winky was intended. Only two were made, and were framed by the owner in mirror glass, on which the artist painted white acanthus, with the letters "U" and "M" in the corners.
Owner: The Lady Ursula D'Abo

265 **WEST HOUSE, ALDWICK,** *c. 1936*
SUSSEX
Water-colour.   *9 in.× 1 ft. 1½ in.*   *Signed, bottom right:*
Rex

A low, white house with a verandah, seen at an angle. To the left, near a tree, Mr. Duff and Lady Diana Cooper and Dr. Rudolph Kommer, seated at a table with a white cloth, on the lawn. "This postcard for Darling Diana with love from Rex." June 27th. Described by him in a letter as "that ridiculous old-lady's-water-colour". Reproduced in *The Light of Common Day* (Hart-Davis, 1959), by the owner, the Lady Diana Cooper.

THE SATYR GATE AT CASTLE HOWARD. Cat. no. 260

266   **THE SATYR GATE AT**   *? 1938*
CASTLE HOWARD

Indian ink.   7 in. × 6½ in.   Signed, bottom right:
Rex Whistler.   (*See page 40*)

A view of the baroque gate seen in perspective from the right, with its grinning satyrs' heads and stone vases of flowers. The wrought-iron gates are shut, and a gardener stoops with a broom in front, to the left.

This drawing would seem to be connected with one of the same gateway reproduced on **p. 45** of *The Emperor Heart*, by Laurence Whistler (no. 481), where the gardener appears in the same attitude, though in the centre of the gateway, which is open. But it was probably intended as an illustration to *Sir John Vanbrugh, Architect and Dramatist* (no. 491), also by the artist's brother.

Owner: Laurence Whistler

267   **THE LAKE AT TRENT PARK,**   *1938*
MIDDX

Water-colour.   1 ft. 3 in. × 1 ft.   Signed, bottom right
Rex Whistler 1938

The lake, with a willow tree. A present from the artist.
Owner: Miss Grace Boyce

268   **THE WALTON CANONRY,**   *1938*
SALISBURY

Pencil and water-colour.   5 in. × 7 in.   Unsigned

Sketch drawn for the artist's mother of their home, 69 The Close, Salisbury, showing the red-brick house in perspective, as seen from the south-east entrance-gate.
Owner: Laurence Whistler

269   **"BURLEY WOOD" HANTS**   *1941*

Water-colour.   c. 9 in. × 1 ft. 2 in.
Signed: Rex Whistler

Described as: a stuccoed neo-Georgian house with a parapet, seen at an angle, and a bay window on the narrower front to the left. Trees to right and left. Mislaid.
Owner: Sir Francis Portal, Bt.

270   **LAVINGTON PARK, SUSSEX**   *1941*
Three Topographical Sketches

Sepia ink and crayon.   Unsigned

Made to encourage the artist's mother, widowed the year before, to accept the home offered to her by Mrs. Herbert Agar in the lodge of Lavington Park.

(1) 5 in. × 1 ft. 1 in. Landscape showing the lodge and village to the left, with the artist's mother bicycling along the drive. "You bicycling to have tea with me and Barbie at Beechwood." There are many other notes, e.g. "The corn was in these lovely stooks when I drew these sketches, but of course you would have only the bare stubble for the rest of the Autumn."

Drawn on two sheets of Lavington Park writing-paper, placed end to end. The remaining two sketches are on the reverse of these sheets.

(2) 5 in. × 6½ in. "View from inside the Park." The porticoed lodge to the left, and the entrance gates.

(3) 5 in. × 6½ in. "Bird's eye view from outside the park." Entrance gates to the left and the lodge beyond them.
Owner: Laurence Whistler

271   **TWO DRAWINGS FOR**   *c. 1941*
SOLDIERS' KIT LAY-OUT

Indian ink.   1 ft. 1 in. × 1 ft. 9 in.   Unsigned

(1) In a cartouche bristling with flags and weapons: "No. 7 Holding Coy. Welsh Guards Correct Lay out of Kit for Barrack Room Inspection." Reproduced in *Rex Whistler*, by Laurence Whistler, 1948, p. 36.

(2) In a similar cartouche: "No. 7 Holding Coy. Welsh Guards Correct lay out for Kit Inspection." Bold and careful drawings to show the private soldier the exact position of each article of his kit.
Owner: Laurence Whistler

272   **A DRAWING OF A COUNTRY**   *1942*
HOUSE

For a book projected by Sir John Squire. Mentioned in a letter to Lady Juliet Duff on July 24th: "What *hell* that book will be—fains I buying it. . . ."
Whereabouts unknown

273   **A DIAGRAM FOR COMPASS**   *? 1942*
MARCHING

Indian ink and wash on canvas.   3 ft. 3 in. × 2 ft. 4 in.
Unsigned

An aerial perspective sketch of fanciful countryside, to teach his men the use of map and compass for circumventing an obstacle and maintaining direction. Bottom left, a large compass representing the point of departure. Top right, the destination: a slender classical pavilion with a dome and cupola. In the centre a wood, supposedly obscuring the latter from the former. A dotted line showing the route of march. Bottom right, a small plan of the same route, giving bearings.   *Owner: Laurence Whistler*

274   **"BUNDI"**   *1943*

Pencil.   8 in. × 1 ft.   Unsigned, but dated by the
artist: April 1943

A sheep-dog lying near the legs of a table, with an indication of the carpet. "Bundi" in flourishes. The artist said that he could not draw animals, but this was a very woolly one. It was begun at lunch-time and finished in twenty minutes, his host not interrupting him.
Owner: The Estate of Sir Henry Channon

275   **HEYTESBURY HOUSE,**   *1943*
WILTSHIRE

Oil on canvas.   9 in. × 1 ft. 2 in.   Unsigned

Erratum before going to press. This work was wrongly described to the authors as a water-colour.

The east and north sides of the house from the Park. A large cedar to the left.   *Owner: Siegfried Sassoon, Esq.*

276   **A DRAWING ON A CHART**   *1943*
Charcoal, coloured chalk and water-colour.
2 ft. 4 in. × 1 ft. 8 in.   *Unsigned*

In the late summer of 1943 the artist went on a patrol in the North Sea in *H.M.S. Pytcheley*, as a guest of the destroyer's captain, Commander Hodgkinson. During a "make-and-mend" period, while the ship took refuge from a gale in Yarmouth Roads, the artist drew on an old chart, in a wreath of oak-leaves, a grotesque crowned head of Neptune crunching up a German E-Boat.

Owner: Commander Hugh Hodgkinson

277   **ATHENE SPRINGING FROM**   *n.d.*
THE HEAD OF JOVE
Body colour.   *8½ in. × 10¼ in.*   *Signed, bottom right:*
Rex Whistler

The huge god recumbent with head on arm, and eyes and mouth as if lit from within. The armed and naked goddess springs from the right side of the head in a gush of stars. Clouds and stars surround the figures.

Underneath, inscribed by the artist's brother, is a quotation from *Paradise Lost*, II, 752–758:

"All on a sudden miserable pain
  Surprised thee, dim thine eyes, and dizzy swum
  In darkness, while thy head flames thick and fast
  Threw forth, till on the right side opening wide,
  Likest to thee in shape and countenance bright,
  Then shining heavenly fair, a goddess, armed,
  Out of thy head I sprung."

In the fourth line the word "right" has been cacophonously substituted for "left", as written by Milton, since the artist has shown Athene springing from that side of the head.   *Owner: Laurence Whistler*

278   **A SHIP IN A STORM**   *n.d.*
Sepia ink and wash.   *5 in. × 7 in.*   *Unsigned*
A small ship with bellying sail on a rough sea. A craggy shore to the left, under scudding clouds. Reproduced in *Georgian Love Songs*, ed. John Hadfield, 1949, p. 64.
Owner: Laurence Whistler

279   **A DOG ON A TOMB**   *n.d.*
Pen and Indian ink.   *4½ in. × 6¾ in.*   *Signed, bottom right:*
Rex Whistler

A table tomb, on which a dog is lying—the owner's pet? Cherubs in reverie at each end. The front is left blank, as if for an inscription. Reproduced in *Georgian Love Songs*, ed. John Hadfield, 1949, p. 1.   *Owner: Laurence Whistler*

280   **AN ENCAMPMENT IN A**   *n.d.*
RUINED TEMPLE
Pen and sepia ink with water-colour.   *6¼ in. × 8¼ in.*
Signed, bottom right: Rex Whistler

A tent pitched in a ruined circular temple, with gypsies cooking over a pot.

On the reverse is a study in sepia ink for a "Triumph of Architecture". A nude female figure in a triumphal car drawn by nude figures and a cupid.
Owner: The University of Oxford, Ashmolean Museum
(Weldon Bequest, 1937)

281   **"THE PALLADIAN BRIDGE,**   *n.d.*
WILTON"
Water-colour.   *8 in. × 5¼ in.*   *Signed, lower margin:*
For Eddie from Rex

Given by the artist to Sir Edward Marsh. To the right, the bridge in perspective from the river bank. To the left, across the river, trees. Dated by the artist "Sept. 1st".
Presented to the Worksop Public Library and Museum by The Contemporary Art Society, in 1954.

282   **A SKULL IN A BONNET**   *n.d.*
Indian ink.   *5 in. × 8 in.*   *Signed, bottom centre:*
Rex Whistler

A skull in a velvet Tudor bonnet with a long feather and a large ruby. Backed by a broken sword and lance, and with an unlettered scroll. Possibly a tail-piece.
Owner: Arthur Fanshawe, Esq.

283   **TWO OLD LADIES**   *n.d.*
Pencil.   *6¾ in. × 5¼ in.*   *Unsigned*
Sketch of two old ladies, left profile and full-face, in elaborate hats and veils, seated at a restaurant table. Probably from the life.   *Owner: Malcolm Fry, Esq.*

284   **THE QUEEN OF SHEBA**   *n.d.*
Pencil and water-colour.   *5 in. × 6¼ in.*   *Unsigned*
In a four-wheeled chariot beneath a plumed pink canopy, with two white horses driven by a negro. Other figures on foot, or riding.   *Owner: Dr. Anne McLaren*

285   **YOUTHS AND**   *n.d.*
SHEPHERDESSES
Sepia ink and wash.   *8 in. × 10 in.*   *Unsigned*
To the right, two bored, pretty shepherdesses. Two youths approaching stealthily, unseen, on a crag to the left. Reproduced in *Restoration Love Songs*, ed. John Hadfield, 1950, opp. p. 120.   *Owner: Laurence Whistler*

Sketch-books and MS. Books

Owner: Laurence Whistler (except where otherwise given)

286   **"BOOK OF SKETCHES &**   *1923*
             NOTES"
9 in. × 7 in.

Now labelled "1923A". An exercise book bound in brown canvas. On the front cover: "Whistler 1923" flourished, and below: "Slade School". 146 pages, many loose, include the following. A title-page drawing, signed *Rex Whistler*. 60 pages of "Architectural Notes" with drawings of details, plans, etc., in pencil. The remainder consists of sketches in pencil, pen, and Indian ink and water-colour. Ideas for the Shadwell Murals (pp. 98, 99, 113–114). Architectural fantasies: e.g. "My Guest House" (p. 106), "Approach to my House" (p. 120), "My Private Bathroom" (pp. 121–122), "Back Stairs to Servants Quarters" (p. 65), etc. Pen and Indian ink and water-colour views of the artist's home at the time, Pinner Wood House, Middx. (pp. 110, 111).

287   **SKETCH-BOOK**   *1923*
6¼ in. × 3½ in.

Now labelled "1923B". A diary and memorandum book, used as sketch-books, in a leather note-case. Signed, *Rex J. Whistler*. 86 of the pages are filled with sketches, nearly all in Indian ink and water-colour, a few in pencil, including a caricature of his brother Laurence, aged 11. Humorous sketches, caricatures, 8 full-page drawings of his home at the time, Pinner Wood House, Middx, with details of stairs, porch, etc., 2 water-colours of Wilsford Manor, and other architectural subjects.

288   **"AN ANTHOLOGY OF MINE"**   *1923*
8 in. × 6½ in.   (*See page* xx)

A ruled exercise-book in original wrappers. 120 pages: pp. 1–73 containing thirty-seven poems by Poe, De la Mare, Herrick, Keats, and others, nearly all richly decorated with drawings in Indian ink and water-colour. A note on p. 3 reads, "Poems, verses & lines that I love most marked thus:★." Those marked are *Annabel Lee*, the Ode *To Autumn*, Selections from Gray's *Elegy*, *The Listeners*, *La Belle Dame Sans Merci*, *Ode to a Nightingale*, and occasional lines *passim*. The title page shows a figure in Tudor costume at a table surrounded with books, cogitating by candle-light, festooned with cobwebs. Signed at the foot, *Rex John Whistler*. Pp. 74–114 are blanks. P. 115 has a pencil sketch of a sea-shore (*Annabel Lee*). Pp. 116–120 contain "Prayers, Charms & Witch recipes", with 3 decorations.

289   **SKETCH-BOOK**   *1924*
9 in. × 7 in.

A black school exercise-book, signed on the front cover, "RJW", paginated 1–123, with elaborate end-paper and title-page, etc. On the front end-paper: "Book of Sketches and Notes. This Book belongs to Rex Whistler of Warren Lodge, Farnham Common Bucks: & The Slade, University College, Gower St. London." The sketches are chiefly in Indian ink and water-colour, and include the following. Architectural details and fantasies: e.g. "Convenient Travelling House for batchelor" [*sic*], a home on wheels (p. 12). Illustrations to books and poems: e.g. Baudelaire's *L'horloge* (pp. 29–30), Poe's *Raven* (p. 34), *An Adventure* (p. 50), etc. Decorated poems and humorous drawings. Dating from the period at the Slade School and the visit to Switzerland and the Riviera.

290   **SKETCH-BOOK**   *1925*
7 in. × 10¼ in.

Taped sketch-book with pencil slot. 55 pages. Inscribed "Rex J. Whistler. 1925. Villa Natalia, Corso Cavallotti, San Remo, Italy"; and with Warren Lodge and Slade addresses. It contains sketches for the Shadwell Murals (Indian and sepia ink and water-colour, pp. 14, 17–19, 21, 31–33, 38); an idea for his bookplate (pen and Indian ink, p. 24); details of Wilton and the Park School (pen and Indian ink, pp. 25–28); sketches for the Slade Summer Competition, "The Merchant of Venice" (pen and Indian ink, pp. 43–46); a pencil sketch of the Tate Gallery Refreshment Room, with a first idea for the main wall and a rough plan with measurements (pp. 50–51). Also other architectural notes.

291   **VISITORS' BOOKS:** *1925–1944*
THE DAYE HOUSE, WILTON

Rex Whistler frequently embellished the visitors' books of houses he stayed in. Outstanding are those belonging to Edith Olivier.

(1) 1919–1925. (5¼ in. × 5 in.)

     In 1925, when the artist paid his first visit to the Daye House, he decorated the opening page of entries for 1922, to mark his hostess's arrival at the house. Thereafter he decorated a title-page (or the first page) for each succeeding year, beginning at 1926.

(2) 1926–1935. (7 in. × 4½ in.)

     In addition to the annual headings, he provided, in 1928, a full-page drawing in Indian ink and water-colour of "The Great Accident. September 9th. 10.55 a.m." This shows, at the top, Edith Olivier driving the Whistler brothers cheerfully to morning church; at the bottom, the end of a disastrous skid—the car totally wrecked against the park wall of Wilton House, though without damage to the occupants. The development of the artist's style over nine years is clearly revealed by the headpiece to 1935: a delicate water-colour of the Palladian Bridge at a distance (*Plate 84*). This is closely followed by his decoration in 1926 on the inside of the back cover: "To be continued (we *hope*). Signed, The Guests."

(3) 1936–1942. (*8¼ in.* × *7 in.*)
Notable in this book is the headpiece to 1939: Edith Olivier advancing to the Town Hall as Mayor of Wilton, reproduced in *Country Moods and Tenses*, by Edith Olivier, 1941, fig. 53; and as a Christmas card. Later headpieces reflect the progress of the war: 1940, Mars and Vulcan, drawn in furious baroque, hammering weapons; 1941, an exploding city; 1942, a vast Jap face vomiting hordes of soldiers.

(4) 1943–. (*6½ in.* × *5½ in.*)
An armed hero in a cavern reaches towards a distant light. His last headpiece, for 1944, remains unfinished.

Owner: Miss Rosemary Olivier

292 **"A BOOK OF MYRTLES & ROSES"** *1926*

10¾ in. × *7 in.*

A MS. anthology written and decorated by the artist, supposedly a printed book. In original wrappers with decorated label (pen and Indian ink, water-colour and gold): "A Book of Myrtles & Roses. Collected by Rex J. Whistler 1926." 12 leaves, chiefly pen and Indian ink, sepia ink, and water-colour. Title-page, with a verse from Poe's poem *For Annie*, which gives the title. Dedication: "To Laurie". 4 poems with head- and tail-pieces and decorations. A full-page, water-colour drawing of an 18th-century nobleman on a terrace, his negro page bearing the coronet on a cushion. A design for the artist's bookplate (unused). A careful elevation and plan, in colour, for a garden pavilion. Ruled margins to seven of the leaves.

293 **SKETCH-BOOK** *1926*

8½ in. × *5½ in.*

Now labelled "1926A". Embossed covers (loose) with artist's bookplate, and decorated title-page. Paginated 1–127. Pencil, pen, and Indian or sepia ink, and 16 water-colours, together with end-page in water-colour and gilt. Opposite p. 1 a finished design for the artist's bookplate (unused). 4 pages of sketches for George Moore's *Peronnik the Fool* (no. 519) (pen and Indian ink). Many architectural details and designs. "Design for my tomb"—a pen and Indian ink urn on a pedestal: on the reverse, a water-colour drawing of an angel beside an urn—"R.I.P. R.J.W."—in an imaginary cemetery. Three sketches of Cranborne Manor. "The Grotto, Amesbury Abbey. Aug. 31st (Edith and Laurie)"—water-colour. The entrance gates to Amesbury—and to Fonthill. A two-page water-colour of Willen Church. A water-colour of one of the Boycott Pavilions at Stowe. Suggestions for headpieces for *The Connoisseur* and for illustrations to articles on Pepys in *English Life*. A poem by Edna St. Vincent Millay with embellishments in water-colour. Grotesques and humorous inventions, including—"A wonderful and beautiful INVENTION for concealing the crude and ugly shape of the Soda-water Siphon" (by enclosing it in a decorated urn); a pencil sketch, "While of unsound Mind" (two feet protruding from an urn)—reproduced in *Rex Whistler*, by Laurence Whistler, 1948, p. 104.

294 **SKETCH-BOOK** *1926–1927*

1 ft. 4¾ in. × *10½ in.*

Now labelled "1926B 1927". Perforated sketch-book containing 19 leaves (21 are missing). A tower of St. John's, Smith Square (pencil). Designs for furniture, and details of mouldings (pencil and Indian ink). An unused idea for the "Spring" plate in *The New-Forget-Me-Not* (no. 419). An unused idea for the London Museum poster, water-colour, 8½ in. × 5½ in.—a view of the Thames and distant St. Paul's (no. 652). Miscellaneous studies.

295 **"BRIEF NOTES ON ANDREA PALLADIO"** *? c. 1927*

11 in. × *7 in.*

Now labelled "Palladio Notebook ? *c.* 1927". In wrappers. Possibly about the time of the Tate decorations, 1926–7, with pencil comments added by the artist in 1935. On the fly-leaf a pen and Indian ink device "R W", followed by 2 blank leaves. Paginated 1–25, followed by 19 blank leaves and a pencilled architectural sketch on the free end-paper. Head-piece to p. 1: "Brief Notes on Andrea Palladio 1508–1580" between (left) broken columns and (right) an urn, etc. Opposite p. 11 a pencil sketch of the Palladian Bridge at Wilton, and pen and Indian ink sketches of the "Bridge at Bassano".

296 **ROME SKETCH-BOOK** *1928*

10½ in. × *6¾ in.* (*Half-title of this book*)

Decorative paper covers torn off and covers loose. 31 leaves remaining. 22 pages blank. The artist's sketch-book during his stay at the British School at Rome, Apr. 22nd–Aug. 7th, with some work of the following nine months. Opposite the title-page, in brown ink, a cartouche with the address of the British School, under a shell containing "R.W.". An elaborate title-page in brown ink with, each side at the top, a flaming urn and a self-portrait bust, both on pedestals, from which hangs drapery with "Rex Whistler 1928". A pair of cloud-borne cherubs below. Brown ink drawings include: screen and terminal figure in the Borghese Gardens, Apr. 25th; fountain at Tivoli, Apr. 26th; design for a covered bridge across the moat at the Fortezza della Brunella, Aulla; tower at Bolsover Hall, Derbyshire, Aug. 27th. Pencil drawings include: Roman Viaduct at Spoleto, May 12th; "Tree on road to Bellegra", July 8th; bridge at Licciana, and boys bathing, July 15th; fountain in P. Navona, Aug. 6th; baroque façade near Lord Berners' house, Aug. 7th. Water-colours: "Ilex in Borghese Gardens"; View from the garden at Renishaw, Derbyshire, between pyramid yews; sketch for the Tate Gallery poster (no. 653). Most of the sketches are referred to in the artist's Rome Diary (see no. 240). The sketch-book was lost in the train to Munich in 1929, and returned to the artist's brother in 1959.

297   **"BAROQUE NOTE-BOOK"**   *1928*

In his diary at the British School at Rome the artist recorded: "July 4th. Spent morning in library. Studying Baroque. Started my Baroque notes"; "July 19th. Drew some things in the Baroque note book." This was evidently distinct from his Rome Sketch-book (no. 296).

Whereabouts unknown

298   **SKETCH-BOOK**   *1929*

$7\frac{3}{4}$ in. × $5\frac{3}{4}$ in.

Now labelled "1929A". On the front end-paper a pen and sepia ink medallion: "1929 RW January", flourished. 81 pages. 3 pages cut out. 18 blank leaves. Pencil notes of architectural details made during a visit to Ireland in January. Two water-colour sketches of the front and side of a castellated house (pp. 11, 13). Sketched pencil portraits of Lord Pakenham (p. 3) and Dame Edith Sitwell, "Edith. Jan:" (p. 31). A pencil sketch for Sir Philip Sassoon's Christmas Card (pp. 68–9).

299   **SKETCH-BOOK**   *1929*

$4\frac{7}{8}$ in. × $8\frac{1}{4}$ in.

Now labelled "1929B". Without front cover. 26 pages perforated, 2 pages loose. Brown or sepia ink drawings include: "The Shelleys' house, Marlow"; Baroque ornaments—"Bellona" at Munich, and elaborate urn (on reverse). Pencil drawings include: Rococo "Pew end at Mittenwald, Untergrainau, drawn with Nanny. May 1929". Sepia ink and water-colour portrait of "John. Nov. 25" (a child, unidentified).

300   **SKETCH-BOOK**   *1929*

9 in. × 1 ft.

Now labelled "1929C". 16 pages, without covers. Pen and sepia ink drawings include: "Villa Julia, July 5th"; Piazza di Castello, Turin. Pencil drawings include: portrait of a man with a bow tie, and Lord Granby (the 10th Duke of Rutland) as a boy, both left profile; details of French Gothic; two sketches for Dame Adelaide Livingstone's bookplate (one in ink). Evidently added to in later years.

301   **"THE WILSFORD THEATRE"**   *1931*

$4\frac{5}{8}$ in. × $3\frac{7}{8}$ in.

Bound in green cloth, with gilt tooling on the front cover (not designed by the artist), containing a gilt "S from R" to his design, and with additional decorations in green ink. On the half-title, "The Wilsford Theatre", above an "S" between crossed sprays. Opposite the title-page, the linked letters "STRW" in a rectangle. Title-page: a rococo cartouche in sepia ink and wash, with a tragic and comic mask to left and right, and a musical trophy below, containing ovals with "S" and "R". In the centre "The Wilsford Theatre—A small collection of Suggested Plans, Elevations, and Drawings made for it. MCMXXXI." The project for the theatre was evidently soon abandoned; for the book only contains one rough pencil sketch of the building, and 16 blank leaves.

302   **Decorations to "PORTRAIT OF**   *1932*
CHRISTABEL" by Osbert Sitwell

Sepia ink and wash, and water-colour.   1 ft. 1 in. × 9 in.

Three copies only of a poem in free verse, in the artist's calligraphy: for Christabel McLaren, Samuel Courtauld, and Osbert Sitwell, with slight differences in the decorations. Bound with green morocco spine and imitation vellum covers painted by the artist. Front cover: a title cartouche in sepia wash, heightened with gold. Free end-paper: a cipher of "C.M." On the reverse: "This Edition is limited to three volumes, of which this is no. *One*" (etc.) *Rex Whistler*. Half-title: an urn with fruit, and a circular plaque, reading "Portrait of C.M. by O.S." Title-page: the wording on a tall rectangular green panel, flanked by elongated terminal figures, supporting cartouches. Ten head- and tail-pieces in colour. Flourished calligraphy.

Owners: Christabel, Lady Aberconway, The Hon. Christopher McLaren (Mr. Courtauld's copy) and Sir Osbert Sitwell, Bt.

303   **ADDRESS BOOK**   *1932–1933*

1 ft. × 8 in.

A morocco-bound dummy of *The Next Volume* by Edward James (The James Press, 1932), with the gilt-tooled rococo design on the front cover. The artist has had his initials, "R.W." inserted in the formal sun. The fore-edge was indexed by himself. The book contains a few pencil sketches, and several flourished embellishments to the names of the artist's particular friends: one in colour.

304   **MISS WELLESLEY'S**   *1932–1940*
VISITORS' BOOK

$6\frac{3}{4}$ in. × $4\frac{3}{4}$ in.

Kept by Miss Elizabeth Wellesley (Lady Elizabeth Clyde) as a child, at Penns in the Rocks, Sussex. Cover decoration in water-colour and sepia ink: "Elizabeth Wellesley" in a wreath, with a little picture of the house at the top. Eight decorations in pencil, Indian ink or water-colour.

Owner: The Lady Elizabeth Clyde

305   **ODE TO THE WEST WIND**   *1934*

$6\frac{1}{4}$ in. × 4 in.

A 6-leaved MS. book, in which the artist has written out Shelley's poem. The covers are decorated, in imitation of printed paper, with alternating "A"s and stars, and with a flourished ADW imposed on them in Indian ink. On the front paste-down end-paper is the following inscription, as if printed:

> This Edition consisting of ..... copies
> only for distribution in the civilized World
> and The United States of America is signed
> by the Author & was specially printed for
> Miss Angela Dudley Ward
> This volume is number ......

The figure 1 has been inserted in pencil in the appropriate places, also the word "not" before the word "signed".

Above, in pencil, "For darling Angie a poem she loves from someone who loves her." The title-page is panelled with rules: "Ode to the West Wind/P. B. Shelley/Specially Published, May 25th/MCMXXXIV/London." In the largest panel "Angie" is written in a leafy wreath (Indian ink and water-colour). To each of the five right-hand pages there is a head-piece in Indian ink, water-colour, and sepia wash. In the centre of the 5 blank pages, opposite, is written "ADW" beneath a star (Indian ink and water-colour). On the final left-hand page a coronal of pink roses contains: "For darling Angie to wish her many happy returns of the day." *Owner: Lady Laycock*

306 SKETCH-BOOK 1939
10 in. × 1 ft. 2½ in.

A "Spirax" Sketch-book with 12 detachable leaves remaining, one of them blank, containing sketches chiefly in pencil and coloured chalk, including: "The Mess from the miniature Range" at Sandown Park; a curtain design for *Love for Love*, and ideas for *War and Peace*.

307 "THE HANDSOME YOUNG MAN" 1940
Water-colour.   7¼ in. × 6¼ in.   Unsigned

An 8-leaved MS. book without covers or title-page. The story consists of captions to the paintings on the right-hand pages. (P. 1) "There once was a very rich and very handsome young man" (p. 2) "who lived in a very beautiful house". (P. 3) "One day while out riding, what should he see coming towards him but . . ." (p. 4) "the most beautiful Nigger Lady bicycling along the path." (P. 5) "It was love at first sight, and" (p. 6) "soon afterwards they got married and . . ." (p. 7) "decided upon a boating and picnicking honeymoon" (p. 8) "and lived happily ever after." The final picture is a family group, with three children—each half-black and half-white, divided vertically.

Subsequently bound and titled, with (in gold on the cover) a small wreath from the front cover of Hans Andersen, here containing the letters "L.R.". On the fly-leaf, but not inscribed by the artist, "For Laura Ridley. Invented and drawn for her by Rex Whistler . . . Jan 15th 1940." *Owner: Mrs. Adrian Carrick*

308 VISITORS' BOOK OF 1942 BINDERTON HOUSE, SUSSEX
Water-colour.   4 in. × 9 in.   Signed: Rex Whistler, 1942
A view of Binderton. *Owner: Sir Anthony Eden*

309 LADY CYNTHIA ASQUITH'S 1944 VISITORS' BOOK
Pencil, ink, and coloured chalks.   8¼ in. × 10 in.
Decorations on pp. 28 and 42–43

In *Haply I May Remember*, 1950, pp. 111–114, Lady Cynthia describes the artist's one-night leave at Sullington Court, Sussex, shortly before D-Day, and the making of two decorations while she read poetry aloud. The first is a head-piece to the Sullington section of the book: a cartouche with a cipher of "C A", backed by flowers, sheaves, etc. The second is on the "1944" pages: a wreathed Corinthian column; and a head-piece across the double-spread, with a wavy pencil note standing for a vine spray: "So sorry haven't been able to finish this scribble. Rex. P.s: I have not stolen any of the pencils." On the page below he added the army numbers to a brother-officer's signature and his own: *Rex Whistler 121651.*

Owner: The Lady Cynthia Asquith

From *THE EMPEROR HEART*. Cat. no. 481

Architecture, Furniture, etc.: Designs and Studies

Architecture and Sculpture

310 **"NETHERHAMPTON HOUSE,** *1925* **IN THE COUNTY OF WILTS"**

Indian ink and water-colour. $6\frac{1}{4}$ *in.* × *10 in.* *Unsigned*

The front of the early Georgian stone-built house, with (bottom right) a detail of one of the parapet urns. Title on a flying scroll, supported by two cherubs. On the reverse: to the right, a detail of the wrought-iron gates; to the left, the "Loggia at Selva Dolce, Bordighera". Signed, bottom right, *R.J.W.*

From the 1925 Sketch-book. Edith Olivier says in her unpublished Journal for May 31st: "To see the Newbolts after tea. Rex mad with delight over their house, which he thinks the loveliest he has ever seen." And next day: "Stopped outside Netherhampton and Rex hastily drew it."
Owner: Laurence Whistler

311 **THE GARDEN PORCH,** *1927* **NETHERHAMPTON HOUSE, SALISBURY, WILTS**

Water-colour

Remembered as a view of the pillared porch with his brother Laurence kneeling beside it. Edith Olivier records in her unpublished Journal for Aug. 29th: "Went to Netherhampton . . . and the boys drew and painted—Rex a water-colour of the garden porch while funny little Laurie crouched about like a goblin 'measuring it up'."
Whereabouts unknown

312 **DESIGN FOR AN OBELISK** *c. 1927*

Pencil. *11 in.* × $8\frac{1}{4}$ *in.* *Unsigned*

With a large classical pedestal, containing the space for an inscription inside a wreath. On a page torn from his brother Laurence's schoolboy architectural note-book.
Owner: Laurence Whistler

313 **DESIGN FOR AN** *c. 1927* **ORANGERY**

Pencil. $8\frac{1}{4}$ *in.* × *11 in.* *Unsigned*

To the left, the end-elevation, partly ruled: an engaged Doric portico with a pediment. To the right, sketches for the side-elevation, and part of the plan. On a page torn from his brother Laurence's schoolboy architectural note-book.
Owner: Laurence Whistler

314 **GARDEN FEATURES AT** *1928* **CAPRAROLA**

Pencil. $8\frac{1}{4}$ *in.* × *10 in.* *Unsigned*

Part of the semicircle of piers, showing the left-hand pier, with "Stone Sculpture, Virgin riding unicorn", and the next feature topped with a large urn.
Owner: Laurence Whistler

315 **SKETCHES OF CAPRAROLA** *1928*

Pencil. *1 ft. 2 in.* × *10 in.* *Unsigned*

"Back of Palazzino." Details of a parapeted wall above steps. "Vignola?"
Owner: Laurence Whistler

316 **SIX DESIGNS FOR A** *1928* **MONUMENT TO LADY GREY**

Sepia ink and wash

"1" 9 in. × 7 in. A headstone containing an upright ellipse between drapery hanging from stars. Above, a smaller ellipse between consoles. Indicated wording includes "In Memory . . . Pamela Grey." A marginal note questions whether the upper ellipse and the stars might not be changed to a shell and knots, respectively. This was done, in the adopted design.

"2"★ On the reverse of the above, a perspective sketch for a table-tomb with richly curved ends and decorative panels. Two figures beside it in serene reverie.

(3)★ 10 in. × 8 in. A headstone with a very rich cartouche involving drapery and cornucopias, and supporting a floral vase between consoles. Suggested size "4 ft. 6 in. × 2 ft.".

(4)★ "Memorial Urn and pedestal." 10 in. × 8 in. A flaming urn on a rich pedestal, which has cherubs' heads all round below the cornice, an elliptical medallion on one side, and flutes below. To the left a sketch, showing a cartouche instead of the ellipse.

(5) 1 ft. 1½ in. × 9½ in. A headstone containing an upright ellipse between drapery which falls from knots in the centre of consoles, and is looped up to the base of a large shell at the top. Crossed sprays of flowers below the ellipse. "Suggested size: 4 ft. 6 in. × 2 ft." To the

★ Reproduced in *Rex Whistler* by Laurence Whistler, 1948, p. 85.

right, details of two possible kerbs, and, top right, a small perspective sketch of the whole, in the churchyard.

This was a development of Design no. 1. The stone in Wilsford Churchyard, Wilts, dated "18 Nov. 1928", was carried out very nearly to this design, with the addition of carved birds on the floral sprays below, and with one of the kerbs suggested. The size is that proposed.

The design was more closely followed in the monument to Mrs. Laurence Whistler (Jill Furse) in Dolton Churchyard, North Devon, dated "MCMXLIV", with the addition of a smiling mask, a pen, and a book of verse, in front of the floral sprays below, and tassels hanging from the shell. Sculptor, George Friend.

Owner: Laurence Whistler

(6) 10 in. × 8 in. A headstone with a large rococo cartouche, and a small one above, beneath a broken segmental pediment with segments reversed.

Owner: The Hon. Stephen Tennant

317 DESIGN FOR A MURAL   1928
MONUMENT IN NORTON BAVANT
CHURCH, WILTS
As executed: approx. 5 ft. high

On Edith Olivier's recommendation, Colonel Benett-Stanford commissioned a memorial to his son, Vere, which was designed on Nov. 28. It hangs in the South transept: baroque, with a broken pediment of segments reversed, and five coats of arms displayed round a central cartouche—the whole being supported on square brackets. The stone is dark, with the arms in heraldic colours, the lettering all in rounded italic—probably only sketched by the artist, who, at this time, could write to Edith Olivier: "I *hate* lettering, and always refuse to do it on my posters, etc!"

Whereabouts of design unknown

DISCARDED DESIGN FOR   1928
THE ABOVE
Pen and sepia ink.   10 in. × 8 in.   Unsigned

A straight-sided mural monument containing an upright ellipse with a profile head in relief in the upper part. Topped by a broken segmental pediment supporting a flaming urn. Ribbons above and below the ellipse, with numerous shields.   *Owner: Laurence Whistler*

318 DESIGN FOR A GOTHIC   c. 1928
ARCADED BRIDGE
Pen and sepia ink.   4¾ in. × 5 in.   Unsigned

The idea of the Palladian Bridge in Gothic Revival terms. Three arches wide above a single river-arch, under pinnacled battlements sloping upwards to a cupola. On the reverse, a classical pavilion on a bridge, with Gothic afterthoughts imposed—the drawing which gave rise to the first-named design.   *Owner: Laurence Whistler*

319 DESIGN FOR GARDEN   c. 1928
ORNAMENTS IN THE GOTHIC STYLE
Sepia ink and wash.   6¾ in. × 5¼ in.   Unsigned

An experiment in translating a complete classical garden into Gothic terms. A fountain, with water poured by small statues under canopies into a basin. A domed pavilion, thickly crowned with pinnacles. A statue on a pedestal; and one on a tall clustered column.

Owner: Laurence Whistler

320 ARCHITECTURAL FANTASY c. 1928
Pen and sepia ink.   11 in. × 8½ in.   Unsigned

An octagonal Gothic pavilion rising to a spire. The whole contained within a vast classical baldachino. This invention was accompanied by an impromptu story. On a page taken from his brother Laurence's schoolboy architectural note-book.   *Owner: Laurence Whistler*

321 ARCHITECTURAL   c. 1928
FANTASIES
Pen and sepia ink.   7 in. × 4¼ in.   Unsigned

On one side, a Gothic pavilion on a very narrow footing which is specified as a monolith. Also, a tower, a bridge, etc., and the figure of a woman.

On the reverse, a spiral Gothic tower on an equally pinched base, with a note on "Method of dovetailing stone". Also, a travelling classical house drawn by a traction-engine, with a detail of "card-board case for covering wheels" when stationary, etc.

Owner: Laurence Whistler

322 DESIGN FOR A GARDEN   c. 1928
PAVILION
Sepia ink and wash.   11¼ in. × 6 in.   Unsigned

"A Garden Pavilion for a knoll commanding extensive views." A circular domed building with narrow pedimented projections every way, faced with superimposed orders. Pedigree: by Thomas Archer out of Sir Charles Barry. Reminiscent of Archer's pavilion at Wrest Park. Below, pencil sketches of the pavilion, (1) buried up to the dome, and (2) flying away, having emerged as a balloon.

On the reverse, pencil and water-colour, a baroque design for a country house with a domed centrepiece, circular in plan, and wings thrown forward by quadrants, all under a single entablature.   *Owner: Laurence Whistler*

323 DESIGNS FOR A GARDEN   c. 1928
PAVILION
11¼ in. × 6 in.   Unsigned

On two pages from the "1926B 1927" Sketch-book.

(1) Sepia pen and ink. A circular building with narrow arched projections, every way, under pediments; and rising above these, through an attic storey, to a circular balustrade and a central cupola. Below, a sketch for the drawing *Samson Destroying the Philistines* (no. 238). On

the reverse (sepia pen and ink), a man unsheathing a scimitar.

(2) Pencil. Three aerial perspective sketches of a similar temple, but crowned with a low dome: one a simplification to show the form of the roof. On the reverse, a pencil sketch for the *Samson*.

The pavilions shown in (1) and (2) are evidently related to the "Garden Pavilion" above (no. 322).

Owner: Laurence Whistler

324 DETAILS OF VEITSHÖCHHEIM *1929*
Pen and sepia ink.   7¾ in. × 5 in.   Unsigned

Sculpture on "garden staircase", and a statue of Athena with an owl, cherub, etc. On the reverse, four masks in pencil including "Janus", "Mars", and "Nept". From the "1929B" Sketch-book (no. 299).

Owner: Laurence Whistler

325 SIX DESIGNS FOR URNS *1932*
Pencil and sepia ink and wash.   1 ft. 1¾ in. × 10 in.
Unsigned

Six alternative ideas, numbered by the artist, for two urns designed for the late Mr. Samuel Courtauld: to be placed in niches at each end of his Long Room at 12 North Audley St. All to the scale of ⅛ in. to 1 ft. They are now in an album in the following order:

(1) Ovoid bowl, with swags of fruit and flowers above flutes, supporting fruit.

(2) Ovoid bowl, with drapery and swags pendant from masks, above acanthus. Pineapple-topped.

(4) Bowl of ogee contour, slant-fluted, above an acanthus cushion. Flame-topped.

(5) Concave bowl with cushioned belly, and a small circular plaque with a classical head. Large rococo handles.

(6) Bowl of flattened ogee contour, with large circular plaque containing a cipher of "S.C." Raised, rococo handles.

(3) Concave bowl with swellings below and above. A frieze of *putti*. Topped with a very large flame. This is the adopted design, very much as carved in wood by M. Marus, except that the *putti* were replaced by a frieze of the nine Muses, round one bowl, and the nine Samuels, round the other.

The sheets have many pencilled variants in the margin. Also in the album is a fragment of a letter from the artist to Samuel Courtauld, with three ideas for circular bases, one of which was adopted.

Owner: Christabel Lady Aberconway

SKETCH FOR URN NO. 3   *1932*
Pencil.   8 in. × 1 ft.   Unsigned

Also sketch for a picture-frame, with details. On a sheet of writing-paper headed Ditchley Park.

Owner: Laurence Whistler

326 TWO DRAWINGS FOR THE *1932* FRIEZES ROUND THE EXECUTED URNS
Pencil.   9 in. × 3 ft. ½ in.   Unsigned

(1) The Nine Muses encircle the bowl, supporting a long floral swag. It falls from an oval medallion in front, containing the cipher of "S.C.".

(2) Eight Samuels similarly employed: Scott, Pepys, Rogers, the Prophet, Johnson, Richardson, Butler, Coleridge. The ninth is represented by the cipher itself.

On the back is a note by Lady Aberconway describing the provenance of this work.

Owner: Christabel Lady Aberconway

327 DESIGN FOR A CORNICE AT *1933* WILTON, WILTS

For the Library: included in "an enchanting pencil sketch of the room". Edith Olivier's unpublished Journal for Nov. 8th.   *Whereabouts unknown*

328 THREE DESIGNS FOR A *1934* PAVILION AT BULBRIDGE HOUSE, WILTON, WILTS
Unsigned

(1) *Pencil and water-colour. 11 in. × 1 ft. 3 in.* Classical, with a central door below a pediment, two sash windows, and flanking niches. To be built out from the house at right angles. An elevation—the house indicated in perspective to the right.

(2) *Pencil and water-colour. 11 in. × 1 ft. 3 in.* ? An alternative design to the above, showing three tall round-topped windows, under a pediment spanning the front. Elevation.

(3) *Pencil. 1 ft. 10 in. × 2 ft. 5 in.* A semicircular portico of four columns under a low dome, flanked by narrow extensions with niches. This pavilion was built, but with Ionic columns replacing Doric, and without the dome. The artist painted urns in the niches, which are now faintly visible, although later he disapproved of them and painted them out.

Owner. The Lady Juliet Duff

329 DESIGN FOR A SUMMER- *1934* HOUSE, AT BULBRIDGE HOUSE, WILTON, WILTS
Water-colour.   Approx. 8 in. × 8 in.   Signed, bottom right: Juliet with love from Rex. June 20th

A trellis-work front containing a flattened ogee arch, and with a concave lead roof. Inside a table, pictures, and a parrot on a perch.   *Owner: The Lady Juliet Duff*

330 PROPOSAL FOR *c. 1934* GROSVENOR SQUARE, LONDON
Pen and sepia ink.   3½ in. × 4½ in.   Signed, bottom right: Rex Whistler

Proposed to the Duke of Westminster: the Square as a cobbled space surrounded by trees, with stone paths

49

radiating from a central feature. This to consist of four rusticated columns enclosing a statue on a plinth, and crowned by an urn. Reproduced in *Country Life*, Jan. 17th, 1947.   *Owner: Loelia Duchess of Westminster*

331 PROPOSED ALTERATIONS *c. 1934*
TO BOLEBEC HOUSE, WHITCHURCH,
BUCKS

(1) *Pencil and water-colour. 6 in. × 1 ft. Unsigned. (Plate 69)* Proposal for extending and re-shaping the front to the road. With a white modillioned cornice; and a door-case with a broken segmental pediment and bust, below a bull's-eye window. A lantern, etc. Several notes.

(2) *Pencil and water-colour. 11 in. × 10 in. Unsigned.* Proposal for the right-hand half of the front only. Somewhat similar to the above, with stone gate piers and balls.

(3) *Sepia ink and water-colour. 4¼ in. × 6¾ in. Unsigned.* Design for steps and a mown circle in the garden. Stone steps mounting a new rampart, with trees along the top. As carried out, but the vase was omitted.

(4) *Sketch. Pencil on 3-ply wood. 1 ft. × 1 ft. 4 in. Unsigned.* For a one-storey extension to the dining-room, with a classical door between sash windows. Drawn on the backing to the frame of his water-colour of Castel Gandolfo, 1928 (no. 247).   *Owner: Laurence Whistler*

Some less ambitious alterations to the front and back of the house were carried out to the artist's design, including doors and windows, and gate piers with pineapples. In the garden he planted a small lime avenue crossed by a cherry avenue at right angles, as well as making the circular earth bastions, and the steps described. Some of these improvements survive.

332 DESIGN FOR A *1936*
SCREEN WALL AT PLAS NEWYDD,
ISLE OF ANGLESEY

(Architect's wash drawing with pencil additions by Rex Whistler.)
1 ft. 4½ in. × 1 ft. 9½ in.   Unsigned

The elevation is signed, *H. S. Goodhart-Rendel 18.8.36.*

The artist's modification was chiefly to rusticate the arch-ways at each end and provide them with grilles over heavily panelled doors. Thus it was built, projecting from the entrance side of the house.

Owner: The Marquis of Anglesey

333 DESIGN FOR A PAVILION *1936*
AT PLAS NEWYDD, ISLE OF
ANGLESEY

Sepia ink and water-colour with gold.   9 in. × 1 ft.
Unsigned

Sent to the late Lord Anglesey with a letter of Apr. 16th: "I meant to have written pages of boring explanation of my suggestion for your new loggia, which I have drawn out & enclosed for you to laugh at." An elegant 18th-century Gothic design, based on a domed octagon, open to the front only, with small wings. Sham red and gold drapery on the back walls. "The painted hangings we could do in one afternoon & the gold stars on top next day."

The artist's letters contain small variant sketches for this pavilion, which was not built. It was to stand in the centre of the new screen wall then building to his design (see above).   *Owner: The Marquis of Anglesey*

334 SKETCHES POSSIBLY *? c. 1936*
FOR A PUBLIC BUILDING

Pencil, pen, and sepia ink.   5¾ in. × 8¾ in.   Unsigned

Several related sketches of, or designs for, a building in two storeys, now straight, now inward-curving in plan, having always the upper storey set well back behind a parapet, but with a central projection of three round-topped windows under bull's-eyes. A canal to the right.

Owner: Laurence Whistler

335 DESIGN FOR A FORECOURT *1937*
AT PLAS NEWYDD, ISLE OF ANGLESEY

Sepia ink and water-colour.   6 in. × 8 in.   Unsigned

An aerial perspective sketch showing part of the house to the right, with a proposed baroque doorcase, and two walls projecting to form a paved courtyard with a central fountain. The sketch was designed to show how the court could be formed by repeating the existing new wall, which is the one nearest the eye.

On the reverse of a sheet of Plas Newydd writing-paper, containing part of a letter to the late Lord Anglesey.

Owner: The Marquis of Anglesey

336 LIFE-SIZE DRAWING OF *? c. 1937*
A KEYSTONE MASK

Charcoal.   2 ft. 6 in. × 1 ft. 10 in.   Unsigned

A hirsute river-god, or Neptune, crowned and bearded. At the bottom a side-view in pencil, showing the projection of the features. The ruled outline shows the key-stone as 1 ft. 7¾ in. high and 1 ft. 4 in. wide at the top. On the reverse an architectural fantasy, etc.

Owner: Laurence Whistler

337 DESIGN FOR CEILING *1938*
PLASTER-WORK AT 15 KENSINGTON
PALACE GARDENS, LONDON

Pencil.   2 ft. × 1 ft. 4 in.   Signed, bottom right: Rex Whistler 29, Fitzroy Square, W.1.   *(Reverse of frontispiece of this book)*

A very rich trophy, chiefly martial, but with the addition of flaming torches, musical instruments, etc.

Designed for Sir Alfred and Lady Beit, for the centre of a ceiling in an oval room. It was devised to conceal small spotlights, which shone down on a set of framed pictures by Murillo round the walls. Five red dots in the drawing show the placing of the lights. The artist's assistant was Victor Bowen. A photograph of the room appeared in *Country Life*, Feb. 25th, 1939.

Owner: Sir Alfred and Lady Beit

SKETCH FOR THE ABOVE
Pencil.   11 in. × 6 in.   Unsigned

A rough sketch squared out for enlargement, probably by the assistant. Scale of 1 in. to 1 ft. shows that the actual trophy would be 8 ft. × 5 ft.   *Owner: Laurence Whistler*

338   A PROPOSAL FOR THE   *1938*
ENTRANCE SIDE OF MOTTISFONT
ABBEY, HANTS
(?) Water-colour

Recalled by Mrs. Russell as a drawing of the existing front door, and Tudor-style windows at right angles, lighting the painted room. Superimposed on this, a design for a new door and façade; also for a new approach with a detachable paper statue. "The idea of the improvements struck him one evening when he was in the big room and he forgot the time and all about bed and worked all through the night on his little drawing."   *Whereabouts unknown*

339   ARCHITECTURAL FANTASY *c. 1938*
Pencil.   9½ in. × 6 in.   Unsigned

A perspective view of a grand entrance: an archway flanked by low extensions and crowned with an equestrian group. A car is entering the circus in front, which is pointed with four obelisks. Above, a design for a four-candled rococo wall-light, in the form of crossed branches —possibly related to those at Mottisfont Abbey (no. 14).   *Owner: Laurence Whistler*

340   A LIBRARY AT   *c. 1938*
34 CHAPEL ST., LONDON

Lady Diana Cooper asked the artist to re-create this very long room, rising two storeys high. On one side, below bull's-eye windows, he designed bookshelves supporting obelisks and globes with draperies. There were to be large rococo cartouches, inscribed "Biography", "History", etc. In a niche at one end an existing sculptured Syren was to be appropriately enthroned. The shelves were built, but little further progress was made when the owner left. The artist wrote to her in July 1940, when there was a possibility that her successor might complete the work: "If she does—surely I'm her man? No one else knows where they ought to go ["spikes and black balls"] or how those plaques should be painted on the tall pilasters or how the white leaves have to be painted (or made) curling up the big curved cornices, or what to paint on the balls, do they? Of course even if she were to want it I couldn't do much of the painting—(if any)—myself now, but I could make out the designs for the different panels for one of my old boys to paint—& oh! how incredibly delighted they would be to have the work to do. . . ." The original drawing has been mislaid. See Lady Diana Cooper, *The Light of Common Day* (1959), pp. 220, 248.

SKETCH FOR THE ABOVE
Pencil on back of menu card.   9 in. × 1 ft. 1 in.
Unsigned

Made during a meal at the Jardin des Gourmets, probably

the earliest sketch. Bookcases each side of the chimney-piece, with pilasters rising to a coved cornice, bearing cartouches. Above, obelisks and globes and between them roundels painted as if containing busts. A detail of a pilaster-top supporting a standing trophy over a crossed "C".

TWO SPECIMEN NAME-   *c. 1938*
CARTOUCHES FOR THE ABOVE
Body colour on (1) cardboard, (2) plywood

Grisaille rococo cartouches in the form of grinning faces, the black open mouth containing the word: "Biography" in yellow (for gold). Proposed in two sizes, (1) 1 ft. 3 in. × 1 ft. 11 in.; (2) 1 ft. 1 in. × 1 ft. 8 in. Sketches of details also appear in the artist's letters to Lady Diana Cooper on [?] June 8th, 1939, and [?] July 27th, 1940.
   Owner: Laurence Whistler

341   DESIGN FOR   *? c. 1938*
REFRONTING KNEBWORTH HOUSE,
HERTS
Sepia ink and wash.   4½ in. × 7 in.   Unsigned

A new classical front of red brick and stone, to be placed between the existing Victorian turrets. Five sash windows in width, with four pilasters of very slender Doric rising to urns and a central escutcheon. In the foreground, an iron grille between piers. Below, a sketch plan: "The new façade *breaks* forward slightly."
   Owner: Pamela Countess of Lytton

342   SMALL MEMORIAL STONE   *1940*
TO THE ARTIST'S FATHER
Pencil.   1 ft. ½ in. × 9¾ in.   Unsigned

An ellipse, cut out to the actual size of the stone to be laid in the grass of Salisbury Close. A brief inscription to Henry Whistler, encircled by a wreath. The design was repeated as a memorial to the artist himself in the same place—his own home and his father's having been the Walton Canonry.   *Owner: Laurence Whistler*

343   DESIGN FOR AN EXTENSION   *1941*
TO BULBRIDGE HOUSE, WILTON,
WILTS
Indian ink and water-colour.   9 in. × 1 ft.   Signed and
dated under inscription, top left: R.W. Dec 7th 1941

"Proposed New Colonade [*sic*] & Garden Room to be thrown out at Bullbridge [*sic*] House, Wilton." Four sketches, three of them in perspective, and a plan: for an L-shaped extension in the form of a "collonade" [*sic*], open only to the garden, leading to a "New room" and a small "Flower Room". It would involve a new forecourt in front of the house, with a "Pavement of stones, brick, cobbles etc", and a central Corinthian column on a pedestal.   *Owner: The Lady Juliet Duff*

344   DESIGN FOR A PROSCENIUM   *1942*
ARCH

For a Nissen Hut Theatre at the Saw Mills, Wilton. For Mr. John North. Edith Olivier records, in her unpublished

Journal for Sept. 13th, that the artist promised a working drawing to scale, based on his sketch.

Whereabouts unknown

345   **DESIGN FOR A DORIC**   *n.d.*
            COLUMN

Sepia ink and wash.   *7 in. × 4¼ in.*   *Unsigned*

With a spiral wreath. On a pedestal. Supporting a spiked ball. The summit of an avenue is indicated, with trees on either side. Possibly an existing column.

Owner: Laurence Whistler

346   **STUDY OF A STATUE**   *n.d.*

Pencil.   *1 ft. × 9 in.*   *Unsigned*

Back view of a naked youth, with drapery over the left shoulder.   *Owner: Laurence Whistler*

347   **STUDIES FOR A STATUE-**   *n.d.*
            FOUNTAIN

Pencil.   *9½ in. × 7½ in.*   *Unsigned.*   *(Plate 37)*

Eros with bow and arrow, on one knee, blindfold. To stand on a circular pedestal with cherubs in relief, supporting a lion-mask fountain. Below, studies of Eros in three different positions.   *Owner: Laurence Whistler*

348 **RUSHBROOKE HALL, SUFFOLK:** *n.d.*
    SKETCHES FOR A FORECOURT

Pencil.   *10 in. × 1 ft. 2 in.*   *Unsigned*

Two geometrical proposals, with an obelisk or urn or other feature in the centre. On the same sheet, a female nude. A leaf from a sketch-book.

Owner: Christabel Lady Aberconway

349   **ARCHITECTURAL FANTASY**   *n.d.*

Sepia pen and ink.   *7 in. × 4¼ in.*   *Unsigned*

A coach crossing a classical bridge into an avenue punctuated by obelisks, urns, a triumphal arch and a wrought-iron grille. On the reverse, a small rusticated entrance arch with extensions for lodges, and with a podium over the Doric entablature, inscribed: "Sitis Famae . . ."

Owner: Laurence Whistler

350   **PROPOSAL FOR THE EIFFEL** *n.d.*
    TOWER RESTAURANT, LONDON

Pencil and water-colour.   *1 ft. ½ in. × 7 in.*   *Unsigned*

An idea for embellishing the restaurant, in order to help the well-known proprietor, M. Stulik. Drawn on an envelope for Miss Viola Tree, and accompanied by an explanatory letter, now mislaid.

Owner: David Parsons, Esq.

Furniture

351   **DESIGN FOR A BOX**   *1928*

For Sir Courtauld Thomson, the agreed price being £50. Mentioned in a letter to Edith Olivier on Jan. 5th.

Whereabouts unknown

352   **DESIGN FOR THE ARTIST'S** *c. 1928*
            BED

Pencil and water-colour.   *10¾ in. × 1 ft. 1¼ in.*   *Unsigned*

A convertible sofa-bed with curved wooden ends and back, and painted drapery at the foot in front. There would be actual red cords, and red and blue painted decoration on a pale blue ground, including, in the centre, a blue-winged cherub supporting a medallion with "R.W.". Also pencil sketches of the construction. The reverse is covered with architectural ideas in pencil.

Owner: Laurence Whistler

353   **STUDY OF TABLES AT** *? c. 1930*
            WILTON

Brown ink.   *8 in. × 5¼ in.*   *Unsigned*

"The 'Kent' tables at Wilton, September 9th." Several studies of tables supported by consoles and dolphins, on both sides of the sheet.   *Owner: Sir Osbert Sitwell, Bt.*

      SKETCHES FOR THE ABOVE

Pencil.   *7 in. × 4¼ in.*   *Unsigned*

Two drawings of dolphins and consoles. On a sheet of The Daye House writing-paper.

Owner: Laurence Whistler

354   **A PAINTING ON AN** *? c. 1935*
    18th-CENTURY MIRROR

Oil on glass.   *6 ft. 6 in. × 4 ft.*

Staying with Sir Philip Sassoon, the artist thought this mirror needed embellishment, and painted on it, in white, a pair of crossed trees, an elegant tent, and a figure; and, below, two bunches of flowers. When it came up for sale, after Sir Philip's death, one agent reported to the intending purchaser, "I wouldn't *touch* it! Someone has painted on the glass and ruined it"; while another firm was planning to break up the mirror and sell it in separate pieces as "Paintings on Glass by Rex Whistler."

Owner: Christabel Lady Aberconway

355 **A PAINTED WRITING TABLE** *c. 1937*

Oil on wood and leather.   *3 ft. 6 in. × 4 ft. 8 in.*
      Unsigned

An existing table with a grey-white ground, on which the

artist has painted panels on the fronts of two drawers in the form of crossed "E"s in grey, twisted with green tendrils; and, above, floral wreaths in grey-white on brown leather, to the fronts of two cupboards. Also narrow wreaths round the top of the table, etc.

Owner: The Estate of the Countess Mountbatten of Burma

356 A DECORATED CLAVICHORD *1939*

Oil on wood.   *Size of main panel: 1 ft. 3¼ in. × 3 ft. 10 in.*

Signed, bottom right: Rex Whistler 1939.   *(Plate 75)*

The clavichord was made by Thomas Goff and J. C. Cobby. Decorated all over by the artist, it is one of his finest works.

Outside of lid (top): On a grey ground "T.R.C.G. MCMXXXIX" in gold lettering with white palm-leaves. Each side there are small gold and white trophies of musical instruments, as if hanging from the hinges. A wreath of leaves all round.

Inside of lid (main panel): Within a border of gold acanthus and corner shells, a painting of Orpheus, with the golden lyre given him by Apollo, charming the animals, which move towards him from all sides. Beside him is Eurydice, in the likeness of Lady Caroline Paget, with a lamb in her lap. Cupid reclines against a stag to her right; and beyond him three naiads are singing, not far from a waterfall, tumbling among rocks. On the extreme left a distant procession climbs, making music, as if in a poem by Keats, towards a circular temple, like that of Vesta.

    This panel was painted on a white ground, which at the artist's request was given an uneven, not smooth, surface in the work-shop by stippling.

Front and ends of case: Continuous white acanthus on grey.

Inside of flap: Small acanthus in the same manner.

Horizontal back-board: A posy of roses, lilac, etc., sprinkled with dew-drops.

Name board: In gold Roman lettering: "T.R.C.G. et J.C.C. fecerunt. MCMXXXIX."

Trestle-stand: Straight wreaths in white on grey.

Photograph in *Country Life*, Mar. 26th, 1948; and

Grove's *Dictionary of Music* (Macmillan, 1954), IV, 736. The original water-colour drawing, the property of the artist, was lost between Mottisfont and London, possibly in transit in his car.   *Owner: Thomas Goff, Esq.*

DETAIL FOR THE ABOVE   *1939*

Pen and Indian ink and sepia ink on tracing paper.

7¾ in. × 1 ft. 5¼ in.   *Unsigned*

Full-size detail of the acanthus and shell border with a note to his assistant, Victor Bowen, on how to draw acanthus: "Dear Vic: Very much the same size as you drew out I think. Only differences are: More rounded tips to all the leaves & more cut up and leafy. Its this *rounded yet delicate tip* to the leaves which is most important of all. If they are too pointed & yet coarse the effect is almost *Gothic*, which I want to avoid. Probably some of the finer tendrils might be painted in by hand afterwards?? In haste R.W." Reproduced in *Rex Whistler*, by Laurence Whistler, 1948, p. 31.   *Owner: Laurence Whistler*

357 DESIGN FOR A BOOKCASE *c. 1940*

Pencil.   *6 in. × 8 in.*   *Unsigned*

A classical bookcase with panelled cupboards up to dado level. Divided into three parts, the centre containing a niche with an urn, below a broken segmental pediment with a bust. Not executed.

Owner: The Lady Elizabeth von Hofmannsthal

358 A PAINTED WIRELESS SET *c. 1942*

? Oil on wood.   *Approx. 2 ft. 6 in. × 2 ft. 6 in. × 3 ft.*

Unsigned

The artist's own property, with five decorations, doubtless in oil. Whereabouts unknown. As described: On the inside of the left-hand door, a shepherd—of the right-hand door, a nymph; in the centre, between the controls, a tree; the ground colour green. Existing at Poole, Dorset, in 1949.

Pottery, Textiles, and Miscellaneous

359 DESIGN FOR CLOVELLY   *1932*
TOILE DE JOUY AND WEDGWOOD POTTERY

Pen and red ink.   *2 ft. 10 in. × 2 ft. 6 in.*   *Unsigned.*

(Front end-papers of this book)

A pictorial design in the manner of the later 18th-century material produced at Jouy-en-Josas by Oberkampf: the artist may have studied examples at the Victoria and Albert Museum. Five views of Clovelly are arranged as a quincunx, with a title-device symmetrically placed at the top, containing the word "Clovelly" in a cartouche, above

a mermaid and a spouting dolphin. In the spaces between these six staggered features there are five smaller devices, consisting of bunches of flowers or marine objects, a lobster-pot, a basket of fish, etc.

    The material was produced in 1933 for Mrs. Hore-Ruthven, by W. H. Haynes, Ltd., of Spring St., London, in four colours chosen by the artist—Jouy red, cornflower blue, black, and green. Later the design was applied to pottery, and produced in the same colours by Wedgwood, in the form of breakfast, tea, and coffee sets, and additional shapes, on "Queen's Ware". It is now in process of being applied to wall-paper by Cole and Son of Mortimer St.,

London. Edith Olivier records in her Journal: "It took him 9 days, *day and night*, and he did not even go out for meals." Photograph and article in *The Times*, Jan. 18th, 1933. *Owner: The Hon. Mrs. Hore-Ruthven*

SKETCHES FOR THE ABOVE *1932*

(1) *Red wash. 7 in. × 9¼ in. Unsigned.* Probably the artist's first sketch, showing two staggered views of Clovelly, topographically incorrect, and two sprays of flowers. In pencil, a suggestion of nets linking these features.

(2) *Pen and red wash. 8¼ in. × 8¼ in. Unsigned.* A sketch for the five views as carried out, arranged in a quincunx, but in different order. There is a suggestion of looped nets and chains linking the various items. These will have been abandoned because of technical difficulty in the execution on fabric. *Owner: Laurence Whistler*

360 **A NEPTUNE CARPET** *1934*
Oil on canvas. 2 ft. 4 in. × 1 ft. 6 in. Unsigned

Mr. Edward James commissioned this carpet, which is now at Monkton House near Chichester, together with the design for it. The artist chose as his subject Neptune surrounded by nereids, sea-horses, and spouting dolphins, in a choppy blue-green sea, which provides the ground of the whole design. At top and bottom are nymphs and dolphins supporting a shell on which the letters "E J" appear, and the same is seen in a small cartouche in the centre.

The carpet was made at the Wilton Royal Carpet Factory and completed in 1935. The design was interpreted in 107 different colours. Edith Olivier records in her unpublished Journal for June 29th that, on seeing the finished work, "Rex now realises how impossible very gradual shading is either in carpet weaving or in my canvas work." Design and photograph of carpet in *The Sketch*, July 17th, 1935.

361 **DESIGN FOR A SILVER** *1934*
      JUBILEE STAMP

Artists were invited to submit designs, to a national competition. In her unpublished Journal for Oct. 28th and 29th, Edith Olivier described Rex Whistler's entry as "drawn most delicately and exquisitely . . . six times the size of the stamp". He told her that Sir Kenneth Clark "said at once on looking at it that it was 'incomparably better than any of the others', so I hope that they will all agree with him. I would *like* to alter Britannia to a Lion if they would let me." His design would have succeeded, but unfortunately he had submitted it too late (much occupied with the scenery he was designing, free, for *Figaro* at Sadler's Wells), and was disqualified. "It means £100", Miss Olivier recorded, "—a great loss to him." The G.P.O. possesses reproductions in four colours, stamp-size, 19 mm. × 34 mm. In the centre an oval medallion with a portrait of King George V, in left profile. To the left, Neptune; to the right, Britannia. Below: 1910 Silver Jubilee 1937. *Whereabouts of original unknown*

SKETCH FOR THE ABOVE *1934*
Pencil on official form. 1 ft. 4 in. × 1 ft. 1¼ in.
Unsigned

Owner: Laurence Whistler

362 **DESIGN FOR A WEDDING** *1935*
      CAKE
Water-colour heightened with white. 10½ in. × 10 in.
Unsigned

A room interior with a black-and-white tiled floor, white walls hung with swags, and a black ceiling decorated with white stars. In the centre, on a table half-draped by a fringed table-cloth and flanked by two dolphin bowls, stands a two-tiered cake. On the second tier a pair of spouting dolphins supports a fountain-basin into which falls a double jet. A vase of flowers on a tall pedestal stands in each corner of the room. Notes by the artist. The cake was made by Messrs. Jackson for Miss Felicity Watts for her marriage to Mr. John Hanbury. The design was shown at the British Art in Industry Exhibition at Burlington House, 1935. *Owner: The Estate of Mrs. Constance Spry*

363 **DESIGN FOR A PLATE** *c. 1935*
Sepia ink and wash. 9¾ in. diameter. Unsigned

An actual-size proposal, with a view of Trent Park in the centre, and four other views of the house and grounds within wreaths round the border, interspersed with small ciphers of "P.S.". For Sir Philip Sassoon. Not carried out.
Owner: Laurence Whistler

364 **DESIGN FOR EDWARD VIII** *1936*
      COINAGE
Pencil. 9 in. × 7 in. Unsigned

Two coins showing Edward VIII facing right, as if in sculptured relief. The inscription in Roman letters: one with a crown above his head, the other in classical style, with a laurel wreath round the brows. On the back, rough ideas for the obverse of the half-crown. Not carried out.
Owner: Laurence Whistler

365 **DESIGNS FOR ROYAL** *1937*
      CIPHERS
Black scraper board. 9¾ in. × 8 in. Signed, bottom right:
Rex Whistler

In Feb. 1937 the artist was commanded by the Queen (Queen Elizabeth the Queen Mother) to design ciphers containing the initials "G.R.I.", "E.R.", and "G.R.E.". Only his design for the latter has come to light. It shows the Crown backed by leaves, above interlinked, flowing, acanthus capitals. On Mar. 1st the artist was sent Her Majesty's "very warmest thanks for the very lovely ciphers". *Owner: H.M. Queen Elizabeth the Queen Mother*

Three sheets exist, covered with pencil sketches for these ciphers, each 8 in. × 6 in. *Owner: Laurence Whistler*

366 **DESIGN FOR A RUG** *c. 1937*

Water-colour. 7½ in. × 9 in. *Signed, bottom right:*
Rex

In a rococo frame, a wreath looped over a flaming urn. Red and green. A detail of the rococo added, top right. "Please forgive such a terribly rough sketch. With love from Rex." Carried out in *gros point* by Lady Juliet Duff, who owns the design.

367 **DESIGNS FOR AN ENGRAVING** *1940*
ON GLASS

Black scraper board. 1 ft. × 9 in.

(1) *Front view.* "Proposed design for a diamond point engraving on a glass goblet for Robert Tritton Esq." A view of Godmersham Park in a rococo cartouche, topped by "T" in a shell. Reproduced in *Rex Whistler*, by Laurence Whistler, 1948, p. 96.

(2) *Side view.* Showing the cipher of "E.T." and part of the inscription at the top: "For Elsie Tritton on her birthday. . . ." Inset, the cipher of "R.T." for the opposite side.

(3) *Back view.* Showing a cartouche containing a blank space. This space was left in order that the stippled view of the house in front should not be confused by another engraving directly behind it.

The glass was executed in 1940. Photograph in *The Engraved Glass of Laurence Whistler*, Cupid Press, 1952, Plates 14 and 15. *Owner: Laurence Whistler*

SKETCH FOR THE ABOVE *1940*

Pencil. 7 in. × 2½ in. *Unsigned*

Rough sketch for the back of the glass, showing the position of the ciphers. *Owner: Laurence Whistler*

368 **DESIGN FOR A RUG** *1942*

Water-colour. 3¾ in. × 6 in. *Signed:* To Mrs Beaton with love from Rex, November 1942

The Royal Arms in a cartouche. Blue, green, yellow, etc. Size suggested by the artist, 3 ft. 9 in. × 6 ft. The design was carried out by Mrs. Beaton in petit-point.
Owner: Mrs. Beaton

369 **DESIGN FOR A FAN** *n.d.*

Sepia ink and water-colour. c. 4 in. × 7 in. *Unsigned*

The design is said to embody scrolls, flowers, and butterflies. Mislaid. *Owner: Mrs. Siegfried Sassoon*

From *THE LORD FISH*. Cat. no. 454

Designs for the Theatre and Cinema

On Feb. 28th, 1944, when his life's work for the Theatre was virtually completed, the artist wrote to Mrs. (Janet) Leeper, the author of *English Ballet*: "I shall be delighted for you to use some of my designs in your book—but I'm afraid *you* will have to look for them. They all belong to me (except the grisaille Act drop [for *The Rake's Progress*] which I sold to the permanent Sadler's Wells Collection) but are always being borrowed, lost and stolen, for one reason and another, and I haven't time, these days, to keep trace. No scene designs are *ever* returned until one has written at least 24 letters." Five months later he was killed in action. This sufficiently accounts for the non-appearance of many original designs in the following pages.

Plays

370   **COMUS by John Milton**   *1930*
(In Betteshanger Park, June 27th)
PROGRAMME AND ENCHANTED CHAIR
PROGRAMME.   *As printed: 8¾ in. × 5½ in.*

Vignette of Comus, seated, raising a goblet. Reproduced in *The Masque*, no. 7.

ENCHANTED CHAIR: Mrs. Leeper recalls: "I think everybody gave a hand with the Magic Chair. It was glorious and flimsy, as far as I remember, and could just about do two performances with impunity." Reconstructed from snapshots, it appears to have consisted of a wicker-work arm-chair, with the covered sides, and the steps on which it was placed, painted with occult symbols. The back was raised and draped in dark red, covered with stars; and in the centre at the top was a large flaming sun on which a face was painted.

371   **BALLERINA by Rodney Acland** *1933*
(Gaiety, October)
PROGRAMME AND COSTUMES FOR FRANCES DOBLE

(1) PROGRAMME. Front cover. As printed, 8¾ in. × 5½ in. Ink and wash, 9 in. × 5½ in., unsigned. "Frances Doble in Ballerina", flourished, with flying ballet girls and a Gothic ruin below. Reproduced in *The Masque*, no. 4, and *Rex Whistler*, by Laurence Whistler, 1948, p. 93.
Owner: Miss Elizabeth Hudson

(2) SCENERY. Water-colour, 9 in. × 1 ft. ½ in., unsigned. Interior with three tall windows to the left; male and crinolined female standing, female figure seated. Inscription concealed by framing. (Not used.) Reproduced in *The Masque*, no. 2.
Owner: Cecil Beaton, Esq.

(3) COSTUMES (Frances Doble's dresses only).
Act I, Sc. 2: Water-colour, 1 ft. 3 in. × 11 in. unsigned. As Paulina Varley. In a pale-blue bodice and flounced skirt, "to *put over* pink ballet dress".
Sc. 3, 4, 5: As Paulina Varley.
Act II, Sc. 1: Water-colour, 1 ft. 3 in. × 11 in., unsigned.

As Lina Varsovina. In a pale-grey bodice and full skirt, with a rose at the breast (crossed out).
Sc. 2 and 4: As Lina Varsovina.
Sc. 5: Water-colour, 10½ in. × 8 in., unsigned. As Lina Varsovina. In a black velvet crinoline with red belt and ermine muff. *Owner: Laurence Whistler*
Act III, Sc. 1: As Lina Varsovina.
Sc. 2: Water-colour, 11 in. × 8 in., unsigned. As Lina Varsovina, in a white and blue crinoline and wide-brimmed hat. "Fontainebleau scene, afternoon dress for Bunny."
Owner: Margaret Countess of Birkenhead
Sc. 3: Water-colour, 1 ft. 2 in. × 11 in., unsigned. As Lina Varsovina. In a dark blue cloak, and cream crinoline, gloves, and ermine muff. Partly torn off.
Sc. 4: Water-colour, 1 ft. 1 in. × 8 in., unsigned. As Lina Varsovina. In a pale-green negligée, trimmed with white.
Sc. 5: Water-colour, 1 ft. ¾ in. × 8 in., unsigned. As Lina Varsovina: "Behind Stage"; "The Snowbird."
In a long brown cloak with brown velvet cape, left profile. "Last scene. Rain."
Owner: Laurence Whistler
Unidentified scene: Indian ink and water-colour, 1 ft. × 10½ in.
As Lina Varsovina. In a yellow and black crinoline, with a chaplet of yellow and white flowers. "Bunny with love from Rex."
Owner: Margaret Countess of Birkenhead

Edith Olivier mentions in her unpublished Journal that the artist had to design sixteen costumes.

372   **?DESIGN FOR BALLERINA** *?1933*
Sepia ink and water-colour.   8½ in. × 11¾ in.   Unsigned.
(*Plate 92*)

A lady in a blue and white crinoline, with her right hand raised, standing in a 19th-century boudoir, with bow windows to the left. Apparently included in the artist's "List of Work lent to Whitechapel Art Gallery, April, 1935", as "Design for Ballerina. Fontainebleau. (Tallulah's)." On the back an inscription in pencil, erased by the artist, who retained the painting: "To darling Tallulah with love always, Rex". Possibly a design for Act III, Sc. 2.—Drawing-room at Fontainebleau, 1862. More probably an illustration to the original novel by Lady Eleanor Smith. *Owner: Hugh Beaumont, Esq.*

373   REUNION IN VIENNA   *1934*
(Lyric Theatre, January 1934)

POSTER AND PROGRAMME

POSTER.   *As printed: 1 ft. 7½ in. × 1 ft. ½ in.*

PROGRAMME.   *As printed: 8½ in. × 5½ in.*

Sepia ink and wash: 12¾ in. × 9¼ in.   *Unsigned*

A yellow rococo frame with looped crimson curtains, and two cherubs supporting a crown and imperial coat-of-arms. On each side a hussar raising a toast. "Gilbert/Miller/presents/Alfred Lunt/ &/Lynn Fontanne/in/REUNION/IN/VIENNA/by/Robert E. Sherwood." Below: "Lyric Theatre/Shaftesbury Avenue."   *Owner: Martin Battersby, Esq.*

Sketch for the Above   *1934*

Ink and water-colour.   *1 ft. 2 in. × 9½ in.*   *Unsigned*

Very much as carried out, but with large volutes behind the bottom trophy, and lettering confined to the names of principals and the title of the play. Reproduced in *The Masque*, no. 4.   *Owner: Laurence Whistler*

374   THE TEMPEST   *1934*
by William Shakespeare
(Stratford-on-Avon, Summer)

COSTUMES ONLY

Pencil and water-colour.   *11 in. × 8¼ in.*   *Unsigned.*

(Plates 99 and 100)

"1. Prospero." Facing left, with folded arms; in a wide-brimmed hat, doublet, and hose "of rich stuff. Faded purple but dark, & very wrinkled & worn"; also a "Cloak: Rusty black. Lined same colour as suit. Binding hanging loose at waiste [*sic*] & shoulder (i.e. in need of repair)." To the left, a rough sketch of a knee-length cloak.

"2. Miranda" in a "'Homemade' dress supposedly of some material saved from the wreck": a loose kirtle with green embroidery and a "thin rope at waist". Reproduced in *The Masque*, no. 7.

3. "Ferdinand" in a red and white striped doublet and round hose, plumed black hat and black belt.

4. "King Alonso" in grey doublet and hose, a purple cloak hanging from his shoulders, and an Order on a blue ribbon from his neck.

5. "Antonio" scowling under a tall-crowned black-plumed hat, in cartwheel ruff, black cloak, black quilted doublet and puffed hose.

6. "Gonzalo", facing right, holding a tall cane, in a black cloak lined with grey, striped grey doublet, and black striped round hose.

7. "Francisco" in a plumed pale-blue beaver, blue-grey doublet and hose with buff stripes and grey-lined cloak. To the right an alternative suggestion in blue-striped doublet and hose and short cloak.

8. "Adrian" in rust-red striped Venetians, embroidered with yellow, a yellow sash and short cloak.

9. "Sebastian" in a white doublet and puffed hose and canions, all embroidered in green, and a red tasselled sash. Reproduced in *The Masque*, no. 4.

10. "Trinculo" in doublet and puffed hose with pale-blue and yellow panes, blue shoes, and black cloak. To left and right, alternative suggestions for the pale-blue sugar-loaf hat.

11. "Stephano" in a grey, black-striped doublet and full slops, with a small ruff, bareheaded. "59 waist." A pencil indication to the right of a tall-crowned hat.

12. "Ariel. No 1." Full-face, the left arm raised. With golden wings, a tunic of "alternate scales gold & silver" and skirt of gold and silver leaves. Round his head "spikes of bright metal . . . coming out of papier maché gilt curls".

13. "Ariel. No. 2." Full-face, poised on right leg, in a dress of "seperate [*sic*] ribbons" of "very dark green sea weed . . . gathered & bound to the body beneath breasts & at waist by ropes of large pearls (showing skin through)". Detail of a strand of seaweed and pencilled indications of headdress and back view. Reproduced in *The Masque*, no. 4, and in *Rex Whistler*, by Laurence Whistler, p. 94.

14. "Ariel. No. 3." In a gold snake-haired mask, ribbed gold wings and "Red gold sequin tights all over".

15. "Caliban." A spiky-haired monster with webbed hands and feet, and a "*Loin cloth*: of some heavy elastic stuff. Rubber or leather." Dark grey-green spotted tights "with a rough 'goose-flesh' texture".

16. "The Reaper (six of them)." Poised on right leg in a "Broad-brimmed straw hat" and spotted deer-skin jerkin.

17. An Elf. In spotted red-brown tights, small golden wings and gold-leaved apron.

18. "Six small Elves." At the top, five elves holding hands, full-face. Below, another, on a larger scale, in right profile. All have gold wings and are clad in tights made of leaves. "The 6 dresses to range in tone from dark bluey green up to light yellow green."

19. "Six Nymphs." One drawn, in right profile, dancing. In a coronet of flowers and a diaphanous blue-starred white dress. Reproduced in *The Masque*, no. 4, and in *Rex Whistler*, by Laurence Whistler, p. 94.

20. "The 12 Strange Shapes." A figure in a yellow antlered mask, and a close-fitting yellow dress, black-spotted, and with "black & white puffs at waist, shoulders & knees": carrying a wine-flagon on a red tray. Pen and ink detail of the trunks and legs, etc.

21. "12 Hounds." Ariel (in costume no. 3) mounted on a glaring horse, lashing from the dark cave the goblin-hounds.

22. "Ceres." Full-face, carrying a cornucopia. The bodice trimmed with pink and puffed at the shoulders, a short kirtle with broad pink bands over a pencilled under-skirt. Above, right: the back view, half-length.

23. "Iris" in a winged and plumed helmet, close-fitting

yellow bodice and pink and pale-blue kirtle, holding a caduceus.

24. "Iris" (2nd costume). In a silver helmet decorated with black leaves and pink and green plumes. In a silver bodice, the "underskirt & sleeves of that hideous 'Rainbow' material with white gauze over it".

25. "Juno." In a blue-embroidered white dress, trimmed with red at waist and shoulders, and a blue-plumed crown.

26. "Juno" (2nd costume). A more elaborate version of the same dress, worn under a dark-red gown trimmed with gold, the mantle looped from the right shoulder across the waist by a gold sash. The drawing is very badly stained, and the left edge torn away.

TWO UNIDENTIFIED DESIGNS

(1) Pencil, 1 ft. 3¾ in. × 10 in. An unfinished sketch. A female figure, with indication of plumed head-dress, and bodice with scalloped shoulder-trimmings. Possibly a first idea for Iris or a Nymph?

(2) Pencil, 10 in. × 8 in. Three-quarter length of a male figure in a belted deerskin tunic, horned and crowned with ivy. Pencilled sketches, unconnected with the play, on the reverse.

On a separate sheet the artist listed the costumes drawn, including "Master", "Bosun", and "4 sailors", and elsewhere noted "16 Dresses, Tempest" in a list of works sent to the Whitechapel Art Gallery in April, 1935.

One sheet (1 ft. 3¾ in. × 10 in.) contains 12 pencil sketches from Inigo Jones's costume designs for Ben Jonson's *Masque of Queens* (1609), from which the artist derived inspiration for the costumes of Ceres, Iris, and Juno. That of Ceres, in particular, is clearly related to Inigo Jones's design for Candace.   *Owner: Laurence Whistler*

375   **VICTORIA REGINA**   *1935*
         by Laurence Housman
(Broadhurst Theatre, New York, December 26)
POSTER, PROGRAMMES, SCENERY, AND COSTUMES
(*Plate 106*)

Most of the original drawings for this complete production were sold for the artist in New York, by the Walker Gallery, or later by the American-British Art Centre, from 1936 onwards.

(1) LEAFLET. As printed: 8¼ in. × 6 in. "Helen Hayes in Victoria Regina." Drawn wording in an oval frame, yellow (for gold), with looped crimson curtains.

PROGRAMME. As printed: 9¼ in. × 6¾ in. "The Playbill." In an oval, a picture of Queen Victoria in old age, seated beside a bust of Albert, with Windsor Castle in the background.

SOUVENIR BOOKLET. Title-page—"Gilbert Miller/presents/Helen Hayes/in/"Victoria Regina"/by Laurence Housman/with/Vincent Price/Abraham Sofaer:/Staged by Mr Miller/entire production designed by/Rex Whistler."

(2) ACT DROP. A distant view of Windsor Castle in a huge wreath of roses, rising from cornucopias.

(3) SCENERY:

Act I, Sc. 1: The Six o'clock Call. 1837. Entrance Hall of Kensington Palace. Water-colour, 9 in. × 1 ft. 3 in., signed bottom left: *Rex Whistler Oct 1935*. A Georgian entrance hall with statues in niches each side of a glazed door, and black and white marble floor. Reproduced in *The Masque*, no. 4.   *Owner: Gilbert Miller, Esq.*

Act I, Sc. 1: Back-cloth. Water-colour, 8 in. × 6 in. Kensington Gardens at dawn: a vista of dim trees. Reproduced in *The Masque*, no. 7.   *Owner: Laurence Whistler*

Act I, Sc. 2: Suitable Suitors.

Act I, Sc. 3: Woman Proposes. A Sitting Room at Windsor Castle. 1839.

Act I, Sc. 4: Morning Glory. Prince Albert's Dressing Room at Windsor Castle. 1840. To the left, a door. To the right, a shaving mirror near the window. A floral wallpaper of a diamond pattern. Sold to Mrs. E. Roland Harriman in 1936.

Act II, Sc. 1: A Good Lesson. Prince Albert's Writing Room at Buckingham Palace. 1842. Water-colour, 8 in. × 11½ in., unsigned. A book-lined room, with an elliptical arch at the back leading to double doors. Yellow and white striped paper above the shelves. To the right, a mirror above the draped mantelpiece. A floral hearth-rug.
                     Owner: Gilbert Miller, Esq.

A photograph of this scene in the New York production shows that the bookcases were omitted, and other details altered.

Act II, Sc. 2: Under Fire. A Room in Buckingham Palace overlooking the Park. 1842. Two ladies in waiting gazing from a central window. Drapery below the cornice, above an acanthus wallpaper. (From a photostat.)

Act II, Sc. 3: The Rose and the Thorn. An antechamber at Windsor Castle. 1846. A central doorway leading to further staterooms, clustered columns to left and right. A piano to the right.

[Act II, Sc. 4: Intervention. Prince Albert's Writing Room at Buckingham Palace. 1861. Scene as for Act II, Sc. 1.]

Act III, Sc. 1: The Queen, God Bless Her. A Garden Tent at Balmoral Castle. 1877. The aged Queen at a table to the left, facing Disraeli to the right. A Gothic plaid screen behind her. The towers of Balmoral in the distance to the right. Sold to Mr. Robert Strauss in 1936. Reproduced in *The New York Sun*, Mar. 28th, 1936.

Act III, Sc. 2: Happy and Glorious. Buckingham Palace. 1897. A great room in perspective, with sunlight flooding in through windows on the right. Corinthian columns. Sold to Mr. Robert O'Hearn in 1945.

(4) COSTUMES:

Act I, Sc. 3. Albert's costume was sold to Mr. Robert O'Hearn in 1945.

Act I, Sc. 4. Victoria's and Albert's costumes were sold to Mrs. Gilbert Miller in 1945.

Act II, Sc. 1: or Sc. 2: Victoria's costume was sold to Mr. Gilbert Miller in Mar. 1946.

Act II, Sc. 2. Victoria's costume was reproduced in *The Masque*, no. 4.

Act II, Sc. 3. Victoria's costume was reproduced in *The Masque*, no. 4.

Act II, Sc. 4. Victoria's and Albert's costumes were sold to Mrs. Richard Rodgers in 1946.

Many Working Copies of the artist's costume designs for this and the London production remain at B. J. Simmons of Shorts Gardens, London.

Reproductions of original designs appeared in "Color Drawings by Rex Whistler", *Stage Magazine*, Aaronson & Lazar, Inc., N.Y., 1936.

376 PRIDE AND PREJUDICE 1936
by Jane Austen
(St. James's Theatre, February 1936)

POSTER, PROGRAMME, SCENERY, AND COSTUMES

(Plates 97 and 102)

POSTER. As printed: 1 ft. 7½ in.× 1 ft. ½ in. In the centre what appears to be a printed copy of the novel, open at the title-page, "Pride/and Prejudice/by/Jane Austen/Drama-tised by/Helen Jerome/The Play produced by/Gilbert Miller/Designed by Rex Whistler/St. James's Theatre/London". The frontispiece, a "View of Rosings in the County of Kent", with three young ladies. Flowers and fruit are bursting from above and below the book, respectively. Printed announcements of the theatre, actors, etc., are in oblong panels above and below. Reproduced, from a printed copy, in *The Masque*, no. 4.

PROGRAMME. As printed, 8½ in.× 5½ in. At the top, "St. James's Theatre" in a ribbon. In the centre two ladies resting by an urn beneath a weeping willow. Below, an oval, with the wording in drawn letters.

ACT DROP. 7 in.× 1 ft. 2 in. Water-colour, unsigned. A book, exactly as reproduced on the poster (see above), but with fruit and flowers to left and right, respectively. Reproduced in *The Masque*, no. 2.

Act I: The Drawing Room at Longbourn. Water-colour, 7½ in.× 1 ft. ½ in., unsigned. Large bay windows to the right on to a portico. Central doors with a view of a further room. Reproduced in *The Masque*, no. 2.

Owner: Hugh Beaumont, Esq.

Back-cloth to the above. Water-colour, 7½ in.× 9½ in. The further room, with three sash windows to the right. Also a design for the lantern to hang in it.

Owner: Laurence Whistler

Act II, Sc. 2. Aunt Gardiner's House in London. Water-colour, 7¾ in.× 11½ in., unsigned. A large three-light window, with a view across the street. Gold-framed pictures on a floral wall. Reproduced in *The Masque*, no. 2.

Owner: Hugh Beaumont, Esq.

Back-cloth to the above. Water-colour, 8¾ in.× 6 in., unsigned. Georgian fronts across the street. "J. Bramwell & Co.", etc. *Owner: Laurence Whistler*

Act II, Sc. 3. Lady Catherine de Burgh's drawing-room at Rosing's Park. Water-colour, 8 in.× 11¼ in., unsigned. A columned opening to a further room: purple-draped walls with plaster palms in the corners. Reproduced in *The Masque*, no. 2. *Owner: Hugh Beaumont, Esq.*

? Back-cloth to the above. Water-colour, 7½ in.× 5 in., unsigned. A small rotondo in a wooded park. Evidently to be seen through a window. Damaged label reads: "Act 2 Scene 3". *Owner: Laurence Whistler*

Rough Sketches for the Above
Pencil. 7¾ in.× 10 in.

Three sheets with sketches on both sides for the sets and details of furniture.

Sketch for the ceiling. Pencil and water-colour, 6 in.× 1 ft. 1 in. Probably for Act I, cut to shape.

Notes of architectural detail. Pencil, 6½ in.× 8 in. Three sheets of lined paper. Studies possibly in connection with this play. *Owner: Laurence Whistler*

COSTUMES
Pencil and water-colour. Nos. 1 and 7: 8 in.× 5½ in.
Nos. 2–6: 10½ in.× 6 in.

1. Mrs. Bennett. In a black bodice and white skirt.
2. Mrs. Bennett. In a black dress with an apron, seated with a teapot in her right hand.
3. Lydia. In a long dark-blue cloak, holding a pair of gloves.
4. Lady Catherine de Burgh. In a purple dress with black gloves, a walking-stick in the left hand.
5. Lady Catherine de Burgh. In a yellow dress and turban trimmed with black. On the right, a back view of the head in pencil.
6. Elizabeth Bennett. The head turned half-right, the right arm resting on a shelf (sketched); a blue-trimmed shawl on table to left. *Owner: Fleming Williams, Esq.*
7. Janet Bennett. Standing by a table, looking down, in a pale pink dress with spots of deeper pink.

Owner: Mrs. Max Bernstein

8. Lady Catherine de Burgh, 10 in.× 8 in. In a brown dress with diagonal stripes, and a plumed turban.
9. Mrs. Bennett, 9¾ in.× 8 in. In a lace cap, striped bodice, and grey skirt.
10. Mrs. Bennett, 8 in.× 6½ in. In a pale-blue gown and white underskirt. On the left, a detail of the white-edged blue shawl.
11. Elizabeth Bennett, 11 in.× 9 in. In white gown edged with black, and a yellow underskirt.
12. Elizabeth Bennett, 11 in.× 9 in. In a pale-blue dress with a white-spotted scarlet sash.
13. Lydia Bennett, 9¾ in.× 7¾ in. Seated half-left in a red-striped white dress and brown sash. Pencilled details of the lace border to the dress, stripes, etc., to left and right.

Pencil Sketches for the Above
11 in.× 9 in.

Eleven studies of hair styles of the Jane Austen period.

An unfinished sketch for the dress of Charlotte Lucas, with a black bodice.

Lady Catherine de Burgh in a cape and plumed hat. To the right, a sketch of the head in a plumed turban.

Study of the back of a gown with a black and white hem.

Two sheets of pencil sketches and colour notes, details, etc., for costumes for the female characters.

Four sheets of costume details and hair styles, 7 in.× 4½ in *Owner: Laurence Whistler*

Many working copies of the artist's costume designs remain at B. J. Simmons of Shorts Gardens, London.

377 VICTORIA REGINA 1937
(The Lyric Theatre, London, June 21st)

POSTER, PROGRAMME, SCENERY, AND COSTUMES

Because of a rule that the grandparents of the reigning sovereign could not be portrayed on the stage, there seemed no likelihood, in 1935, that this play could be put on in London in the near future. The artist therefore rashly sold, in 1936, nearly all his original drawings for the American production. George V's death altered matters, and the artist was compelled to re-draw the entire production. As his new drawings closely followed the earlier set, it is not always possible to assign them to one or the other production. The order of scenes was as before, except that Act I, Sc. 2, was now cut out, so that Sc. 3 and 4 in that Act became 2 and 3 respectively.

PROGRAMME. Much as before, but with printed lettering. Above the design: Lyric Theatre/Shaftesbury Avenue. Within the oval, the details of the production. Also used as a poster, 2 ft. 6 in. × 1 ft. 8 in.

ACT DROP. Water-colour. A distant view of Windsor Castle in a huge wreath of roses, rising from a regal trophy. The whole as if under Gothic groining. Only the left-hand half of the latter and of the wreath is completed. Reproduced in *The Masque*, no. 4. Mislaid.

Owner: Laurence Whistler

SCENERY. Act I, Sc. 2: Water-colour, 9 in. × 7 in., unsigned. Back-cloth, a long avenue at Windsor Park under a bright blue sky.

? Sketch for the above, pencil, 8 in. × 11 in. A traceried window with a mirror to the right above a console table. On the reverse a chimney-piece.

Act II, Sc. 2: Water-colour, 9 in. × 8 in., unsigned. Back-cloth, the Mall at an angle under a blue sky with the Duke of York's column and St.-Martin-in-the-Fields in the distance. "All the houses and columns, etc.: *very* bright indeed."

Act II, Sc. 3. Water-colour, 8½ in. × 6¾ in., unsigned. ? A first idea for the back-cloth, showing the interior of a vaulted conservatory full of palms, with a night-blue sky.

Act II, Sc. 3. Water-colour, 9 in. × 11 in., unsigned. Back-cloth: "Ballroom from above." A great room with a lamp-lit arcaded gallery, in perspective.

Act III, Sc. 2. Water-colour, 8 in. × 6½ in., unsigned. Back-cloth to tent. A large conifer and other trees at Balmoral.

Act III, Sc. 2. Water-colour, 1 ft. 1½ in. × 5 in., unsigned. Detail of a mahogany door and upper panel for Buckingham Palace.

There are also 14 sketches and detail drawings on sheets of varying size, mostly in pencil. Also two small note-books with sketches.

COSTUMES:

Act II, Sc. 2. Water-colour, 11 in. × 8 in., unsigned. Albert in a grey top hat, dark-blue tail-coat, and grey check trousers.

Act II, Sc. 3. Lady Jane. Water-colour, 11 in. × 8¼ in., unsigned. Looking half-left, holding a rose, a girl in a crinoline of "fine tulle over pink-striped satin".

There are also two sketches for this costume, but possibly for the New York production. Each, water-colour, 11 in. × 8¼ in., unsigned. Variants for the "pink & white stripe" dress.

"The Duchess." Pencil, 11 in. × 8¼ in., unsigned. Flounced dress, described as "wine" and "cream".

"Q. Victoria's Dresses with decor"—11 small sketches

on one sheet. Indian ink and water-colour. 11 in. × 8¼ in. The artist's record of colour schemes throughout the production: dresses and furniture, etc., with written notes. Damaged, top left, by fire. On the reverse, pencil sketches of dresses.

Owner: Laurence Whistler

378 OLD MUSIC by Keith Winter *1937*
(St. James's Theatre, August 18th)
SCENERY ONLY

Act I. (1) The Nursery of the Deckers' house in London. Afternoon, Dec. 1853. Pencil and water-colour, 10 in. × 1 ft. 2 in., unsigned. Reproduced in colour in *The Masque*, no. 7. On the reverse, a pencil sketch for Act II, Sc. 1.

(2) "Nursery Windows backing." Water-colour, 7 in. × 10½ in., unsigned. A London street-front to be seen through the window.

(3) "Ground row for nursery windows." Water-colour, 9 in. × 1 ft., unsigned. Detail of roofs outside window.

(4) "Nursery fireplace." Water-colour, 4 in. × 7 in., unsigned.

(5) "Backing for Nursery double doors." Water-colour, 8 in. × 8½ in., unsigned. Design for wall-paper and suggestion for a real picture to be seen when the doors are opened.

Owner: Laurence Whistler

Act II, Sc. 1. The Drawing Room of the Yales's House in London six months later.

(1) (Probably for *Old Music*) "Backing for Drawing-Room Window." Water-colour, 8½ in. × 11¼ in., unsigned.

A view of distant spires, buildings, and blue hills seen over the blue-green tree-tops of the park, the position of the two windows being indicated.

Owner: Alick Johnstone, Esq.

(2) Detail of picture frame. Water-colour, 5½ in. × 7 in., unsigned. (?) For picture between the windows.

(3) Detail of ceiling. Pen and Indian ink, 6 in. × 8 in. "I haven't *coloured* it as it must match in, of course, with your existing cornice and frieze."

Act II, Sc. 2. An open glade on the outskirts of a wood. Water-colour, 8 in. × 1 ft., unsigned. Reproduced in colour in *The Masque*, no. 4.

Sc. 3. Full-size detail for wall-paper. Water-colour, 2 ft. 6 in. × 1 ft. 10 in., unsigned. A large bright-coloured posy in a diamond. But possibly for *Victoria Regina*, Act I, Sc. 3 (Albert's Dressing Room).

Owner: Laurence Whistler

Rough Sketches for the Above

Pencil. 1 ft. 1 in. × 1 ft. 4 in.

Two ideas for the Nursery; 3½ in. × 5¾ in., an idea for Act II, Sc. 1. *Owner: Laurence Whistler*

Act III, Sc. 1. London six months later.

Sc. 2. Lord Trensham's Study.

Sc. 3. Dining-room of the late Lord Trensham's house, 1883.

379 FROM QUEEN ELIZABETH TO *1937*
ELIZABETH THE QUEEN

(A Special Matinée for King George's Pension Fund,
Winter Garden Theatre, December 16th)

PROGRAMME.   *As printed: 11¼ in. × 9 in.*

A drawn title, in an oval bearing the Garter motto: contained in a strap-work cartouche, with a crowned "E" at the top between cherubs, and dolphins at the bottom.

380   THE LUCK OF THE DEVIL   1939

(The Players' Theatre, June, 1939)

SCENERY

Water-colour.   7 in. × 11 in.   Unsigned

An artist's attic studio overlooking Paris. Reproduced in *The Masque*, no. 7.   *Owner: Leonard Sachs, Esq.*

BACK-CLOTH

Scenic paint on linen.   8 ft. 8 in. × 15 ft.   Unsigned

The roof-tops of Paris visible through the window. This back-cloth was entirely painted by the artist himself, working behind the scenes during evening performances at the theatre.   *Owner: The Players' Theatre*

381   LOVE FOR LOVE   1943
by William Congreve

(Phoenix, April)

SCENERY.   (*Plate 101*)

Curtain. Pencil and Indian ink wash, heightened with gold. 1 ft. 1½ in. × 1 ft. 7¾ in., unsigned. The silhouette of a William and Mary gallant and lady springing to greet one another, encouraged by Cupid, between huge columns also in silhouette. The figures are made slightly three-dimensional by gold modelling. Behind them, in pencil, a vista of classical buildings under a cartouche: "Love for Love by Mr Congreve". Not used. Reproduced as a head-piece (the figures alone) in *The Masque*, no. 4.

Sketches for the above, Indian ink wash, 4½ in. × 7 in., on both sides of a sheet of 29 Fitzroy Square writing-paper. The principal figures greeting one another (1) between trees, (2) by an obelisk.   *Owner: Laurence Whistler*

Act I, Sc. 1: Valentine's Lodging. Sepia ink and water-colour, 6 in. × 9 in., unsigned. A panelled room with a bed in the alcove to the left and a figure reclining. A circular table to the right. Reproduced in *The Masque*, no. 4.
          Owner: Sir John Gielgud

Act I, Sc. 1: Detail drawings, pencil and water-colour, unsigned. (1) For back and right-side wall, treated as one, 1 ft. 3 in. × 2 ft. 4 in. (2) For left-side wall with two windows, 1 ft. × 11 in.   *Owner: Hugh Beaumont, Esq.*

Act I, Sc. 2: Foresight's House. Sepia ink and water-colour, 6 in. × 9 in., unsigned. A saloon with Corinthian pilasters and mural paintings. Four figures to the right. Reproduced in colour in *The Masque*, no. 7.
          Owner: Sir John Gielgud

Act I, Sc. 2: Detail drawings, pencil and water-colour, unsigned. (1) Back-cloth, 11 in. × 1 ft. ½ in. Corinthian order, and frieze reading ASTRA REGUNT OMNES SED REGIT

ASTRA DEUS. (2) 1 ft. × 11 in. Coupled columns of the same order, with fireplace to left and arch to right. (3) Border, 6 in. × 1 ft. 7½ in. "Border 38 ft. × ? 8 ft.", looped and fringed curtains across the top of the set.
          Owner: Hugh Beaumont, Esq.

Studies for the scenery: (1) Indian ink and pencil, 7 in. × 9½ in., unsigned. Showing Valentine on the bed, and at the table. (2) Pencil and blue ink, 9 in. × 7 in., unsigned. For both scenes and for the curtain. The latter will be the sheet referred to by Sir John Gielgud, in a letter to Laurence Whistler, as containing ". . . sketches done by Rex in front of me while dining at the Ivy one night".
          Owner: Laurence Whistler

Sir John also mentions "the backcloth [to Act I, Sc. 2] which was an elaborate Thornhill decoration with gods and goddesses . . . drawn out in some detail".

382   AN IDEAL HUSBAND   1943
by Oscar Wilde

(Westminster, November)

SCENERY AND COSTUMES

(*Plates 108 and 110*)

SCENERY

Act I. The Octagon Room in Sir Robert Chiltern's house. Water-colour, 9 in. × 1 ft., unsigned. A late Victorian interior with a saucer-domed ceiling and striped panels between columns. Central doors leading to the head of a staircase. Reproduced in *The Masque*, no. 2. This drawing, like the other scene designs, is copiously annotated by the artist, e.g. "Bogus Adam satinwood . . .", "'Gunther's' type of little gilt chairs . . .", "Aubusson carpet", etc.

Act II. Morning Room in Sir Robert Chiltern's House. Water-colour, 8½ in. × 11¾ in., unsigned. A red carpet; red-patterned wall-paper; heavy green curtain to the window in the right-hand corner. Much bric-à-brac. Reproduced in *The Masque*, no. 2.

Act III. Library of Lord Goring's House in Curzon St. Water-colour, 9 in. × 1 ft., unsigned. A bow-ended room beyond a screen of columns, blue-and-white striped silk panels. "Yellow gathered lampshades." Reproduced in *The Masque*, no. 2.

COSTUMES

Water-colour, 1 ft. × 9 in., unsigned. In three frames.

(1) Act I: Lady Chiltern; Mrs. Cheveley. Act II: Lady Chiltern; Mrs. Cheveley.

(2) Act I: Mabel Chiltern; Act II: Lady Markby (reproduced in *The Masque*, no. 7); Act IV: Lady Chiltern; Act IV: Mabel Chiltern.

(3) Act I: Lady Basildon; Act I: Lady Markby; Act II: Mabel Chiltern.   *Owner: Hugh Beaumont, Esq.*

Act I: Mrs. Marchmont; and Act III: Mrs. Cheveley, are missing. The latter is described as "green and silver; black satin cloak, lined dead rose-leaf".

Thirteen small sketches of the women's costumes on one sheet, pencil and water-colour, 4½ in. × 7 in. The artist's record of designs.

Act II: Lord Goring. In a grey frock-coat with a red buttonhole.

Act IV: Lord Goring. "4 button morning coat" and "yellow waistcoat". *Owner: Laurence Whistler*

Many working copies of the artist's costume designs remain at B. J. Simmons of Shorts Gardens, London.

383   **STRICTLY BETWEEN**   *1944*
OURSELVES
(Hippodrome, Eastbourne, May)
SCENERY
Indian ink and water-colour.   1 ft. × 8 in.   Unsigned
The officers of the 1st Bn. Welsh Guards, reviving on the eve of invasion—for the benefit of troops in the Eastbourne area—this security play, asked the artist to design some simple scenery. For a back-cloth he drew two huge heads of Welsh Guards officers, eagerly telling, or listening to, a military secret. This was enlarged to 12 ft. × 8 ft. and finished by the artist himself. He also painted two side-panels (lifted from the closed Pier Theatre, to the manager's indignation): on the right, a disguised Goering eavesdropping on the officers; on the left, an unidentified listener, with Hitler peeping below his arm. This small production contained his last work for the theatre.

Owner: Captain Michael Ling

Ballets

384   **THE INFANTA'S BIRTHDAY**   *1932*
(Camargo Society, Adelphi, December)
SCENERY AND COSTUMES

SCENERY.   Back-cloth.   Water-colour,   11 in. × 7¼ in. Inscribed by the artist: "Bogus 'El Greco'. For wall behind throne." Placed centrally between pretended mirrors, the main or only painted decoration.

Owner: Laurence Whistler

COSTUMES. Pencil and water-colour, 7 in. × 4½ in. (except no. 5, approx. 8 in. × 5 in.), unsigned.

(1) "Boy Hobbyhorse rider", running right, in white tights, with sword, leopard-skin cloak, etc.

(2) "Acolite", in white cardinal's hat, cape, and tights, carrying a large candle.

(3) Captive Moor, in blue costume with red tassels.

(4) "Tight-rope dancer." A hooded nun in black and white with a black mask, holding, as if on the rope, a red wand horizontal above her head. This character was suggested by the artist, but it shocked Mme. Karsavina and was dropped. *Owner: Mrs. Barman (Miss Penelope Spencer)*

(5) "The Pages." Yellow puffed sleeves and black slant hat.   *Owner: W. B. Morris, Esq.*

Other costumes included—The Infanta, The Dwarf, Bull and Toreador, Maids in Waiting.

385   **THE RAKE'S PROGRESS**   *1935 &*
(Sadler's Wells Co., May 1935)   *1942*
SCENERY AND COSTUMES
(Plates 93–96 and 103)

In 1940 the Sadler's Wells Ballet Company was nearly caught by the German invasion of Holland, and scenery and costumes were left behind. When this ballet was to be revived in 1942, it was found that the original drawings had disappeared, the artist having failed to achieve their return to him, though his property. He agreed to re-create them, if assisted, and he provided quick sketches in colour for Miss Vivien Kernot, who, from them, and from photographs and recollections, made more careful coloured drawings. These in turn were submitted to the artist, who wrote his comments on them, and in some cases partly re-drew the costumes or faces, so as to indicate exact form, colour, complexion, or hair-style. The re-drawings are therefore to be included among his works. Subsequently 22 of the original 1935 costume designs came to light and were returned to the artist's brother.

ACT DROP   *1942*
Pencil, sepia ink and wash, heightened with white.
1 ft. 3 in. × 1 ft. 10¼ in.   Unsigned

A classical street in perspective, with a tower and portico on the left and a statue in the centre. "The Rake's Progress" on a flying cartouche, supported by cherubs. Bottom right, a pencilled note by the artist to the scene-painters: "I don't want a slavish copy & should be glad of slight corrections where they seem necessary if columns, pinnacles etc are found to be out of the upright for example. I should like about *the same degree of finish, not more than* I show here, but I have added in borders some details of cornice mouldings etc etc: to show what my rough scribbling in certain places was meant to convey. The colour & technique is meant to suggest a *faded Engraving* or 18th cent: pen & bistre wash-drawing. But keep the engraved idea mostly in mind."

Note to sketched statue in margin: "William III or Marlborough type of statue, enveloped in whirling drapery. Charles I on Whitehall type of pedestal."

Reproduced in *Rex Whistler*, by Laurence Whistler, 1948, p. 95, and in *The Masque*, no. 4.

Owner: The Royal Ballet Benevolent Fund

A comparison with a photograph of the actual curtain of 1935 shows that the original drawing must have been architecturally somewhat less eventful. The central statue was then equestrian, which the artist may have thought too prominent at the time of re-drawing.

Sketch for the First Curtain   *1935*
Sepia ink and wash.   9¾ in. × 1 ft. 3¾ in.   Unsigned
Owner: Laurence Whistler

COSTUMES   *1935*
Twenty-two costume designs for the first production, re-discovered after the second. In two frames, water-colour, each drawing 10 in. × 5½ in., unsigned.

(1) The Trumpeter; the Jockey; the Fencing Master; Madman as Pope; Madman as King; Madman with rope; Mad Musician; the Rake's Friend; the Dancing Master; the Betrayed Girl; the Rake (in green dressing-gown with piece of material attached); the Gamester.

(2) The 3rd Harlot; the 4th Harlot; the Dancer; the 2nd Harlot; the Black Servant; the Girl's Mother; the 1st Harlot; the Rake (in red coat trimmed with gold); the 5th Harlot; the Ballad Singer.

The Dancing Master and the Betrayed Girl were reproduced in *The Masque*, no. 4.

COSTUMES   *1942*

Twenty sketches on both sides of a single sheet, pencil and water-colour. 10 in.× 1 ft. 2¼ in., unsigned. One sheet of the artist's rough guide for the use of Vivien Kernot, with notes and indications of colour. Some of the postures are exactly similar to those in her re-drawing, based on them.
Owner: Laurence Whistler

COSTUMES AS RE-DRAWN BY   *1942*
VIVIAN KERNOT AND REVISED BY THE ARTIST
Pencil and water-colour

(1) The Rake, the Tailor, the Bravo, the Horn-Blower, the Jockey on one sheet, 1 ft. 7 in.× 1 ft. 4 in. The artist's touching-up can be seen especially in the faces of the Bravo and the Jockey, and in a sketch for the Rake's bow and frogging.

(2) The Ballad Singer, 1 ft. 4 in.× 11 in.

(3) The Rake, 1 ft. 4 in.× 11 in. The artist has touched up the face, and drawn sketches at the side showing front and back view, to illustrate his note: "The coat should be stiffer than it was before. Possibly slightly *wired*? It should certainly *not* hang in limp folds as this drawing (& the photograph) shows."

(4) The Negro Woman, 1 ft. 4 in.× 11 in. The face repainted by the artist, with an additional sketch of head and shoulders, to illustrate his notes: "Very dark make-up. . . . If it were possible, a very amusing and negroid effect could be gained by the dancer putting one of those sham sets of white teeth in her mouth—but probably it would be too uncomfortable."

(5) The Young Girl, 1 ft. 4 in.× 11 in. The frilled cap altered by the artist and ribbons from one shoe removed.

(6) Seven Girl's Costumes: Brothel Scene, 1 ft. 7 in.× 1 ft. 3¾ in. Slight alterations by the artist, with a colour note. On the reverse he has drawn the head and shoulders of a harlot, with this note: "Make up for all the women—except the young girl and her mother. Crude use of rouge on the cheeks and placed rather lower than is the fashion now. Also skin generally rather *greasy* and unwashed looking."

(7) The Dancing Master, the Friend, and the Horn-Blower on one sheet, 1 ft. 7 in.× 1 ft. 3¾ in. Slight alterations by the artist, and a sketched head to show the wig. Many notes.   *Owner: The Royal Ballet Benevolent Fund*

SCENERY   *1942*

Five Flats, the pieces of a model. Sepia ink and water-colour, 8 in.× 10½ in. Cut to shape and sent to the artist, who carefully painted them. 1 and 2 are for the permanent side walls of the set; 3 and 4 are two of the changing back-cloths.

(1) Left wall. With Doric columns and an oval window over a square-topped door. ". . . I would prefer the walls to be rather taller than they were [i.e. in 1935] and square-headed as shown here . . . (If doors already made see other flat.)"

(2) Right wall. Similar to (1) but with an elliptical-topped door. Sketch of the correct moulding for the pilasters.

(3) Back-cloth for the Rake's House. A Venetian window, with this note across the bars: "Lit pale Amber or Straw outside".

(4) Back-cloth for the Mad House. The elliptical-topped arches each with a face in the keystone (one manic, the other depressive), below oval windows. Grilles in the arches, behind which would appear the "King" and the "Pope".

(5) Ceiling Flat. Undecorated.

(The remaining back-cloths provided a Gaming House and the Debtors' Prison. Other scenes took place in front of the Act Drop.)

Two illustrations in *Ballet Design Past and Present*, by C. W. Beaumont (*Studio*, 1946); six in *Stage Designers II: Rex Whistler* by Janet Leeper (*Ballet*, June 1948). The inspiration was, of course, the Hogarth series of paintings in the Sir John Soane's Museum, London.
Owner: The Royal Ballet Benevolent Fund

386   **THE SLEEPING PRINCESS**   *1939*
(Vic-Wells Ballet Co.)
PROGRAMME AND ROYAL BOX

PROGRAMME (Royal Command Performance in honour of the French President, at the Royal Opera House, Covent Garden, Mar. 22nd, 1939).

As printed: 1 ft. 3½ in.× 9 in.   *(Plate 112)*

A splendidly elaborate programme in the shape of a baroque cartouche (both the covers and the pages so cut as to conform to this shape) with a gold cord and tassels along the spine. The cartouche border is embossed, blind, with palms and Gallic trophies; and with the crown and "G.R." in gold at the top. In the centre is a large device embodying the arms of both nations, with flags, flowers, the crowing cock and the couchant lion.

The Royal Arms in red supported by the lion and unicorn form a head-piece to the first page, above a flourished "Royal Opera House". This is by the artist, as is also the formal sun on the back cover, but the remaining, smaller head- and tail-pieces are antique.

The cover is reproduced in *The Masque*, no. 4, and in *Rex Whistler*, by Laurence Whistler, 1948, p. 92. The Royal Arms were used on the cover of the programme for the Season of International Opera, 1939: in red, under the flourished heading: "Royal Opera Company, Covent Garden", in black.

Drawings for the Above   *1939*

(1) Small-scale model for the programme. Sepia ink and wash, with gold, 9¼ in.× 5¼ in., unsigned. Drawing for the front cover very much as carried out, the embossed border indicated by line. The centre-piece in pen and

wash. Drawn on thick paper cut out by the artist to the required shape. Pencil sketches of a head-piece and letter-press, on the inner leaves.

(2) Full-sized drawing of half the embossed detail for the front cover. Pencil and Indian ink, 1 ft. $3\frac{1}{4}$ in. × $8\frac{3}{4}$ in., unsigned. It is the left side which is drawn, to be reversed for the right side.

(3) Final drawing for the central device, and the lettering. Sepia wash on white scraper-board, approx. 1 ft. 2 in. × $10\frac{1}{2}$ in. Signed, bottom left for reproduction: *R.W.* (on central device). Signed, bottom right, off drawing: *R. Whistler*. The embossed border in faint pencil outline.

On his own copy of the printed programme the artist has painted the panelling of the embossed border all round, in grey marbling. On the inside he has sketched in pencil, probably at the actual performance, the Royal Box made to his design, and in it the King and Queen, with the French President and his wife. They are standing for the National Anthems with part of the audience seen above and below. *Owner: Laurence Whistler*

THE ROYAL BOX

In the centre of the Grand Circle. The artist provided elaborate decorations in yellow velvet, trimmed with white, gold, and silver. Above looped pelmets were the Royal Arms richly displayed, flanked by crowing cocks. The Box, three bays wide (divided by tossing palm trees), was enclosed between huge symbols of the French Republic, axe and fasces. The whereabouts of the final design is unknown, but in the collection of the artist's brother there are eight variant ideas in the form of pencil, ink, and coloured sketches.

Reproduced in *The Masque*, no. 4.

387 **THE WISE VIRGINS** *1940*

(Sadler's Wells Theatre, May 20th)

SCENERY AND COSTUMES

DROP CURTAIN

Pencil and water-colour. *$10\frac{3}{4}$ in. × 1 ft. $7\frac{1}{2}$ in.* *Unsigned*

(Plate 105)

In the centre, half concealing a perspective of walls, a flaming urn. Its voluminous smoke supports two angels, who display a drapery inscribed with Matthew XXV, 1 and 2. At the top, a gold crown in a glory surmounts crossed palms. To each side there is a pilaster with a panel of five cherubs standing on one another's shoulders. The right side is a sketch only.

Reproduced in *The Masque*, no. 4.

The artist wrote to Edith Olivier on Apr. 18th: "I fear the scenery and dresses are going to be intolerably hideous, but we must all *face the music*, I suppose (or Constant will be offended—not to mention Willie)." The reference was to Messrs. Lambert and Walton.

Sketches for the Above

Pencil. *Three sheets: 1 ft. $5\frac{1}{2}$ in. × 1 ft. $9\frac{1}{4}$ in.*

Three alternative architectural treatments, always with the text in the centre, in a cartouche, or on drapery. Two sheets: (1) $8\frac{3}{4}$ in. × 11 in. Drapery surrounded by figures, and held up by Virgins. (2) $4\frac{1}{2}$ in. × 7 in. A panel in Jacobean strap-work.

BACK-CLOTH

Water-colour. *1 ft. $5\frac{1}{2}$ in. × 1 ft. $9\frac{1}{4}$ in.* *Unsigned*

In a plain rusticated wall a studded doorway is framed by angel caryatides, supporting an entablature and a flaming heart. Pink and green. The right figure is only sketched. Reproduced in *The Masque*, no. 7.

Rough Sketch for the Above

Pencil and water-colour. *9 in. × 11 in.*

COSTUMES

Pencil and water-colour. *11 in. × 9 in.*

The Bride. "White cloak" to the floor, from which white-gloved hands appear. The head crowned.

The Bridegroom. In a black coat to the thighs, with gold embroidery and red striped stockings.

Angel. In a yellow dress with swirling red drapery. A smaller sketch of the same to the right.

Four Foolish Virgins (on one sheet) in pink and blue, gaily dancing.

(*Wise Virgins* missing.) *Owner: Laurence Whistler*

388 **LES SYLPHIDES** *1941*

(International Ballet Company, Lyric, August)

SCENERY

Water-colour. *1 ft. $7\frac{1}{2}$ in. × 1 ft. $1\frac{1}{2}$ in.* *Signed, bottom right:* Rex Whistler, Welsh Guards, Whyteleafe, Caterham

A Gothic ruin in moonlight, tree-grown and creepered. The scale shows that the back-cloth would be 25 ft. × 46 ft. Reproduced in *The Masque*, no. 4.

DESIGN FOR WINGS

Water-colour. *8 in. × 10 in.* *Unsigned*

The left wing: a piece of ruinous wall and the lower part of a column. Also little sketches in pencil to show how the two book wings should stand each side.

Owner: Mrs. Derrington (Miss Mona Inglesby)

? DISCARDED IDEA FOR SCENERY

Pencil. *9 in. × 1 ft. $\frac{1}{2}$ in.*

The ruin of a classical building on a curving plan; columns and leafy arches in perspective. Reproduced in *The Stage*, Sept. 10th, 1959. On the reverse, an unidentified costume design for ballet: a red dress with flared skirt and raised hips. "5 Duchesses."

Owner: Mrs. Derrington (Miss Mona Inglesby)

389 **EVERYMAN** *1943*

(International Ballet Company, Lyric, July)

SCENERY

Water-colour. *$4\frac{1}{2}$ in. × $3\frac{1}{4}$ in.* *Unsigned*

Stone towers each side, with a back-cloth of blue sky over very low mountains. "I want the sky to be painted quite *even*, pure blue, fading imperceptibly down to white. . . . Only the clouds to break perfect smoothness." And a note on the towers: "I hope every effort will be made to make these appear round."

Small cut-outs for the set in four pieces: gauze with interior of the castle; two pillar flats; ground row of mountains; blue sky back-cloth.

Owner: Mrs. Derrington (Miss Mona Inglesby)

390 **LE SPECTRE DE LA ROSE** *1944*
(New Theatre, February)
SCENERY AND COSTUMES
(1) DESIGN FOR DROP CURTAIN
Water-colour. 11 in. × 1 ft. 1 in. Unsigned.
(*Plate 111*)

A great red rose, dew-sprinkled, on a night-blue sky of stars. The Spirit of the Rose seen faintly, reclining in the centre.

(2) STAGE DESIGN
Water-colour. 11 in. × 1 ft. 1 in. Unsigned.
(*Plate 107*)

A room with windows open to the moonlight: the girl's bed in an alcove to the right: rose-fringed lattices.

Both the above, destroyed by fire, were reproduced in *The Masque*, no. 4.

(3) COSTUME DESIGN
Ink and water-colour. 7 in. × 4½ in. (Plate 109)

The girl's ball-dress. Low-necked, with puffed shoulders and bow at the back. Photograph in the Witt Library at the Courtauld Institute, London. Destroyed by fire.

(4) DESIGN FOR STAGE PROPERTIES
Water-colour. 10 in. × 1 ft. 2 in. Bottom right corner missing. Unsigned

Sofa, table-cloth, chair, and detail of moonlit roses by window, all with copious pencil notes by the artist. On the reverse, pencil notes and sketch of a vase of flowers. The sofa and roses were reproduced in *The Masque*, no. 7.

Owner: Laurence Whistler

Operas

391 **FIDELIO** *1934*
(Covent Garden, April)
SCENERY
Water-colour. Unsigned. (Plate 91)

(1) Act I, Sc. 1. The Jailer's House. 9½ in. × 1 ft. ½ in.
In a stone-floored room with groined ceiling a girl in a yellow dress irons at a table, to the left, under a barred window. On the right, between the two doors, a cowled chimney-piece with a cauldron. Reproduced in *The Masque*, no. 4.

(2) Act I, Sc. 2. The Prison Yard. 8½ in. × 11½ in.
On the left, from a dark doorway with a portcullis, a group of figures stumbles into the yard. Light streams on them through a tall arch to the right. A sentry stands on the battlemented wall behind them. Reproduced in colour in *The Masque*, no. 4.

(3) Act II, Sc. 1. The Dungeon. 8½ in. × 11½ in.
To the left, a man lies prostrate on the dungeon floor, lit by a torch smoking from an iron basket on the wall behind him; before him in the floor yawns an open grave. In each wall is an arch. Through the central one an ascending stairway is visible.

(4) Act II, Sc. 2. Forecourt of the Prison. 8½ in. × 11½ in.
On the left is part of the Vanbrugian prison tower, with figures emerging from the giant door. On the right, a lightly pencilled group of figures. Reproduced in *The Masque*, no. 7. *Owner: The Hon. James Smith*

(5) Act II, Sc. 1. Detail of "Grave-mound".
Pencil and Indian ink. 8 in. × 10 in. Careful drawing of stones and earth. *Owner: Laurence Whistler*

Sketches for the Dungeon Scene *1934*
(Act II, Sc. 1)

(1) Water-colour. 7½ in. × 10½ in., unsigned. Through the left-hand arch, and again through the central arch, are seen the ascending stairs. A figure lies on the right against a stone with an iron ring in it. On the reverse is a pencil and wash sketch of the dungeon without the figure or the hole in the floor.

(2) Pencil and ink wash. 7½ in. × 10½ in. Much as the above, except that a figure is seen through the central arch, ascending the stairs. On the reverse is a rough charcoal sketch of the central arch and stairs beyond.

Owner: The Hon. James Smith

392 **THE MARRIAGE OF FIGARO** *1934*
Sadler's Wells Opera Company
(Sadler's Wells, October)
SCENERY AND COSTUMES

A programme note records: "The Management owe the new scenery to the generosity of Mr. Rex Whistler, to whom they are deeply indebted." And Edith Olivier says in her unpublished Journal for Nov. 30th: "He has painted and *given* the scenery, very beautiful, especially the last dark woodland scene, with a long alley leading to the Wilton Column against a night sky."

Revues

393   **WAKE UP AND DREAM**   *1929*
A Cochran Revue
(London Pavilion, March)

(1) CURTAIN. For Operatic Pills. Indian ink and water-colour. Sheet cut in two, each 1 ft. 4 in. × 1 ft. ½ in. Left-hand sheet signed on the back: *Rex Whistler*. Right-hand unsigned. The Red and Blue Ladies' Choirs at the Albert Hall. Hideous females in short white dresses, with red or blue sashes and angels' wings, banked in front of the great organ, and bellowing.

Sketch for the Above

Sepia ink and water-colour.   1 ft. 2 in. × 10 in.
Signed on back: Rex Whistler

Smaller-scale view of the entire organ and part of the building above, with the red and blue choirs massed to left and right, and Sir Thomas Beecham conducting. Note on the architecture: "Cream & grey. All Corinthian Capitals. Ionic bastards on Organ."

(2) CURTAIN. For Pastorale. Indian ink and water-colour. 1 ft. ¾ in. × 1 ft. 9½ in. Signed on back: *Rex Whistler*. Figures in lederhosen seated with raised tankards. A pastoral Bavarian landscape, with a cliff-top castle. Reproduced in *The Masque*, no. 7.

Owner: Laurence Whistler

394   **EVERGREEN**   **A Cochran Revue**   *1930*
(London Pavilion, March)

CURTAIN. For At the Seaside.

395   **COCHRAN'S 1930 REVUE**   *1930*
(London Pavilion, March)

(1) CURTAIN. For Piccadilly 1930. Water-colour and coloured chalks. 9¾ in. × 1 ft. 2¼ in.
  (a) Rough sketch for the above. Figures swarming from hansom cab and an open-topped bus towards the London Pavilion, seen among clouds and cherubs. Below, a black chalk sketch of the London Pavilion.
  (b) Architectural sketch: "London Pavilion & Scott's". Sepia ink and wash. 5½ in. × 7½ in. Probably sketched on the site, and afterwards inked over.
  (c) Part of working drawing. Sepia ink and water-colour. 1 ft. ¼ in. × 5 in. Showing the centre of the London Pavilion, as if in a picture frame with a cherub and "C.B.". A gesturing policeman.
(2) CURTAIN. For Catch As Catch Can.
(3) CURTAIN. For Tennis (London only). Indian ink and water-colour. 8 in. × 10 in. An endless perspective of hard tennis courts, with violently leaping figures. Squared out for enlargement.
(4) CURTAIN. For The Wind in the Willows. Not used. Sepia wash, 7¾ in. × 1 ft. 4½ in. Four brown weeping willows: a figure indicated as concealed in the one to the left, with this note beside it: "On her head and in

each hand branches of willow with *brown* leaves. Dress of green gauze decorated."

COSTUMES for above. Pencil and water-colour, 9¼ in. × 6 in. Constructional sketch to show the figure enclosed in a "wire frame", representing a tree-tunk. Arms raised in "canvas sleeves" along the line of the branches. A small sketch to the right, showing the appearance of tree-trunk, twisted with ivy. No scenery was used for this number.

(5) CURTAIN. For At the Gate (Provinces only). Water-colour. 1 ft. ½ in. × 1 ft. 4½ in. Signed, bottom right: *Rex Whistler*. Very blue and blue-green landscape, with a winding path and skipping lambs. "Field gate scene. Royston and Ada May." Reproduced in *The Masque*, no. 7.
(6) CURTAIN. For The Bakerloo (Provinces only).

Owner: Laurence Whistler

396   **COCHRAN'S 1931 REVUE**   *1931*
(London Pavilion, March)

(1) CURTAIN. For A Suburban Street. Water-colour, continuous on two sheets, each 1 ft. 3 in. × 1 ft. ½ in., unsigned. A suburban street in perspective, with suburban inhabitants: identical 1920-ish villas, leading to the gas-works. The right-hand sheet overlaps the left by an inch. The artist forgot this in painting the latter, so that the Vicar is obliterated when they are joined.
(2) CURTAIN. For The General's Dilemma. Indian ink and water-colour. 11 in. × 1 ft. 5 in., unsigned. Swiss scenery. A peasant girl with a St. Bernard, divided from a figure in lederhosen, leaning on a cow by a torrent.

Owner: Laurence Whistler

397   **PETER'S PARADE**   *1932*
(Gate, December)

The Tango Mask referred to in *The Masque*, no. 7, in the list of the artist's Designs for the Theatre, was a ready-made mask improved by him, and destroyed after use.

398   **STREAMLINE**   **A Cochran Revue**   *1934*
(Palace, September)

(1) *Scenery and Costumes for The First Waltz*

SCENERY

Sepia ink and water-colour.   10 in. × 1 ft. 3 in.   Unsigned
A Gothic arcaded room with the moon through a lattice. Energetic musicians and spinning couples. An old lady on the stairs, amazed, with a candle. Reproduced in *The Masque*, no. 4, *The Artist*, Nov. 1935, *Art Review for 1935* (Artist Pub. Co.).

COSTUMES
The Viennese Governess

Pencil and water-colour.   1 ft. 1½ in. × 10 in.   Unsigned
A black dress with white stars and a red belt. Inscribed

"Tilly" (Miss Tilly Losch). Reproduced in *The Masque*, no. 7.

Six Girls (flared skirts and narrow waists)

Pencil and water-colour.   *11 in. × 8¼ in.*   *Unsigned*

635: scarlet stripes, green bow at waist.
636: red and black pattern, black bow.
637: blue bodice, blue and white skirt.
650: green stripes with green belt.
651: green stripes, lace-trimmed, with black belt.
652: white dress with pink belt.

Eight Girls (as above)

Pencil and water-colour.   *1 ft. 3¾ in. × 10 in.*   *Unsigned*

625: yellow trimmed with white.
626: pale-blue, pink trimmings and belt.
629: lilac with black trimmings.
630: slant pale-green stripes, black bows.
631: red, with white trimmings.
★632: pale-blue stripes, edged with black.
633: grey with jade-green piping.
634: pale cinnamon with black zig-zags.

★ Reproduced in *The Masque*, no. 4.

Two Designs

Pencil and water-colour.   *1 ft. 3¾ in. × 10 in.*   *Unsigned*

628: "Aunt Amelia", purple.
641: "Capt. Havelock", blue tunic with red sash and scarlet-striped buff trousers.

(2) *Scenery and Costumes for The Private Life of Napoleon*

CURTAIN. For Prologue. Water-colour and Indian ink. 10 in. × 1 ft. 3¾ in., unsigned. A black door: in a pink wall with white lines and a hanging map of the world. The schoolmistress standing, to the left. Four girls seated, to the right.

SCENE I

Water-colour.   *10 in. × 1 ft. 4 in.*   *Unsigned*

An antechamber at Amiens. A blue and yellow room with a central door, draped; two niches with statues; and a figure seated at a table. Reproduced in *The Masque*, no. 7.

SCENE II

Napoleon's Tent before Waterloo. Curtain.

SCENE III

Pencil and water-colour.   *8½ in. × 1 ft.*   *Unsigned*

The Duchess of Richmond's Ball. Interior with crimson curtains and urns between Ionic columns. Figures indicated in the foreground. Reproduced in *The Masque*, no. 4, and *The Artist*, Nov. 1935.

Sketch for the Above

Pencil, sepia ink, and water-colour.   *10 in. × 1 ft. 1¼ in.*
Unsigned

To show outlines of wings. Decoration barely indicated.

COSTUMES

"The Governess" and "The 3 pupils"

Indian ink and water-colour.   *7 in. × 5¼ in.*

The Governess in grey with a white spotted handkerchief and white belt; a pupil in a knee-length white dress, with a grey bow at neck and a grey belt. On a sheet of "Bolebec House, Whitchurch" writing paper.

Nineteen Costume Designs

Pencil and water-colour.   *1 ft. 3¾ in. × 10 in.*
Unsigned

600: "Josephine." Seated, with a white skirt and red bodice.
601: "Josephine." Standing, in a blue and white dress with stars. Also pencilled details.
602: "Madame Buonaparte" in a black satin dress and black and white bonnet, with black plumes.
603: Girl's dress, yellow with white decoration; yellow and white feathered cap.
604: Girl's dress, green, gold-edged, and starred.
605: Girl's dress, black, slashed and puffed with white.
606: Girl's dress, white velvet overskirt and bodice, with pink-striped skirt.
607: Lady's ball-dress, white and green-striped, with puffed sleeves.
608: Lady's ball-dress, pale-blue with white lace.
609: Lady's ball-dress, crimson, embroidered with gold.
610: Lady's ball-dress, scarlet striped, with long scarlet gloves and white-edged scarlet bodice.
611: Lady's ball-dress, grey trimmed with white wreaths.
612: Lady's ball-dress, white with purple spots and sash.
613: Official's dress, black coat and cream breeches, seated at table.
614, 615: Napoleon, a black epauletted coat, white waist-coat and breeches, and red sash; another drawing, in a grey cape carrying a black hat.
616: Madame Buonaparte, in a green, black-spotted dress with black tassels and white kerchief, arm-in-arm with Jerome in a black coat and buff breeches.
619: Flunkey in crimson livery with white facings to his coat.
Lady's ball-dress, orange with black trimmings and black feathered cap.
Napoleon, in gold-embroidered grey, with crimson sash and black stock.

? *Costumes for The Private Life of Napoleon*

"Conde de Lousada" in a pale-blue tunic decorated with gold braid, white breeches, and gold-edged top-boots. With a drawing, top left, of a black cocked hat with a red feather.
Plethoric military man in scarlet tunic and white trousers. Reproduced in *The Masque*, no. 7.

Owner: Laurence Whistler

? SKETCH FOR STREAMLINE—   ? *1934*
EYE-VOLUTION

Pencil.   *9¾ in. × 1 ft. 3¾ in.*   *Unsigned*

A proscenium arch with figures in boxes to the left—one, nearest to the stage, being prominent. Sir Charles Cochran recalled that in this number, designed by Cecil Beaton (showing three ages of the chorus-girl), an actress impersonated Lady Cunard in a box; which gave offence. The artist may have made this rough sketch when discussing the number with Mr. Beaton.

Owner: Laurence Whistler

399   BIG TOP   A Cochran Revue   *1942*
(His Majesty's, May)

(1) CURTAIN. For A Paris Street. The artist wrote to Lady Juliet Duff on July 24th, 1942, from his army camp: "I have written to C.B.C. to ask him to send back to me that sketch for the Paris scene which I did at Bulbridge.... When (& if) it arrives I shall try & make the little oil painting from it for your new friend Mrs Maizell."

(2) CURTAIN. For Johnny One Note. "Ground Row for Johnny One Note." Indian ink and water-colour. 1 ft. 1 in. × 1 ft. 3 in. Signed top right: *Rex Whistler*. A large scroll, to be 13 ft. high, in which a single musical note is creating havoc among Egyptian columns, statuary, modern and ancient figures, and animals. Below, an area of blue: "This blue to match the blue of the back curtain." The scene was produced on tour but omitted from the London production. Reproduced in *The Masque*, no. 7.

Owner: Laurence Whistler

400   TWO DESIGNS FOR   *1934 (or*
COAL MINERS   *earlier)*
Indian ink and water-colour.   8½ in. × 11 in.   *Unsigned*

Almost identical scenes, heavily framed in black, of a distant colliery across moors, and an old man under a bare tree with a dog. On the back of one, a similar scene in water-colour but without the tree, and with a row of (?) unemployed miners. The title Coal Miners is not written on either drawing but appears in an incomplete list of his designs for Cochran Revues, written by the artist on the typescript of The Private Life of Napoleon.

Owner: Laurence Whistler

401   SCENERY   *n.d.*
Water-colour.   9¼ in. × 1 ft. 1 in.   *Unsigned*

A cream-coloured interior with blue niches each side, containing statues. The back wall taken up by two large square windows on to a balcony, with a vase of white flowers on a pedestal between them. Beyond is the vista of a formal garden ending at the sea. The style of this and the two following drawings suggests that they may have been made for revues.   *Owner: Laurence Whistler*

402   DESIGN FOR A DOOR   *n.d.*
Water-colour.   1 ft. 3 in. × 10 in.   *Unsigned*

A white door, with the number "35", its black panels having white masks and trophies in them. Bottom left, a bust [? of Napoleon].   *Owner: Laurence Whistler*

403   SCENERY   *n.d.*
Pencil and water-colour.   10 in. × 1 ft. 3½ in.   *Unsigned*

A circular room with yellow drapery and six black busts on pedestals. A cornice with white swans, crowned, above two doors. A Rape in grisaille on the ceiling. A lady with a bustle entering, right, from the clamour of "The party" (in another room).   *Owner: Laurence Whistler*

Unused Designs for the Theatre

404   DESIGN FOR A   *c. 1927*
PROSCENIUM ARCH
Pen and sepia ink.   10 in. × 1 ft. 4¾ in.   *Unsigned*

Drapery supported from the tops of obelisks each side. Over the centre, two cherubs holding a crown beneath an elliptical coffered ceiling. Sketch of a play in action. From the artist's 1927 Sketch-book. Partly reproduced as a headpiece in *The Masque*, no. 7.   *Owner: Laurence Whistler*

405   "DESIGN FOR THE   *1930*
PERMANENT CURTAIN FOR A
THEATRE"
Ink and water-colour.   8½ in. × 11½ in.   *Signed:* "R" *in
cartouche at top of proscenium arch*

A proscenium arch with a drop curtain. To the left, "Comedy", a laughing warrior reclining; to the right, "Tragedy", an Elizabethan with a skull on his lap. In the centre a romantic landscape with a misty castle, trees, ruins, and a waterfall behind a horseman.

A wedding present. On the reverse (above two hearts transfixed by an arrow): "For Dick with love and all good wishes from Rex, June 5th 1930." Shown at the exhibition of Decorative Work and Stage Scenery, at the Goupil Gallery, Jan. 1930.

Owner: Richard de la Mare, Esq.

406   LAME DUCK   by Ronald Hall   *c. 1934*
(Not produced)
SCENERY
Pencil and water-colour.   *Unsigned*

(1) A room in the early 19th century manner. 6¾ in. × 11½ in. "White walls with green stars ... green curtains with white stars ... all the furniture white ...", etc.

(2) Back drop. 5½ in. × 4½ in. Detail of view through french windows across a town garden: trees and Georgian houses against an evening sky.

Owner: Mrs. Henzell Case

407 THE BOY DAVID by J. M. Barrie *1935*
SKETCHES FOR COMPLETE SCENERY
Pencil.   9¼ in. × 1 ft. 2¼ in.   Unsigned

A page from a sketch-book covered with rough ideas for the five sets. This project was offered to the artist by C. B. Cochran in the New Year, but he did not continue with it.

Owner: Laurence Whistler

408   THE HAPPY HYPOCRITE   *1935*
Sepia ink and water-colour.   8 in. × 1 ft.   Unsigned.
(Plate 98)

A sketch for the Play Scene in Clemence Dane's dramatized version of the story by Max Beerbohm. A proscenium arch under moon and stars, among trees. Boxes in perspective, in one of which Lord George Hell is watching the play. Made for Ivor Novello, but not used. On the night before he left for America in November, Edith Olivier found "heaps of packing on bed and everywhere, and in the midst of this confusion sat Rex painting a little scene for The Happy Hypocrite, which he had promised for 12.30 tonight. Left at 20 to 1 when it was nearly done." (Unpublished Journal.)   *Owner: Richard Addinsell, Esq.*

409   WAR AND PEACE   *c. 1938*
Sketches for projected décor. A large-scale production, involving a permanent set and changing scenery in the form of projections thrown on a back-cloth, probably with cinema sequences.

(1) Two sheets of yellow paper, pencil, 8 in. × 1 ft. ½ in. Rough sketches for 25 changes of scene, annotated "Czar's Ball", "Mad Rush", "Napoleon in the tower", etc.

(2) Six sheets, pencil and blue and red chalk, 8¼ in. × 11¾ in. Rough sketches developing the ideas in the two sheets above. The 1939 Sketch-book contains further ideas.

Edith Olivier records in her unpublished journal for Aug. 11th, 1938, "Rex is to do the décor for War and Peace—and go shortly to Zurich to plan it with the producer". He abandoned the project at the beginning of the war. In 1945 "War and Peace" was produced in London by Julius Gellner with 32 scenes by Hein Heckroth.

Owner: Laurence Whistler

410   A MIDSUMMER NIGHT'S   *1943–*
DREAM by William Shakespeare   *1944*
Five sketches, possibly for the above, pen and blue ink, 7 in. × 9 in. On writing paper, headed "John Gielgud". The principal sketch shows fairies running through a glade near an urn and a fallen column.

Owner: Laurence Whistler

In discussing a production of this play with Sir John Gielgud, the artist expressed weariness with the conventional "fixed forest". He would have used festoon curtains in the form of great branches, which, sweeping together across the stage, would have provided for rapid changes of scene behind them. He was thinking of the effect of walking through a beechwood, and constantly opening the branches to discover a new glade.

In a letter to Mr. Hugh Beaumont, on May 29th, 1944, he referred to his military commitments and wrote: "nothing I would have loved more to do for the theatre, and feel I would have done nothing else so well: so if you haven't done it by the time I am free again, remember. . . . (It was to have been 'Classical'—Not Bogus Baroque classic but à la Claude or Poussin) [and he sketched the fairy court in a glade by a ruined arch]. Or a little earlier still, and plum contemporary with author William himself."

411   UNIDENTIFIED DESIGN   *? 1944*
FOR SCENERY
Sepia ink and water-colour.   6 in. × 7½ in.   Unsigned

The interior of a large room, backed by two tall french windows, with a garden beyond, and with a grand staircase rising between columns to the right. A man, perhaps in modern dress, stands looking out of one window. The artist's copious notes, on both sides of the sheet, indicate that it was for a one-set production at the Westminster Theatre. "To make a difference between the acts, I suggest that the window backings are triplicated, with *Summer* effect, *Spring & late Autumn* (bare trees) and *Winter* in heavy snow. . . . To help mark the differences between the acts: In the earlier part of the century lace curtains would be used as well as the heavy velvet ones", etc. Possibly for *The Banbury Nose*, by Peter Ustinov. Found in the artist's pocket, and given by his mother to Mr. John Bromley.

Films

412　**A PLACE OF ONE'S OWN**　*1944*

(Eagle-Lion Studios)

From the book by Sir Osbert Sitwell (Macmillan, 1941)

SCENERY

Sepia ink and wash.　Unsigned.

(Back end-paper and Plate 104)

1. The Entrance Gates of Bellingham Towers, 10 in.× 11¾ in. To the right, Mr. and Mrs. Smedhurst looking up at a notice-board: "To be Sold", above the garden wall of the house.

2. Bellingham Towers, 10 in.× 1 ft. 10 in. To the left, a mid-Victorian mansion with a conservatory, to the right the entrance gates and drive, with a glimpse of the garden beyond. Many notes of details, e.g. "White lace curtains showing at the windows", "chimneys probably yellow 'earthenware'", "Red earthenware 'frills' along roof-ridges", "elaborate Iron window Box holders", etc. On the reverse, a pencil sketch of the Drawing Room.

3. The Garden Party, 11½ in.× 1 ft. 2¾ in. Edwardians in the gardens of Bellingham Towers. In the left foreground a lady and gentleman on a "Park-like cast iron 'rustic' seat" before a "cast-iron ornamental table probably painted white"; two "frightful black-booted children bringing tea" to them; two croquet-players to the right, and a buffet in the middle distance. In the background a glimpse of the house, among "Wellingtonias", "a lot of shrubberies of laurel & privett [sic] etc:" a "Monkey puzzler"—"*most* useful for atmosphere", etc. Reproduced in *Rex Whistler*, by Laurence Whistler, 1948, p. 90.

4. The Band, 10 in.× 1 ft. 2½ in. To the right in front of a rustic summer-house a group of bowler-hatted bandsmen beside a fountain; in the background garden-party guests strolling by the conservatory. Many annotations— "The fountain: Castiron, ready made look about it might be a little smaller and still more insignificant", "I feel that a rather absurd & very typical contrast might be made, by having a rustic thatched summer house, near a fountain with its implications of 'grandeur'". Reproduced in *Rex Whistler*, by Laurence Whistler, 1948, p. 91.

5. The Conservatory, 10½ in.× 1 ft. ¾ in. Interior, showing a glimpse of the garden beyond the open door, towards which walk two garden-party guests. "There might well be a number of frosted glass globed gas lamps", "Cast iron seat with a 'fern' motif very popular at this date", etc.

6. The Hall, 10 in.× 10 in. Mrs. Smedhurst looking down from the staircase-landing at the maid with a tray below. "Bogus 'Elizabethan' strap work on plaster freize [sic] & under stairs", "Doors 'grained' & highly varnished. Black china handles & finger plates", "ornate new looking grandfather clock", etc. Reproduced in *The Masque*, no. 7.

7. The Drawing Room, 11¼ in.× 1 ft. 2¾ in. Two ladies having tea in a room full of bric-à-brac. "There should be more objects on the closed & draped piano", "gilt 'Gunter' type of small chair", "Japanese bamboo screen", etc. Reproduced in *The Masque*, no. 7, and *A Literary History of Wallpaper*, by E. A. Entwisle (Batsford, 1960).

Rough Sketches for the Above

1. Fountain and band. Pencil, 10 in.× 7½ in. Very rough.

2. Studies of cast-iron garden seats. Pen and sepia ink, 3¾ in.× 5¾ in. "I drew these from actual examples. Very typical of their date."

3. Using as a sketch-book a publisher's dummy, 10 in.× 6¾ in., he covered five pages with pencil details, evidently taken from actual Victorian houses—possibly studied in Scarborough (he was stationed at Pickering). Several details are incorporated in his designs. There is also a first sketch for drawing no. 2, and a bird's-eye-view of his own home, The Walton Canonry, Salisbury (see no. 268), and the adjoining house—doubtless made for a brother-officer.　*Owner: Laurence Whistler*

413　**AS YOU LIKE IT**　*n.d.*

(**20th Century Fox**)

FILM CREDITS: issued as a Souvenir Booklet. 9½ in.× 1 ft. ¼ in.

P.1. Elizabethan strapwork frame with a head of "W.S." at the top, containing the drawn lettering, "Twentieth Century Fox Film Corporation Presents".

P. 2. Two trees with the letter "R" cut in the bark, separated by the drawn lettering, "Elisabeth Bergner as Rosalind."

Pp. 3–15. A parchment torn at the edges and imposed on thick foliage. Used for the remaining credits in drawn lettering, and a printed synopsis of the story, together with 14 small decorations.

Sketch for p. 4 of the above, sepia ink and pencil, heightened with white, 10 in.× 1 ft. The torn parchment, backed by leaves at each side only, and with the wording: "In As You Like It Written by William Shakespeare. MDXCIX." A small decoration, similar to that on p. 14. On the reverse a light pencil sketch for a different treatment of the credits. Reproduced in *The Masque*, no. 7.

Owner: Laurence Whistler

Printed Books:
Illustrations and Decorations

Sizes of the available original drawings are only given when they markedly differ from those of the reproductions.

414   ARABELLA IN AFRICA
by Frank Swettenham   (*Lane, 1925*) $7\frac{1}{2}$ *in.* × 5 *in.*
Frontispiece, figure at entrance to Oriental palace. *12 full plates*: 1. Arabella beside car at quayside. 2. Arabella at head of stairs with gesticulating Frenchman. 3. Arabs and a girl at dining-table. 4. Arabella in bathroom, a black servant climbing through the window. 5. On the stage. 6. Three figures beside car on a precipitous road. 7. Native street scene. 8. Two figures descending palace steps. 9. "Consulting the Oracle." 10. Group with luggage in the hall. 11. "Africa jeers at Arabella." 12 (in colour). Two figures right and left of half-opened palace door, round which a woman peers. *11 head-pieces*: 1. Arab and Arabella between two palms. 2. The Desert. 3. Reclining woman. 4. Timgad. 5. Seascape. 6. Stork on roof. 7. Prone figure on steps at doorway. 8. Squatting snake-charmer. 9. Candle, decanter, etc. 10. Luggage-laden car (the number-plate "R.J.W. 19"—for the artist's age) in winter landscape. 11. Woman's head. *8 tail-pieces*: 1. Trophy of flower-crowned skull. 2. Comic and tragic masks, etc. 3. Trophy of luggage and boots. 4. Arab head against crossed knife and fork. 5. Reclining woman. 6. Gladiator and retiarius. 7. Bearded turbaned head with veiled woman's head on each side. 8. Revolver, truncheon, candle, etc.: "L'Amour est mort. Vive l'Amour." Other illustrations by Mary Foster-Knight.
Sketch for Pl. 7: Indian ink and wash, $10\frac{1}{2}$ in. × $5\frac{3}{4}$ in., unsigned. A similar composition, with differences of detail. On the reverse a pen and Indian ink sketch of Pinner Wood House, Middlesex, from the island: a standing figure in a punt, with the dog, Tyke.   *Owner: Laurence Whistler*

415   MILDRED   Essays by various hands
(*High House Press, Shaftesbury, 1926.   Privately printed*)
$7\frac{1}{2}$ *in.* × 6 *in.*   *8 decorations*
Original designs: pen and Indian ink, unsigned: 1. Wilton column ($4\frac{1}{2}$ in. × 4 in.). 2. Palladian Bridge, Wilton ($3\frac{3}{4}$ in. × $5\frac{3}{4}$ in.). 3. The yew walk (4 in. × 6 in.). 4. 18th-century man and woman ($3\frac{1}{4}$ in. × $2\frac{3}{4}$ in.). 5. Pastoral with shepherdess (3 in. × $3\frac{1}{2}$ in.); 6. Urn with flowers ($1\frac{3}{4}$ in. × $2\frac{1}{2}$ in.). 7. Silhouette portrait with vase and books ($4\frac{1}{4}$ in. × $3\frac{1}{2}$ in.). 8. "The End" ($1\frac{3}{4}$ in. × 3 in.). *Owner: James Archibald, Esq.*

416   THE TREASURE SHIP
Edited by Lady Cynthia Asquith
(*Partridge, 1926*)   10 *in.* × 7 *in.*
1 full-page illustration, King Melon and Princess Caraway, the latter holding a cushion; *title-scroll*; *3 decorations*, the

King exhorting two soldiers; pistol, quiver, bag of gold; departing galleon; *tail-piece*, vase of flowers—"The End". Illustrating *Fat King Melon and Princess Caraway*, by A. P. Herbert.
Original design for full-page illustration, pen and Indian ink, 6 in. × $4\frac{3}{4}$ in., signed bottom right: *Rex Whistler 1926*.
Owner: Archibald Black, Esq.

417   THE LOVE CHILD   by Edith Olivier
(*Secker, 1927*) $7\frac{1}{2}$ *in.* × $4\frac{1}{2}$ *in.*
Dust-wrapper and *inset in title-page*, girl and woman in a garden at a tea-table. Reproduced in *Rex Whistler* by Laurence Whistler, 1948, p. 73. *End-piece*, a formal sun, star, and cloud—"Finis".

418   AS FAR AS JANE'S
GRANDMOTHER'S   by Edith Olivier
(*Secker, 1928*) $7\frac{1}{2}$ *in.* × $4\frac{1}{2}$ *in.*
Dust-wrapper and *inset in title-page*, a carriage entering the gates of a country mansion. Reproduced in *Rex Whistler*, by Laurence Whistler, 1948, p. 73.
Original design for Frontispiece, pen and Indian ink, 8 in. × $6\frac{3}{4}$ in. Signed, bottom left: *Rex Whistler 1928*.
Owner: James Archibald, Esq.
The artist decorated his own copy, presented to him by the authoress ("My 320 pages of exposition in exchange for your two inspired ones"), with five tail-pieces in pen and Indian ink.   *Owner: Laurence Whistler*

419   THE NEW FORGET-ME-NOT:
A CALENDAR
(*Cobden-Sanderson, 1929*)   9 *in.* × 6 *in.*
Dust-wrapper and *cover*; *Presentation page*; *Title-page device*, a vase with forget-me-nots, as on spine of cover; *4 full plates*, Winter, Spring, Summer, Autumn; *40 head-pieces*: 1. Charlie Chaplin. 2. The Boat-Train. 3. Musical trophy. 4. Greyhounds and Challenge Cup. 5. "To My Valentine." 6. Crowd outside theatre. 7. "Tussaud in Flames!" 8. Boat Race. 9. Grand National. 10. Pastoral with sheep and lovers. 11. Box at Covent Garden. 12. Mermaid and Marble Arch. 13. Faces at Private View. 14. Debutante. 15. Flower decoration. 16. F.O. Party. 17. Fourth of June. 18. Derby Crowd. 19. Trooping of the Colour. 20. Royalty at Ascot. 21. Tennis. 22. Henley Regatta. 23. Eton and Harrow at Lords. 24. Spectators at Air Pageant. 25. Yachting trophy. 26. Urban summer. 27. Fishing trophy.

28. Cricket. 29. Britannia and the circus. 30. Highland trophy. 31. The River. 32. Golfing trophy. 33. Shooting. 34. Arriving for the week-end. 35. Lord Mayor's Show. 36. Fox-hunting. 37. Ballet. 38. Rugby football team. 39. Quiet evening. 40. Christmas presents.

350 copies were signed by the artist. Head-pieces were provided for every contribution—all previously written, except Max Beerbohm's, where the process was reversed: with amusing results (see *Rex Whistler*, by Laurence Whistler, 1948, p. 26).

Original designs for title-page, cover, and presentation page, four plates, pen and Indian ink and water-colour, signed bottom right: *Rex W. 1929;* and 39 head-pieces, pen and Indian ink. These were bound as a book, 10¼ in. × 7½ in., in blue parchment, and presented by Mr. Christian A. Zabriskie to the Metropolitan Museum of Art, New York, in 1939.

Original design for head-piece no. 7, pen and Indian ink, 5½ in. × 8¾ in., unsigned, given to the writer of the poem, Dorothy Wellesley.　　　　*Owner: The Lady Elizabeth Clyde*

ROUGH SKETCHES FOR THE　*1929*
ABOVE

(1) Dust-wrapper, pencil, 10 in. × 8 in.
(2) Two sketches for head-piece no. 34, one idea not adopted. Pencil, 10 in. × 8 in. On the reverse, head and shoulders of a smiling rustic.
(3) Sketches for the flower-pot and watering-can for front and back covers, water-colour, 11½ in. × 3¾ in.
　　　　　　　　　　　Owner: Laurence Whistler

REJECTED DRAWINGS FOR　*1929*
THE ABOVE
Brown ink.　　8¼ in. × 5½ in.　　(Plates 55–58)

Four drawings for the full plates, which were considered too delicate for reproduction. Somewhat as in final drawings, but with differences of detail.

(1) *Winter.* A freezing cherub hugs himself, on a plinth. Background, a snow scene with a sledge drawn by reindeer approaching a castle.
(2) *Spring.* The figure of Spring throws flowers which the cherub catches; lambs in background.
(3) *Summer.* A cherub bored with holding a parasol over a naked Flora asleep.
(4) *Autumn.* Ceres with a basket of fruit on her head and three cherubs, one eating an apple.
　　　　　　　　　　Owner: Kenneth Rae, Esq.

420　　**CHILDREN OF HERTHA**
　　　　by Laurence Whistler
(*Holywell Press, Oxford, 1929*)　　7½ in. × 5 in.
300 copies privately printed.

Complete title-page (also reproduced on the cover of a number of copies); 2 *head-pieces:* ruined arch in wooded landscape; landscape with castle in rococo cartouche; *decoration:* stream with classical pavilion and reclining figure; *tail-piece:* skull, flowers, sword, hour-glass, etc. The artist coloured the decorations in several copies,

including his own. The title page was reproduced in *Country Life*, Oct. 20th, 1950, and in *Rex Whistler*, by Laurence Whistler, 1948, p. 75.

421　　**THE POETS ON THE POETS**
　　　　(*Faber, 1929*)　　8 in. × 5 in.
(1) *Andrew Marvell*, by V. Sackville-West. (2) *Dante*, by T. S. Eliot. (3) *Tennyson*, by Humbert Wolfe. (4) *Dunbar*, by R. Taylor, etc.
　Dust-wrapper and *cover* (the same).

422　　　　**THE THIRD ROUTE**
　　　　　by Philip Sassoon
　　　(*Heinemann, 1929*)　　9 in. × 6 in.
Dust-wrapper and *end-papers* (the same), and *device on cover*.

423　　**THE BOOK WITHOUT A NAME**
"An 18th Century Journal"　Edited by E.R.P.
　　　(*Faber, 1929*)　　8½ in. × 7 in.
Dust-wrapper.

424　　　**AN ANGLER'S PARADISE**
　　　　　by F. D. Barker
　　　(*Faber, 1929*)　　8¼ in. × 5 in.
Dust-wrapper and *title-page device* (from spine of wrapper).

425　　**HARRIET HUME**　by Rebecca West
　　　(*Hutchinson, 1929*)　　8 in. × 5 in.
Dust-wrapper.
　Original design, ink and water-colour.
　　　　　Owner: Miss Rebecca West (Mrs. Andrews)

426　　　　**GULLIVER'S TRAVELS**
　　　　　by Jonathan Swift
　　(*Cresset Press, 1930*)　　1 ft. 2 in. × 10 in.
　　　　　(*Plates 63–68*)
(*Wrapper-front of this book, with substituted lettering*)

A special edition in two super-royal quarto volumes, printed in 18 pt. Baskerville by the O.U.P.; limited to 195 copies on hand-made paper, bound in parchment and green niger, 10 being on Roman vellum, in whole niger, with an extra set of the plates (coloured by another hand) in a separate portfolio. No. 1 of the vellum copies was specially decorated for Miss Elizabeth Godley, inscribed, "For E.G. from R.W. The colouring of the Plates & the extra decorations", with two wash-drawings (vol. I: Gulliver bearing a fragment of Lilliput on his back. Vol. II: a military trophy).

Title-page device, a bust of Swift and a medallion, "Lemuel Gulliver. Rex Whistler delineavit 1929", flanked by globe, book, ink-pot, etc.

12 full plates with descriptive titles bottom centre, each illustrated within a decorative frame (an idea which the artist probably derived from Richard Bentley's *Designs for*

Six Poems by Mr. T. Gray, 1753). 1. Within a marine frame, topped by spouting dolphins, Gulliver and Capt. Pritchard seated outside an inn; the title in a rococo acanthus cartouche between mermaid and triton. 2. Within a ruinous classical arch with terminal figures, Gulliver thigh-deep in the sea, surrounded with tiny ships, "cuts with his knife the cables that fasten the anchors . . ." 3. Within a classical arch surmounted by a broken pediment, Gulliver kneels before the King of Lilliput, who stands on a high canopied dais; below, a Palladian stairway curves to right and left of the title-inscription. 4. Within a frame of rustic tools wreathed with vines, the top formed by two crossed scythe-blades supporting a pumpkin, a kneeling Brobdingnagian cutting corn, alarmed by the sight of Gulliver. 5. Within an arch, below which stone heads spout water into a shallow circular basin, the Brobdingnagian dwarf shaking apples down on Gulliver. 6. Within a frame composed of two busts on pedestals above piled books, a globe, an hour-glass, an ink-pot spilling over on to a skull, etc., Gulliver addresses the King of Brobdingnag from his box. 7 (frontispiece to vol. II). Gulliver climbing from a foreground rock in a frame of rocks and trees to scan Laputa floating above the sea. 8. Within a frame of fantastic architecture, with figures in attitudes of perplexity and cogitation, the Town of Lagado, where Gulliver rides in the Lord Munodi's chariot. 9. Within a frame of two cloaked skeletons standing on globes, each skeleton supporting on his head a flaming brazier, whose smoke wreathes round the Pentacle, (top centre) Gulliver startled by the conjuring-up of Alexander's army by the Governor of Glubbdubdrib. 10. Within a classical arch with two busts on the cornice above urns, Gulliver with drawn sword, his back to a tree, confronts the Yahoos. 11. Within a rococo frame, twined with leaves and flowers, Gulliver "sees approaching a curious Vehicle drawn by four Yahoos". 12. Within a frame composed of two terminal figures ("Truth" and "Wisdom") carrying cornucopias and supporting flaming urns, with cupids above, unveiling a medallion, Gulliver "writes a faithful history of his travels . . ."

5 Maps. 1. In the foreground a spouting dolphin, top left a rococo cartouche, supported by triton and trumpeting mermaid: "The Kingdoms of Lilliput and Blefuscu . . ." 2. A shell, bottom left, supported by dolphins and surmounted by Neptune with a trumpet at his lips between a cupid and a reclining Venus: "The Kingdom of Brobdingnag . . ." 3. On a fringed and tasselled drapery supported by two cherubs, with two others blowing trumpets beneath: "The Kingdoms of Laputa, Balnibarbi, Glubbdubdrib and Japan . . ." 4. On an oval, set in a rusticated wall: "A Diagram showing the Method by which the Island of Laputa is conveyed to different parts of the Dominion of Balnibarbi." 5. On a cartouche, bottom centre, supported by triton and mermaid and surmounted by a crowned horse: "The Country of the Houyhnhnms . . ."

4 Head-pieces: 1. Gulliver with a Lilliputian in his hand, in the right background the Temple and entrance arch. 2. Gulliver pushing up the lid of a Brobdingnagian ink-well and lifting a huge quill; behind him, to the right a packet of envelopes, with "R.W." beneath a coronet on the flap; in the foreground a signet ring, with "R.W." reversed. 3. Landscape of the island, with Laputa in the air above Gulliver, seated on a boulder in the foreground. 4. In a rococo frame Gulliver kneeling to kiss the hoof of a Houyhnhnm.

4 Tail-pieces: 1. In a rococo cartouche, Gulliver greeting his family. 2. In a rococo cartouche flanked by triton and mermaid, a boat from a distant sailing ship rescuing Gulliver in his Box. 3. A Japanese landscape of streams and mountains, with high-pitched bridges, over the central one of which seven Japanese conduct Gulliver. 4. Gulliver at the stable door talking to two horses.

The following were reproduced in *Rex Whistler*, by Laurence Whistler, 1948 (page numbers in brackets): plates 2 (56), 4 (49), 8 (50), 9 (51), 11 (53); map 1 (52); head-pieces 3 and 4 (54); tail-pieces 2 and 4 (55).

Original Designs (complete set) for 12 full plates, pen and sepia ink, and *5 maps,* sepia ink and wash, 1 ft. 2 in. × 10 in.; for *title-page device,* pen and sepia ink, 7½ in. × 7 in.; for *4 head- and 4 tail-pieces,* sepia ink and wash, 7 in. × 10 in.

Study for Plate 1, Indian ink and water-colour, 10 in. × 8 in., signed bottom right, *Rex Whistler.* The frame roughly indicated, with mermaid and triton reclining against cartouche, and only one dolphin at the top. The clouds and birds would disappear in the final version, and Gulliver's bag be replaced by a trunk.

Study for Plate 6, pencil, 10 in. × 7¾ in., unsigned. Without the frame, and showing the King leaning on his right hand.

Two studies for Head-piece 1: (1) Pencil, 5½ in. × 9¾ in., unsigned. The Temple in the left background; in the right, figures on a bridge and a tree indicated; Gulliver reclines left, on the cartouche. (2) Pencil, 8 in. × 10 in., unsigned. Much as finally carried out.   *Owner: Laurence Whistler*

427   **DESERT ISLANDS**
by Walter de la Mare   *(Faber, 1930)*
10½ in. × 6¼ in.

Dust-wrapper and *end-papers* (the same): Crusoe and a mermaid, mutually surprised; *cover device,* gilt: "W de la M" as compass-face; *spine,* alternate pineapple and formal star in panels; *complete title-page;* *2 head-pieces:* Crusoe with dog, cat, and parrot; Treasure-chest, with skull, map, books, and coins; *2 tail-pieces:* shorescape, with ship, mermaid and spouting dolphin; Crusoe stirring a cauldron over a smoking fire.

A Large Paper Edition of 650 copies, signed by the author, lacks end-paper decorations; the illustrations printed from plates (not blocks, as in the ordinary edition). Title-page and first head-piece were reproduced in *Rex Whistler*, by Laurence Whistler, 1948, p. 60–61.

428   **THE TRIUMPHANT FOOTMAN**
by Edith Olivier   *(Secker, 1930)*   7¼ in. × 5 in.
Dust-wrapper and *inset in title-page.*

Original design for dust-wrapper. Indian ink and water-colour, 8 in. × 7 in., signed, bottom, *Rex Whistler.*
Owner: Miss Rosemary Olivier

429 DR. DONNE AND GARGANTUA
by Sacheverell Sitwell
(*Duckworth, 1930*)   10 in. × 6¼ in.

Frontispiece, only in 215 copies signed by the author: to the left, crossed trees above a broken balustrade; in the foreground, a naked figure seated on a cartouche inscribed: "Dr. Donne and Gargantua", Dr. Donne standing beyond him to the right. Reproduced in *Rex Whistler*, by Laurence Whistler, 1948, p. 57.

Original design, green ink and wash, signed bottom right: *Rex Whistler 1930*.

Rough sketches of seated figure, etc., Indian ink, green ink and sepia wash, 8 in. × 5½ in., unsigned.
Owner: Laurence Whistler

430 ALEXANDER POPE by Edith Sitwell
(*Faber, 1930*)   9 in. × 6 in.

Dust-wrapper, portrait of Miss Sitwell placing a wreath of bays on a bust of Pope. Also bound in. A Large Paper Edition, signed by the author, was issued without the dust-wrapper but with the design bound in.

2 studies for the above: (1) water-colour on green paper, 6½ in. × 9½ in., unsigned. (2) Indian ink and water-colour, 7 in. × 5½ in., unsigned. As carried out, except that Miss Sitwell holds a quill pen and a scroll, instead of the bay-wreath.
Owner: Laurence Whistler

431 THE FRIEND OF SHELLEY
by H. J. Massingham
(*Cobden-Sanderson, 1930*)   9 in. × 6 in.

Dust-wrapper.

Original design, Indian ink and water-colour, signed bottom right, *Rex Whistler*, with pencilled instructions by the artist on reverse.
Owner: Laurence Whistler

432 LEIGH HUNT by Edmund Blunden
(*Cobden-Sanderson, 1930*)   9 in. × 6 in.

Dust-wrapper. Within oval frame, Leigh Hunt at a table with a quill pen and ink-pot.

Study for the above, Indian ink and water-colour, signed, bottom, *Rex Whistler*, a vase of flowers instead of the ink-pot, and two children beside Leigh Hunt.
Owner: Laurence Whistler

433 CANNIBAL CORYTON
by G. P. Robinson (*Duckworth, 1930*)   7¼ in. × 5 in.

Dust-wrapper.

Original design, pen and Indian ink, with red and green inks, 8¼ in. × 6¼ in., presented in 1954 by Mr. Thomas Balston to the Ashmolean Museum.

434 COLOPHON FOR   *1930*
MESSRS. COBDEN-SANDERSON

A flaming urn with flowers at the base, flanked by "C" and "S". On a proof the artist has pencilled round the smaller print an oval topped by a coronet; round the larger, a border with indented corners. The device was reproduced in *The Art of the Book* (Studio Ltd., 1938), p. 46.

SKETCH FOR THE ABOVE
Pen and Indian ink.   3 in. × 3½ in.   Unsigned
Very much as carried out.   *Owner: Laurence Whistler*

435   THE NEW KEEPSAKE
by various contributors
(*Cobden-Sanderson, 1931*)   9½ in. × 5½ in.
(*See pages* xvii, 14, 34, 74, *and* 113)

Dust-wrapper, cover, presentation page, and 24 head-pieces: 1. Youth reading, two figures playing croquet in background. 2. Four officers listening to gramophone. 3. Boy pursued on seashore. 4. Leda and the swan. 5. Park Lane. 6. The thaw.★ 7. The bay of Pomodoro. 8. Classical buildings in landscape with river and fisherman. 9. Lovers by a waterfall. 10. Trophy of Death's head in a ruff, scythe, hour-glass, etc. 11. Explosion at sea. 12. Arrival of postman. 13. Revolutionary scene.★ 14. Travellers in a carriage, admiring rocks shaped like a man's head.★ 15. Bicycle beside a porch. 16. Sea-serpent. 17. Trophy of flags, fasces, crown, etc. 18. Car approaching house. 19. George Washington breaks a vase. 20. Scholastic trophy with bust in mortar-board. 21. Child and governess by a waterfall. 22. Flames from a rock, figures with scythe and torch. 23. Fanciful view of Roman Forum. 29. Man and woman at a table, smoking.

A Large Paper Edition of 60 copies, signed by the artist, was bound in red cloth, gilt extra, with the same dust-wrapper as the ordinary edition.

★ Reproduced in *Rex Whistler*, by Laurence Whistler, 1948, pp. 58, 27, and 59 (nos. 6, 13, and 14, respectively).

Rough sketch for dust-wrapper, Indian ink and water-colour, 7 in. × 4¼ in., signed in cartouche, bottom centre: *Rex Whistler*. As carried out, but with incomplete, scribbled list of contributors.   *Owner: Laurence Whistler*

Original designs for: (1) dust-wrapper and spine, Indian ink and red ink, 8¼ in. × 7 in., signed in cartouche, bottom centre: *Rex Whistler*; (2) cover, Indian ink and water-colour, 8½ in. × 6¼ in., unsigned; (3) 24 head-pieces, pen and Indian ink, 5 in. × 7 in.   *Owner: Laurence Whistler*

From *THE NEW KEEPSAKE*. Cat. no. 435

436 THE TRAVELLER'S COMPANION
by P. and M. Bloomfield *(Bell, 1931)* *7½ in. × 5 in.*
Dust-wrapper, also bound in, *cover spine*, and *7 full plates:*
Part 1. Traveller at wayside fountain. 2. Disgruntled
passengers in railway compartment. 3. "Food and Drink."
4. Youth observing nymphs bathing. 5. Guide declaiming
to spectacled tourists. 6. "Women and Cities", figures
appreciating nude statue on pedestal. 7. Artist at easel
among ruins. Plates 4 and 6 were reproduced in *Rex
Whistler*, by Laurence Whistler, 1948, p. 59.

A copy of the book was grangerized for the artist, with
all the original designs bound opposite their reproductions,
the dust-wrapper bound in at the end, and the book boxed.
This was given to Miss Penelope Dudley Ward (Lady
Reed) with a cartouche on the fly-leaf embodying a
miniature portrait of her, and the lettering: "P.W. With
love from Rex. June 12th." *Owner: Lady Reed*

Rough sketch for dust-wrapper, sepia ink and water-
colour, 7½ in. × 5 in. *Owner: Laurence Whistler*

437 GREEN OUTSIDE by Elizabeth Godley
(Chatto & Windus, 1931) *8½ in. × 7 in.*
Dust-wrapper, cover, complete title-page, frontispiece in colour
("Extremely naughty children" misbehaving at tea-table).
11 decorations in text: Round tower in the "Woods of
Pottle". 2. Ink-pot and envelope. 3. "Pictures for
Katharine"—Fairy on milk-churn. 4. L.M.S. van. 5. Mouse
in "Pottle Tree House".★ 6. Princess at a table. 7. Omnibus.
8. Top hat and gloves, etc. 9. Hammer, anvil, armour.
10. Dragon carted away by St. George.★ 11. King and
throne. *12 head-pieces:* 1. Trophy of skull, books, astro-
nomical scroll, etc. 2. Hot tap happily gushing, cold tap
disconsolately dripping. 3. Pingo flying a kite. 4. Girl in
window-seat watching the rain. 5. Vase of flowers.
6. "Eel, Adder, Cod and Bee." 7. "Ragged Robin."
8. Military trophy. 9. Sealed-up goblet on tray. 10. Two
crouching beldames. 11. Girl with dog catching Autumn
leaves. 12. Man with fork walking down cottage path.
3 tail-pieces: 1. Flowers and sickle.★ 2. Man returning to
snow-covered cottage.★ 3. Ermine drapery with crown,
crossed banners, etc.

★ Reproduced in *Rex Whistler*, by Laurence Whistler,
1948, pp. 7, 8, 47, and 48.

Studies for 16 head- and tail-pieces, on two sheets,
1 ft. 4 in. × 10 in. Pencil.
Studies of flowers, on one sheet, 9 in. × 1 ft. 1 in. Pencil.
Owner: Laurence Whistler

438 DWARF'S BLOOD by Edith Olivier
(Faber, 1931) *8 in. × 5 in.*
Dust-wrapper, complete title-page, and *tail-piece* (Prometheus
and the vulture, in a cartouche).
Original design for dust-wrapper: coloured inks and wash,
8 in. × 6½ in., unsigned.
Original design for title page: Indian ink, 6½ in. × 4½ in.,
unsigned. *Owner: Miss Rosemary Olivier*

439 BROOME STAGES by Clemence Dane
(Heinemann, 1931) *8¾ in. × 8¼ in.*
Dust-wrapper and *title-page* (a rejected design for the dust-
wrapper).
Original design for dust-wrapper, sepia ink and water-
colour, front: 9 in. × 6 in., spine: 9 in. × 1¾ in., signed
Rex Whistler on a floating sheet of paper.
Owner: Richard Addinsell, Esq.

Original design for title-page, sepia ink and wash.
Owner: Miss Clemence Dane

440 THE RED KING DREAMS
by C. G. Crump *(Faber, 1931)* *7½ in. × 5 in.*
Dust-wrapper.

441 THE NEXT VOLUME
by Edward James
(The James Press, 1932) *11 in. × 7½ in.*
(Plates 81 and 82)
Cover (rococo cartouche enclosing formal sun surrounded
with bees, stars, and planets, with clenched hand device
at the four corners; inside dentelles with devices of clenched
hand and coiled serpent). Complete *title-page*. *4 full plates:*
1. Woman kneeling in pillared chapel. 2. New York. 3. In
rococo cartouche, a figure leaning against pedestal of an
urn regarding classical pavilion. 4. Cupid asleep on tree-
trunk above a cartouche: "To Ottilie." *Dedication page*, a
map, "Veduta di Monte Soracte", with flute and dagger
among reeds, etc. *Title-decoration*, full page: "Six Sonnets
written near Naples", a sea-horse. *10 head-pieces:* 1. The
children of Leda. 2. Waterfall among rocks. 3. "A maiden
with a scarf of gauze." 4. "Night in the Roman Forum."
5. A sickle and sheaves below landscape of moonlit corn-
field. 6. Father Time asleep, obelisk, pyramid, etc., in
background. 7. Venice in a rococo cartouche. 8. Mediaeval
girl in landscape with castle. 9. In a rococo cartouche,
Castle Howard. 10. Sleeping negro. *10 tail-pieces:* 1. The
grave of Shelley. 2. Urn and acanthus. 3. Trophy of arms.
4. Vine-encircled column. 5. Head of Hadrian in relief on
stone slab. 6. Medallion with sculptured head, "Vivarini",
with hill and coach in background. 7. Medallion with
sculptured head, "Joseph Haydn", framed in leaves above
a musical trophy. 8. New York, seen across sea, as if
through porthole. 9. Trophy of skull, torch, banner, sickle,
etc. 10. Mounds of desert sand forming recumbent female
figure, the smoke of a distant volcano appearing to issue
from her mouth. *Colophon device:* a clenched hand issuing
from leaves.

500 copies were bound in cloth without cover decorations, 25 on hand-made paper, signed on title-page by
author and artist, and bound in full blue morocco, gilt
extra, numbered 1–25. No. 12 was presented to the British
Museum, with a dedication drawn in sepia ink and water-
colour below the half-title: "Presented to the British
Museum by Edward James", in a medallion encircled with
leaves and surmounted by a crown, signed bottom right,
Rex Whistler. The prospectus says: "Mr. Rex Whistler

will also draw for each of these 25 copies a different and particular design upon the leaf before the title-page, which illustration will incorporate the name of each particular subscriber." The following were reproduced in *Rex Whistler*, by Laurence Whistler, 1948 (pages in brackets): title-page (as title-page with altered lettering); head-piece 7 (63); tail-pieces 4 and 5 (end papers).

Original designs, sepia ink and wash, heightened with white, unsigned. For full plate no. 1; head-pieces nos. 6, 7, 9; tail-pieces nos. 4, 6, 7, 8, 9: 6 in. × 8¼ in. For colophon device: 5½ in. × 4½ in. *Owner: Laurence Whistler*

442   **ARMED OCTOBER**
by Laurence Whistler
(*Cobden-Sanderson, 1932*)   9 in. × 6 in.   (*Plate 83*)
Dust-wrapper and *cover* (the same); *title-page device*: trophy of arms with cipher of "L.W." on shield, repeated in miniature on cover. *12 head-pieces*: 1. Vine-wreathed stone head. 2. Neptune in scallop-shell chariot drawn by sea-horses. 3. The mountain stream. 4. Blackbird's nest. 5. Figure reclining beside fountain. 6. Broken column in grass. 7. Face of Pan in trophy of flowers, reed, crook, etc. 8. Landscape in moonlight with hills beyond a plain littered with skulls and bones. 9. Hour-glass, foxgloves, and sickle. 10. The invalid. 11. Reclining figure with book beside stream. 12. A gale at night: reproduced in *Rex Whistler*, by Laurence Whistler, p. 29.
Original design for title-page, pencil, sepia ink, and wash, the trophy of arms as carried out, with pencilled indications of lay-out.
Original designs for *12 head-pieces*, sepia ink and wash, 5 in. × 7 in.   *Owner: Laurence Whistler*

443   **DOWN THE GARDEN PATH**
by Beverley Nichols   (*Cape, 1932*)   8 in. × 5¼ in.
Dust-wrapper and *end-papers* (the same: aerial perspective of cottage and ground). *Frontispiece*, "Flora" with gardening trophy; complete *title-page*; *4 full plates*: "Spring"— sowing grain; "Summer"—pool with nymph and satyr; "Autumn"—apple-picking; "Winter"—man sheltering before a fire; *head-piece*: cherubs gardening; *2 tail-pieces*: a couple walking along a road to the village; a vase of flowers and gardening implements. Full plate "Spring" was reproduced in *Rex Whistler*, by Laurence Whistler, 1948, p. 74.
Original designs, pen and Indian ink, for (1) Frontispiece, (2) "Spring", (3) "Autumn".   *Owner: Laurence Whistler*

444   **BELL'S MUSICAL PUBLICATIONS**
(*Bell, 1932, 1933*)
Six vols., edited by [Sir] Adrian C. Boult, each with the same musical trophy on the half-title, containing a bell.

445   **FOUR FANTASTIC TALES**
by Hugh Walpole   (*Macmillan, 1932*)   8 in. × 5½ in.
Dust-wrapper and *inset in title-page*.
Original design for dust-wrapper, sepia ink and wash

and water-colour, signed bottom left of front cover: *Rex Whistler*, and bottom right of spine: *R.W.*
Owner: Martin Battersby

Study for dust-wrapper, pencil and water-colour, with only two figures in the right foreground, the hour-glass and background only lightly pencilled in.
Study for title-page, pen and Indian ink, with notes by the artist on the lay-out.   *Owner: Laurence Whistler*

446   **A MAN NAMED LUKE**
by March Cost   (*Collins, 1932*)   8½ in. × 5¼ in.
Dust-wrapper and *title-page device*.
Original design, Indian ink and water-colour, much as carried out, but with trophy on spine reversed.
Owner: Laurence Whistler

447   **CHAUCER G. K. Chesterton**
(*Faber, 1932*)   9 in. × 6 in.
Dust-wrapper.
Original design, Indian and sepia ink and wash.
Owner: Laurence Whistler

448   **LITTLE INNOCENTS**
by Dame Ethel Smyth and others
(*Cobden-Sanderson, 1932*)   8¼ in. × 5½ in.
Dust-wrapper.
Original design, green ink and wash.
Owner: Laurence Whistler

449   **THE DISCOVERY OF POETRY**
by Hugh Lyon   (*Arnold, 1932*)
Library edition, using sheets of 1931 reprint of original schools edition.   7½ in. × 5 in.
Dust-wrapper and *spine of cover*.
Original design, sepia ink and water-colour, 9 in. × 7 in.
Destroyed

450   **BOOMERANG by Helen Simpson**
(*Heinemann, 1932*)   8 in. × 5½ in.
Dust-wrapper.

451   **BATH by Edith Sitwell**
(*Faber, 1932*)   9 in. × 6 in.
Dust-wrapper (also bound in).

452   **THE SERAPHIM ROOM**
by Edith Olivier   (*Faber, 1932*)   7¼ in. × 5 in.
Dust-wrapper.
Original design, Indian ink and water-colour, 8¼ in. × 7 in., unsigned.   *Owner: Miss Rosemary Olivier*

453   **LOUDER AND FUNNIER**
by P. G. Wodehouse   (*Faber, 1932*)   7¼ in. × 5 in.
Dust-wrapper.
Original design, Indian ink, green ink and wash.
Owner: Laurence Whistler

454 THE LORD FISH by Walter de la Mare
(*Faber, 1933*)   8 in. × 5 in.   (*Plate 61*).
(*See pages xii, 55, 77, 99, 104, and 106. Plate 61*)
Dust-wrapper, complete title-page (the same), *spine* of cover.
3 full plates: 1. "The walls of a high dark house, with but two narrow windows in its stone surface." 2. Ruined arch and castle turret—"At the top of a flight of tumbledown steps stood a wizened pigmy hunched-up old man". 3. Small boy and scarecrow—"No Farmer Jones that, & not even one of his Men! It was just Old Joe."
7 head-pieces: 1. Frog fishing—reproduced on front cover and end-papers. 2. Hunchback sweeping kitchen. 3. Small boy and elderly man opposite each other at a table in high-backed window-seats. 4. Small boy on stool opposite a giant having his supper. 5. Scare-crow in wintry landscape. 6. Behind stage footlights, a man bowing to a monkey in Imperial robes. 7. In a frame of jeering figures bearing aloft "Poison" and "Physic", a negro boy sits beneath a tree.
An Edition of 60 signed and numbered copies published on hand-made paper, bound in vellum. Head-piece no. 3 was reproduced in *Rex Whistler*, by Laurence Whistler, 1948, p. 61.
Original designs for spine of wrapper and title-page, sepia ink and wash, 9 in. × 4 in.; for plate of small boy and scare-crow (opp. p. 188), sepia ink and wash; for 7 head-pieces, pen and Indian ink, 4½ in. × 6 in.
Owner: Laurence Whistler
Rough sketch for dust-wrapper and title-page, sepia ink and water-colour, 5½ in. × 4½ in.

From *THE LORD FISH*. Cat. no. 454

455   A THATCHED ROOF
by Beverley Nichols   (*Cape, 1933*)   8 in. × 5½ in.
(*See page viii*)
Dust-wrapper; cover; end-papers, vase of flowers, with books, decanter, spectacles, etc. *Frontispiece*, trophy of household utensils. *Complete title-page*. 4 full plates ("The Garden Room", "The Kitchen", "The Study", "A Bedroom"). *2 head-pieces*: 1. Dog beside beehive, with cottage in background—used as cover device without the dog. 2. Angry woman at cottage porch. *1 tail-piece*: hands at the open window of a bedroom.

Original designs for (1) dust-wrapper, Indian ink and water-colour, 9 in. × 10 in.; (2) title-page, pen and Indian ink, 8 in. × 5½ in. As carried out, but with the (later discarded) title "Under the Thatch"; (3) for Frontispiece and 4 full plates, pen and Indian ink, 2 head-pieces, and 1 tail-piece, pen and Indian ink, 6 in. × 4½ in.
Owner: Laurence Whistler

456   YOUR NAME IS LAMIA
[by Edward James]
11½ in. × 8¼ in.
(*The wrapper-back and front cover of this book*)
[The James Press] 1933; privately printed. Limited to 30 copies. Bound in green full morocco.
9 decorations, excluding the colophon design and those on pp. 1 and 8: 1. A rococo cartouche. 2. Cherub with lute. 3. Cherub with spear against rococo decoration. 4. Palm and two pyramids. 5. Two spears within rococo device. 6. Dish of fruits. 7. Pineapple on pedestal. 8. Trumpet in wreath of flowers. 9. Flaming urn inscribed "Finis". *5 flourished titles* and initial letters to poems.

457   MEN OF GOOD WILL
by Jules Romain   (*Lovat Dickson, 1933*)   8 in. × 5½ in.
Books I–VIII (separate)—*dust-wrapper* and *complete title-page* (the same), each with appropriate lettering by the artist. Books I and II (together)—*another dust-wrapper* and *complete title-page* (the same), used again as dust-wrapper to Books XV and XVI (together).

458   THE GOWK STORM
by N. Brysson Morrison   (*Collins, 1933*)   7½ in. × 5 in.
Dust-wrapper and *inset in title-page*.

459   HAG'S HARVEST   by J. B. Morton
(*Heinemann, 1933*)   8 in. × 5½ in.
Dust-wrapper.

460   GENTLEMEN—THE REGIMENT!
by Hugh Talbot   (*Dent, 1933*)   7½ in. × 5 in.
Dust-wrapper.

461   BREDON AND SONS
by Neil Bell   (*Collins, 1933*)   8½ in. × 5½ in.
Dust-wrapper.
Original design, Indian ink and water-colour. 8¾ in. × 7¾ in., unsigned.   *Owner: Kenneth Rae, Esq.*

462   SPORT   by W. Bromley Davenport
(*Maclehose, 1933*)
Complete title-page.

463   PRINTER'S DEVICE FOR THE 1933
CENTAUR PRESS
Sepia ink and wash.   5½ in. × 4 in.   *Unsigned*
A leaf-fringed oval containing a centaur drawing a bow, and inscribed: "The Centaur Press MCMXXXIII".
Owner: Miss Peri Cotgrave

464 **A VILLAGE IN A VALLEY**
by Beverley Nichols (*Cape, 1934*) *8 in. × 5¼ in.*

Dust-wrapper, end-papers, and *cover* ("B.N." in flower cartouche); *Frontispiece*, a youth in a window-seat, a tankard on the sill, and view of church through window; *complete title-page*; *4 full plates*, "The Church", "The Pond", "The Shop", "The Inn"; *2 head-pieces*, church interior, woman seated reading in garden; *1 tail-piece*, man and dog in tree-lined avenue.

The American Edition (Doubleday Doran, 1934) has part of the dust-wrapper design on cover spine, redrawn by another hand.

Original designs for dust-wrapper and title-page, pen and Indian ink, 9½ in. × 8 in. As carried out, but with the (later discarded) title "Allways". For frontispiece and plates, pen and Indian ink, and head- and tail-pieces, 3½ in. × 5½ in.; and 2 end-papers, 5½ in. × 5 in. and 6 in. × 4½ in.
Owner: Laurence Whistler

465 **THE SILVER COLLAR BOY**
by Constance Wright
(*Dent, 1934*) *8 in. × 6¼ in.* (*Plate 62*)

Dust-wrapper and *frontispiece* (a Lady of Quality with bow and arrow, offered a shell of rubies by negro page); *4 full plates*: Pt. 1: "The Boy"; Pt. 2: "The Lady"; Pt. 3: "The Portrait"; Pt. 4: "A Storm at Twickenham". Plates 1 and 4 were reproduced in *Rex Whistler*, by Laurence Whistler, 1948, pp. 64–5.

Original design for dust-wrapper and frontispiece, sepia ink and water-colour. For 4 plates, sepia ink and wash.
Owner: Laurence Whistler

466 **PARABLE FOR LOVERS**
by Lewis Gibbs (*Dent, 1934*) *7½ in. × 5 in.*

Dust-wrapper and *frontispiece* (same as dust-wrapper front) —Lovers sheltering from hunters; spine of dust-wrapper and *title-page device* (the same)—Cupid with bow, holding aloft a smoking torch.

The dust-wrapper was reproduced in *Rex Whistler*, by Laurence Whistler, 1948, p. 77.

467 **SEVEN GOTHIC TALES**
by Isak Dinesen (*Putnam, 1934*) *8 in. × 5¼ in.*
(*Plate 76*)

Dust-wrapper and *frontispiece* (the same, reduced).
Original design for dust-wrapper, Indian ink and water-colour, 9 in. × 8¼ in., signed bottom right: *Rex Whistler 1934.*
Owner: Laurence Whistler

468 **THE ECCENTRIC LIFE OF ALEXANDER CRUDEN** **by Edith Olivier**
(*Faber, 1934*) *9 in. × 5¼ in.*

Dust-wrapper and *frontispiece* (the same), and *title-page device*.
Original design for dust-wrapper, sepia ink and wash. 11 in. × 8 in., signed: *Rex Whistler.*
Owner: Miss Rosemary Olivier

469 **FIRST CHILDHOOD**
by Lord Berners (*Constable, 1934*) *8 in. × 5¼ in.*

Dust-wrapper and *frontispiece* (the same).
Original design for dust-wrapper and title-page inset, sepia ink and wash, 5 in. × 4½ in. For *title-page lay-out*, Indian ink and red ink, 10 in. × 6½ in. For *spine of dust-wrapper*, pen and Indian ink and red ink, 10 in. × 2 in.
Owner: Laurence Whistler

470 **POEMS OF TEN YEARS**
by Dorothy Wellesley (*Macmillan, 1934*) *7½ in. × 5 in.*

Dust-wrapper and *complete title-page* (the same).
Original design for dust-wrapper and title-page, sepia ink and wash, 11 in. × 7½ in. For *spine of dust-wrapper*, sepia ink and wash, 11 in. × 4½ in. *Owner: Laurence Whistler*

471 **THE ENCHANTED** **by Barbara Mdivani**
(*Privately printed, 1934*) *10½ in. × 6¼ in.*

Cover device, spine, and *complete title-page*.
Original design for title-page, sepia ink and wash, 10½ in. × 7½ in., signed, bottom left: *Rex Whistler 20 Fitzroy St. W.1.* *Owner: Laurence Whistler*

472 **DECORATION** **by Sarah M. Lockwood**
(*Doubleday Doran, U.S.A., 1934*) *10 in. × 8 in.*
Dust-wrapper.

473 **FULL FLAVOUR** **by Doris Leslie**
(*Lane, 1934*) *8½ in. × 5½ in.*

Dust-wrapper.
Original design for dust-wrapper and spine decoration, Indian ink and water-colour, 9 in. × 8¾ in., as carried out, except that the spine decoration was printed in monochrome.
Owner: Laurence Whistler

474 **FOUR WALLS** **by Laurence Whistler**
(*Heinemann, 1934*) *9 in. × 5½ in.*
Dust-wrapper device, reproduced on cover of some copies.

475 **FAIRY TALES AND LEGENDS**
by Hans Andersen
(*Cobden-Sanderson, 1935; John Lane, 1942, etc.*)
8½ in. × 5½ in. (*See pages vii, xxiii, opposite 1, 30, 79, and 93*)
Dust-wrapper, cover, and *end-papers* (the same), *complete title-page. 10 full plates*: 1. "The Emperor walked under his high canopy. . . ." 2. The Little Mermaid watching the Prince's ship. 3. Witch drawing boat to land with crutch. 4. Mourner at Columbine's grave. 5. "The savage ways of the little creature." 6. "The Old Maid leant out to look at the Balloon." 7. "He hit the old Grandmother on the head. . . ." 8. "Some were blind, some crawled about. . . ." 9. Death at the Emperor's bed. 10. "Do you see yonder rock, & the large cave?" *16 illustrations in text*: 1. Woman at loom with two children. 2. Two weavers showing empty loom to Minister. 3. Sick boy in bed beside cellar-window.

4. The Mountain-chief and the Elfin-Maiden. 5. Statue of boy under weeping willow. 6. Gerda and Kay on the roof-top. 7. Gerda on the reindeer. 8. Child with open Bible on mother's bed. 9. Christmas tree, with four adults and nine children. 10. Boy reveals Troll's head to King and Princess. 11. Boy on bridge with sack. 12. Top-hatted shadowless figure bowing to Princess. 13. Hand ironing collar. 14. Old man in a dark street. 15. Girl with basket stepping across stream. 16. Two boys with crossbows followed by girl with box. *33 head-pieces:* 1. Children shouting at storks on a roof-top. 2. Swans flying from castle turret. 3. Three snails among burdock leaves. 4. Tin soldier and Dancer in the flames. 5. Karen dancing to the Headsman's door.

30. Ship and swans on a river beside a palace. 31. Servant with darning needle at a chest-of-drawers. 32. Prince and the old woman by a fire. 33. Steam air-ship. *15 tail-pieces:* 1. Classical pavilion and waterfall. 2. Floral trophy. 3. Military trophy. 4. Landscape with ruined classical arch. 5. Castle on hill within rococo cartouche. 6. Swan. 7 .Two lovers beside a waterfall. 8. Musical trophy. 9. Skull and broken pot. 10. Skull and trophy of sword, sickle, etc. 11. Horse and cart on a bridge before a town. 12. Ruined arch and fallen tree. 13. Cottage in landscape. 14. Corpse on a bier. 15. The Forum, with fallen statue.

The tail-pieces (nos. 1, 4, 5, 10) appearing respectively on pp. 21, 50, 95, 324 (and elsewhere) were reproduced

From *HANS ANDERSEN:* 'The Tin Soldier'. Cat. no. 475

6. Swineherd kissing the Princess. 7. Princess on 20 mattresses. 8. "The Elfin-Mount." 9. Servant and small child with hoop. 10. Cupid at the old Poet's door. 11. Soldier in tree with a witch standing beneath. 12. Ugly Duckling at the canal's edge. 13. Mandarin between China Shepherdess and Chimney-Sweeper. 14. Peasant woman discovers Thumbelina in the tulip. 15. Boy writing at moonlit window. 16. Man reading letter under a street lamp. 17. Boy and girl in elder-tree. 18. Two magicians examine a drop of ditchwater. 19. The naked Princess and the Marsh King. 20. Boy helping washerwoman to carry tub. 21. Willows beside stream. 22. Picnic health to bride and groom. 23. The little match-girl. 24. Mother and Death either side of child in cradle. 25. The merchant's son in the flying trunk. 26. Boy and old gentleman in ancient town. 27. Toy nightingale in cage. 28. Goblin by a tub with a bowl of gruel. 29. Owl watching four hens on a perch.

from *Children of Hertha* (no. 420), with some alterations; nos. 2 and 8, on pp. 26 and 157 (and elsewhere) from *The New Forget-Me-Not* (no. 419); nos. 3, 7, 11, 12, 15, on pp. 38, 151, 337, 351, 470 (and elsewhere), from *The New Keepsake* (no. 435), with some alterations. No. 13 was a first experiment in scraper-board, made in the publisher's office; 51 of the remaining illustrations were designed on scraper-board.

A Limited Edition of 200 copies, signed by the artist on the half-title page, was bound in cream-coloured buckram, gilt extra. In 1942 a new dust-wrapper was devised, incorporating on the spine the figure of the Emperor from pl. 1, p. 37, on the front the title-page inset, on the back pl. 6, p. 291. The following were reproduced in *Rex Whistler*, by Laurence Whistler, 1948 (page-numbers in brackets): dust-wrapper (67), title-page (68), plate 1 (69), plate 2 (72); text illustrations, 5 (70), 7 (71), 23 (70), 30 (71).

Original design for dust-wrapper, Indian ink on white scraper-board, 10 in. × 9 in.

Original designs (complete set of those specially drawn) for 35 head- and tail-pieces, Indian ink on white scraper-board, 4½ in. × 7 in.; 2 head-pieces, 4 in. × 5 in.; 3 head-pieces, 3½ in. × 4½ in.; 10 head- and tail-pieces, pen and Indian ink, 4 in. × 5 in.; for 10 full plates, Indian ink on white scraper-board, 10 in. × 7½ in.

Owner: Laurence Whistler

476   THE PRINCESS ELIZABETH GIFT BOOK
Edited by Cynthia Asquith and E. Bigland
(*Hodder & Stoughton, 1935*)   10 in. × 7 in.

Decorative end-papers, half-title device (a coach and four, with footmen) and *complete title-page*.

477   ALCIBIADES, BELOVED OF GODS AND MEN
by Vincenz Brun   (*Putnam, 1935*)   8 in. × 5¼ in.
Dust-wrapper and *frontispiece* (the same).

480   THE DARK GLASS
by March Cost   (*Collins, 1935*)   8½ in. × 5¼ in.
Dust-wrapper, end-papers, title-page device and *cartouche* on following page.

Dust-wrapper reproduced in *The Artist*, Sept. 1937.

481   THE EMPEROR HEART
by Laurence Whistler   (*Heinemann, 1936*)
8¾ in. × 5½ in.   (*See reverse of half-title and pages* x, xviii, 46, and 80)

Device on dust-wrapper, cover, and *title-page* (the same)—crown and heart above crossed sprays in oval cartouche. *8 head-pieces:* 1. Winged cherub's head, "Requiescat in Pace". 2. Nude figure falling through starlit space. 3. Naked child and spray of flowers. 4. Skull among leaves. 5. Landscape with church spire. 6. Mother with two children at fireside. 7. House and ruined tower on cliff.* 8. Satyr Gate at Castle Howard† (see no. 266).

Original designs for 8 head-pieces, Indian ink on white scraper-board, 5½ in. × 4 in.   *Owner: Laurence Whistler*

* Reproduced in *Rex Whistler*, by Laurence Whistler, 1948, p. 58.

† Reproduced in *The Imagination of Vanbrugh*, by Laurence Whistler, Batsford, 1954, p. xvi.

From *THE EMPEROR HEART*. Cat. no. 481

478   BRIGHTON
by Osbert Sitwell and M. Barton
(*Faber, 1935*)   9 in. × 5¼ in.
Dust-wrapper.

479   I AM YOUR BROTHER
by G. S. Marlowe   (*Collins, 1935*)   8¼ in. × 5¼ in.
Dust-wrapper.

482   KINGDOMS FOR HORSES
by James Agate   (*Gollancz, 1936*)   9 in. × 7 in.
Dust-wrapper and *inset in title-page* (the same)—an Elizabethan youth and horse. *4 full plates:* centaur astonishing horseman; village cricket match; 18th-century golfers; boxing-match outside inn. *4 head-pieces:* old lady approaching mansion in a carriage; a 19th-century cricket team framed in aspidistras; golf-course with sleeping dog; children boxing in street.

483 ALCIBIADES, FORSAKEN BY GODS AND MEN by Vincenz Brun
(Putnam, 1936)   8 in. × 6 in.
Dust-wrapper and *frontispiece* (the same).

484 LORD BIRKENHEAD and other titles by Ephesian   (Private Lives Library. Newnes, 1936)
7½ in. × 5 in.
Dust-wrapper.

485 SAN FELICE by Vincent Sheean
(Hamish Hamilton, 1936)   8 in. × 5 in.
Dust-wrapper, reproduced in *Rex Whistler*, by Laurence Whistler, 1948, p. 76.

486 CONVERSATION PIECES by Sacheverell Sitwell (Batsford, 1936) 10 in. × 7½ in.
Dust-wrapper (based on a plate in N. Heideloff's *Gallery of Fashion*, 1794) and *title-page border*.

487 PORTRAIT OF A LADY by Lady Eleanor Smith
(Hutchinson, 1936)   7½ in. × 5 in.
Dust-wrapper.
  Original design, water-colour, 8 in. × 7½ in.
Owner: Laurence Whistler

488 THE HUNDRED YEARS by Philip Guedalla
(Doubleday Doran, U.S.A., 1936)   9 in. × 6½ in.
Dust-wrapper.

489 NARRATIVE PICTURES by Sacheverell Sitwell (Batsford, 1937) 10 in. × 7½ in.
Dust-wrapper.

490 FLOWERS IN HOUSE AND GARDEN by Constance Spry
(Dent, 1937)   10 in. × 7½ in.
2 head-pieces: portly butler behind laden buffet; a raised pie above crossed sprays; and *2 tail-pieces*: dolphin dishes of fruit; heads of two children gazing at silvered plant on a table. All were reproduced in *A Constance Spry Anthology* (Dent, 1953).
  Original designs for head-piece 1, Indian ink and pencil with touches of white, 7¼ in. × 10 in.; head-piece 2, sepia ink and wash and pencil, 6½ in. × 10 in.; 2 tail-pieces, sepia ink and wash, 9 in. × 6 in. and 5½ in. × 6½ in.
Owner: The Estate of Mrs. Constance Spry

491 SIR JOHN VANBRUGH, ARCHITECT AND DRAMATIST by Laurence Whistler   (Cobden-Sanderson, 1938)
10 in. × 7 in.
Dust-wrapper; device on cover and *title-page* (the same—an architectural trophy).

Original design for dust-wrapper front, sepia ink and wash, 1 ft. × 8 in. For spine of dust-wrapper, sepia ink and wash, 1 ft. × 9 in. On the left a pencil sketch of alternative design, an obelisk inscribed "J.V.".
Owner: Laurence Whistler

492 WITHOUT KNOWING MR. WALKLEY
by Edith Olivier   (Faber, 1938)   9 in. × 5¼ in.
Frontispiece, a reproduction of the water-colour *Conversation Piece at the Daye House*, 1937 (no. 192).

493 A DAY OF BATTLE by Vincent Sheean
(Hamish Hamilton, 1938)   8 in. × 6 in.
Dust-wrapper.

494 IN TIME OF SUSPENSE
by Laurence Whistler (Heinemann, 1940) 8 in. × 5 in.
Device on dust-wrapper and *title-page* (the same)—reproduced, with alterations, from *Children of Hertha*, 1929 (no. 420).

495 SWAN OF USK by Helen Ashton
(Collins, 1940)   8 in. × 5½ in.
Dust-wrapper.

496 LOVER'S MEETING by Lady Eleanor Smith
(Hutchinson, 1940)   7½ in. × 5½ in.
Dust-wrapper.

497 COUNTRY MOODS AND TENSES
by Edith Olivier   (Batsford, 1941)   8¼ in. × 5½ in.
Dust-wrapper and reproduction (fig. 53) of drawing (Rural Mayor in procession). Fig. 53 was used by Edith Olivier as a Christmas card in 1941.
  Original design for dust-wrapper, sepia ink and water-colour, 1 ft. × 8¼ in., unsigned.
Owner: Miss Rosemary Olivier

498 A HOUSE THAT WAS LOVED by K. M. R. Kenyon   (Methuen, 1941)   9 in. × 6 in.
Dust-wrapper.
  Original design for dust-wrapper, water-colour, 1 ft. 1 in. × 8½ in.; with design for spine of dust-wrapper, on the back of a letter, attached.
Owner: Laurence Whistler

499 THE LAST OF UPTAKE by Simon Harcourt-Smith
(Batsford, 1942)   10 in. × 7½ in.   (*Plates 85 and 86*)
Dust-wrapper.
Colour frontispiece: ". . . the whole of Uptake was roaring and crackling." *11 full-page illustrations*: 1. Aged butler with cloak over his arm. 2. Uptake—"a nobleman's

mansion". 3 (in colour). Old lady in bath-chair under porch of garden pavilion, beside her a maid and gardener. 4. A classical bridge over a tumbling torrent. 5. Figures beside a horse-drawn sledge and a ball-topped pyramid in the snow. 6. Two figures in a yew alley. 7. Old lady and gardener in richly-decorated circular grotto. 8. Two toy figures dancing in pavilion, watched by old lady through the window. 9. Two figures on a terrace. 10. ". . . Deborah, hunched upon a marble bench." 11. "The carriages rolled out of the handsome gates." *10 illustrations in the text:* 1. Old lady and gardener by ruined Corinthian columns. 2. The gardener in the hot-house. 3. Child by a sphinx. 4. Young man before fireplace addressing his family. 5. "A little pavilion. . . ." 6. Figure of mechanical Wood-cutter. 7. Old lady by terrace balustrade. 8. Wall-light and decoration of mirror, with old lady walking up gilt steps. 9. Aunt Lavinia standing with her hand on door-handle. 10. Old lady beside luggage-piled carriage on country road.

Original designs, sepia ink and wash for 10 full-page illustrations, 1 ft. 2 in. × 10 in.; for 10 illustrations in text, approx. 10 in. × 8 in.; for frontispiece and full-page illus. no. 3, water-colour, 9 in. × 8 in.

Three sheets of pencil studies for the above, 10 in. × 1 ft. 2½ in., including the Bridge, Uptake (full-page illus. 2, 4), the gardener, the young man, Her Ladyship, Aunt Lavinia, border decoration—with obelisk instead of Corinthian columns, the carriage, etc. (text illus. 2, 4, 7, 9, 10).

One sheet, 10 in. × 1 ft. 2½ in., pen and sepia ink: studies of the mechanical Wood-cutter, old lady, etc. (text illus. 6,7). One of the sheets also has rough drawings for *Königsmark* (no. 516), the title-page and 10 miniature sketches for all the plates. *Owner: Laurence Whistler*

500 THE ENGLISH COUNTRYMAN
by H. J. Massingham (*Batsford, 1942*) *9 in. × 6 in.*
Dust-wrapper.

501 DOVER HARBOUR
by Thomas Armstrong (*Collins, 1942*) *8 in. × 5 in.*
Dust-wrapper.
Original design, water-colour, unsigned.
Owner: Thomas Armstrong, Esq.

502 A BATSFORD CENTURY
by Hector Bolitho (*Batsford, 1943*) *10 in. × 6½ in.*
Dust-wrapper (also bound in).
Original design, sepia ink, 10½ in. × 8 in., unsigned.
Owner: B. T. Batsford, Ltd.

503 NIGHT THOUGHTS OF A COUNTRY LANDLADY **by Edith Olivier**
(*Batsford, 1943*) *8½ in. × 5½ in.*
Dust-wrapper and *frontispiece* (the same)—the landlady going out through the gate of a walled garden into meadows beyond. *10 illustrations:* 1. The lady writing in bed. 2. "Between two and three hundred children had arrived." 3. "The whole party opened the door." 4. "He danced a few rounds with each." 5. Tanks down the village street. 6. Man in pyjamas pouring himself a whisky. 7. "We clustered round the overflowing basin." 8. Leading the dinner procession. 9. "He turned the telescope heavenwards." 10. Moon over field of stooks.

Original designs. For dust-wrapper, sepia ink and water-colour, 9¾ in. × 8 in. For 10 illustrations, sepia ink and wash, nos. 2–9, 9¾ in. × 8 in.; no. 1, 5¾ in. × 9 in.; no. 10, 4½ in. × 9 in. *Owner: Miss Rosemary Olivier*

504 ALBERONI, OR THE SPANISH CONSPIRACY **by Simon Harcourt-Smith**
(*Faber, 1943*) *9½ in. × 6 in.*
Dust-wrapper and *portrait bust on cover,* repeated from dust-wrapper.

505 AND NOW TOMORROW
by Rachel Field (*Collins, 1943*) *8 in. × 5½ in.*
Dust-wrapper.

506 THE WELSH GUARDS AT WAR
by L. F. Ellis (*Gale and Polden, 1946*)
Dust-wrapper incorporates a reproduction of the Regimental Badge from the Brighton murals, 1944 (no. 15). Colour-reproduction opp. p. 38: "Welsh Guards Officer": oil portrait of Lieut. R. Whiskard (no. 115).

507 ¡OHO! **by Rex and Laurence Whistler**
(*Lane, 1946*) *9¾ in. × 7½ in.*
A "reversible" book, which can be read from either end. *Dust-wrapper and cover* (the same), designed by Laurence Whistler, incorporating the artist's Cinderella X the Fairy Godmother. *End-papers,* reversible faces reprinted from the plates, with additions, in borders designed by Laurence Whistler. *Title-page,* designed by Laurence Whistler, incorporating, in the four corners, four reversible faces. The title-page appears at both ends of the book. *15 full page plates:* 1. Midshipman X Commodore. 2. Old Man X Young Man. 3. Patrolman X Policeman. 4. Headmaster X Chauffeur. 5. Doris X Bert. 6. Tripper X Taximan. 7. Lord Littleray of Sunshine X Lady Cardigan Fitz Baddeley. 8. Mr. Habakkuk X Ernie. 9. Mad Wife X Farmer. 10. Manchild X Old Man. 11. Troubled Pilot X Happy Pilot. 12. Intellectual X Pugilist. 13. Madam Mayor X Mr. Mayor. 14. Fireman telephoning X Householder telephoning. 15. Patient X Nurse.

The dust-wrapper illustration was reproduced from the original (no. 687), also face no. 10 above (no. 633); nos. 3, 4, 6, 9, and 12 were re-drawn from the original sketches made for Shell. All the remainder were re-drawn from the printed Shell advertisements (no. 633). The dust-wrapper drawing was reproduced in *Rex Whistler,* by Laurence Whistler, p. 62 (no. 510).

508   THE TIMELESS QUEST,
STEPHEN HAGGARD

by Christopher Hassall   (*Barker, 1948*)   *8½ in. × 5½ in.*

Dust-wrapper and *title-page* (the same) derived by Laurence Whistler from designs by Rex Whistler.

509   WINE IN PEACE AND WAR
by Evelyn Waugh

(*Saccone and Speed, [1948]*)   *9 in. × 6 in.*

Decoration in colour on front and back cover (the same)— title framed in barrel, round which peer three alarmed faces. *2 full plates* in colour: 1. Opening lines of the book framed by a barrel, on top of which a naked Silenus sits waving a bunch of grapes and a spilling goblet. 2. Silenus' body forms frame to opening lines of Part 2—seated, a glass in each hand, his head tilted to catch wine spilling from a bottle lying on table. Reproduced from letters to Prince Vsevelode.

510   REX WHISTLER, HIS LIFE AND
HIS DRAWINGS   by Laurence Whistler

(*Art and Technics, London, 1948*)   *9 in. × 7 in.*

Dust-wrapper and *title-page* derived from *The Next Volume* (no. 441); end papers, from the same; cover device from dance programme (no. 618); 5 head- or tail-pieces, the last from Sketch-book 1926A (no. 293); 8 illus. in the text and 48 plates. These include reproductions from the following books, as listed in the Table of Contents:

The Love Child, by Edith Olivier, 1927; *As Far as Jane's Grandmother's,* by Edith Olivier, 1928; *Children of Hertha,* by Laurence Whistler, 1929; *Gulliver's Travels,* by Jonathan Swift, 1930; *Dr. Donne and Gargantua,* by Sacheverell Sitwell, 1930; *Desert Islands,* by Walter de la Mare, 1930; *Green Outside,* by Elizabeth Godley, 1931; *The New Keep-sake,* 1931; *The Traveller's Companion,* by P. and M. Bloomfield, 1931; *The Next Volume,* by Edward James, 1932; *Armed October,* by Laurence Whistler, 1932; *Down the Garden Path,* by Beverley Nichols, 1932; *The Lord Fish,* by Walter de la Mare, 1933; *The Silver Collar Boy,* by C. Wright, 1934; *Parable for Lovers,* by Lewis Gibbs, 1934; *Hans Andersen's Fairy Tales,* 1935; *The Emperor Heart,* by Laurence Whistler, 1936; *San Felice,* by Vincent Sheean, 1936; *Königsmark,* by A. E. W. Mason, 1940; *¡OHO!* by Laurence Whistler, 1946.

511   THE WORLD'S ROOM
by Laurence Whistler

(*Heinemann, 1949*)   *8¾ in. × 5½ in.*

Dust-wrapper and *end-paper*. The central device derived from a decoration on the free end-paper of a copy of *The Emperor Heart* (no. 481) by the same author, with the letters "C P" altered to "L" and "R". (Lettering added by the author.) Twenty-one decorations reproduced from *Armed October* (1932) and *The Emperor Heart* (1936), by the same author.

512   ASHCOMBE   by Cecil Beaton

(*Batsford, 1949*)   *8¾ in. × 5½ in.*

Dust-wrapper. A reproduction of the oil painting of house and studio, 1936 (no. 69). Four sketches reproduced as decorations: 1. Reverse of half-title. 2. Design for a door to the studio, p. 9. 3. Heading to Visitors' Book, 1930, p. 10. 4. Letter-heading, p. 15. Also photographs of oil paintings (no. 70) and bed (no. 659).

513   GEORGIAN LOVE SONGS
Edited by John Hadfield

(*The Cupid Press, 1949*)   *9¼ in. × 6 in.*

Frontispiece: a classical bust, wreathed (no. 575). *5 full plates:* 1. Two Georgian figures with long canes (no. 579). 2. An urn of flowers (no. 575). 3. A ship in a storm (no. 278). 4. A Georgian lady with a fan to her lips (no. 579). 5. A wigged Georgian figure with a sword (no. 579). *4 head-pieces:* 1. A wreath, with cupids (no. 582). 2. A carriage approaching a Georgian country house (no. 579). 3. A dog on a tomb (no. 279). 4. A straw-hat full of flowers (no. 575).

514   RESTORATION LOVE SONGS
Edited by John Hadfield

(*The Cupid Press, 1950*)   *9¼ in. × 6 in.*

Frontispiece (colour), Queen Anne alighting from a coach at a race-course, from *Nash's Magazine,* June 1935 (no. 557); and *6 plates:* 1. Venus crowned by cherubs, from a sketch for the upper staircase hall at 19 Hill St. (no. 4). 2. Musical trophy, from a sketch for Brook House, panel A3 (no. 13). 3. Festive trophy, from sketch for the same, panel A6. 4. A masked head pouring water into a basin, from the same, panel C7. 5. A statue on a pedestal, from a sketch for 19 Hill St., East Wall (no. 4). 6. A reproduction of *Youths and Shepherdesses* (no. 285).

515   THE MASQUE LIBRARY
Edited by Lionel Carter

(*Curtain Press, 1946–1950*)   *7½ in. × 5 in.*

Dust-wrapper device. Festive Trophy from Brook House, panel A.6 (no. 13). Decorations to nos. 2, 4, and 7, Parts I, II, and III respectively of *Designs for the Theatre by Rex Whistler,* with text by Cecil Beaton, James Laver, and Laurence Whistler.

Pt. I: *2 head-pieces:* crossed sprays tied with ribbon; floral spray tied with ribbon. *Tail-piece,* a head-piece from *Armed October* (no. 442), the face of Pan in floral trophy, repeated as title-page device for Pts. II and III. 8 reproductions in colour of designs for the theatre.

Pt. II: *Head-piece:* curtain design for *Love For Love* (no. 381), 17th-century man and woman greeting each other, a cupid between. 24 reproductions, 8 in colour, of designs for the Theatre.

Pt. III: *Head-piece:* an arch formed by two obelisks and drapery, surmounted by two cupids holding a crown with a smoking urn to right and left of them (no. 404). 22 reproductions, 4 in colour, of designs for the theatre.

Decorations to no. 5, *The Masque of Christmas,* text by Laurence Whistler.

Title-page border from "The Wilsford Theatre" (no. 301), but with "S" and "R" replaced by "BJ" and "IJ" in the two ovals, and with new wording.

Contents page border, repeated in reverse on left-hand page: a column draped by a curtain to which two cupids cling in alarm, a third soaring above to the left (no. 583). Repeated in advertisement pages, and later.

Head-piece: a wreath tied at the base with ribbon, a winged cupid to left and right (no. 582). Also reproduced in *Georgian Love Songs* (no. 513).

Nos. 1–9 bound as *The Masque Library*, with front cover label, the face of Pan (see above).

516   **Illustrations to**   *1952 (1941)*
"KÖNIGSMARK" by A. E. W. Mason
(*Plate 88*)

10 drawings, sepia ink, water-colour, and wash, 1 ft. 2 in.× 10 in. Signed, bottom right, *R.W.*

Commissioned in the summer of 1940 by A. E. W. Mason, to be bound up with the MS. of *Königsmark* (pub. 1938), but instead framed and hung in Mason's flat at 51 South St. Bequeathed to the Tate Gallery, where they now hang on the wall opposite the Refreshment Room.

(1) *Title-page:* A triumphal arch, inscribed "Königsmark. A. E. W. Mason"; and, on a rococo cartouche in the foreground, supported by a man in early 18th-century dress and a turbaned negro, "Illustrated by Rex Whistler".★

(2) Philip Königsmark and Princess Sophia meet in the garden.★

(3) "Bernstorff . . . was holding in his hands a thin, strong cord with a slip-knot at one end of it."

(4) Two jewelled women with a negro page, flaunting themselves at the Palace window.

(5) Philip, in the uniform of Colonel of the Guards, on the steps of the Palace.

(6) The lovers embrace in the garden.★

(7) "Philip reached forward and slowly turned out the lamp, and this time Sophia did not stay his hand."★

(8) Clara von Platen with Philip in the summer-house, dropping the incriminating glove as she is surprised by her husband.

(9) "He passed under the bridge and guided the skiff to the stone steps which led up to the small private door below Sophia Dorothea's apartment."★

(10) "Philip's head had fallen back . . . his eyes were glazing. . . . Pointing a shaking finger loaded with diamonds, she screamed to the guards."★

The ten drawings were reproduced in facsimile in *Rex Whistler, The Königsmark Drawings* (Richards Press, 1952) with an Introduction by Laurence Whistler, the edition being limited to a thousand copies.

★ Reproduced in *Rex Whistler* by Laurence Whistler, 1948, frontispiece and pp. 79–83.

Owner: The Tate Gallery

Three sheets of pencil studies for the above:

(1) 1 ft. 2½ in.× 10 in., unsigned: full-size drawing for no. 7, very much as finally carried out, but in reverse. In a ruled border.

(2) 10 in.× 1 ft. 2½ in., unsigned: studies for nos. 3, 4, and 6, similar to the final drawings, with alternative suggestions for 3 and 7.

(3) 10 in.× 1 ft. 2½ in., unsigned: on one side probably the very first ideas for the 10 illustrations. Nos. 1, 3, and 10 were to remain as first conceived, the others include a portrait of Königsmark, "Sophia Dorothea & her Mother", Trial scene, Sophia on a terrace, a coach in a street, "Clara & Platen", the two lovers before steps, etc. On the same sheet is a pencil sketch of four Welsh Guardsmen, on a charge at Battalion Orderly Room, and a sepia sketch of the R.S.M. On the reverse are two sketches for a bookplate for Lady Lytton (not carried out). *Owner: Laurence Whistler*

517   **THE SATURDAY BOOK**
nos. 13 and 15, edited by John Hadfield
(*Hutchinson, 1953, 1955*)   9 in.× 6 in.

No. 13: *2 head-pieces:* a crown on a cushion, both made of flowers (no. 575); a family of ten Victorians dancing round a candle-lit Christmas tree (no. 557).

No. 15: Rebus Letter to Miss Elizabeth Wellesley (Lady Elizabeth Clyde), pp. 230–1.

518   **THE STORY OF MR. KORAH**
by Christabel Aberconway
(*Michael Joseph, 1954*)   10 in.× 7½ in.

Frontispiece and *2 full plates* in colour: Mr. Korah stepping from his front door into earthquake chasm; escaping up the chimney; crashing on to bed while angry nurse admonishes him. *14 full-page drawings:* 1. Rough sketch for frontispiece. 2. Mr. Korah falling down the cleft. 3. A "curling tentacle" shooting out to seize him. 4. Mr. Korah in the octopus' tentacles. 5. In bed with the octopus. 6. Climbing up the chimney. 7. Pursued by a tentacle. 8. Still climbing. 9. Emerging from factory chimney. 10. Anchored to balloon. 11. Octopus in balloon. 12. Mr. Korah falling from balloon. 13. Fall into sky-light. 14. Wakes up. *2 tail-pieces:* rough sketch for colour-plate, escaping up the chimney; rough sketch for colour-plate, crashing on to bed.

This was a story invented by Lady Aberconway and illustrated by Rex Whistler on a writing-pad, as she told it. Later the artist suggested the publication of the story "after the war", painted the three coloured designs and proposed doing several more.

Original designs for 3 colour plates, water-colour, 10 in.× 7 in. 14 drawings and 2 tail-pieces, pencil, 3¾ in.× 4¾ in. *Owner: Christabel Lady Aberconway*

519   **PERONNIK THE FOOL**   *1926*
by George Moore

(1) *Design for title-page*, pencil, pen and Indian ink, 1 ft. 1 in. × 9½ in., signed bottom left: *Rex Whistler 1926*.

A classical arch, with cherubs climbing each flanking column. Above, singing angels, evidently suggested by Della Robbia; below, a satyr pierced by a sword, which has transfixed the title-scroll. Pencilled on the scroll: "Peronnik the Fool by George Moore. Decorated by Rex Whistler."

(2) *Initial letters* for the 4 chapters, pen and Indian ink.

Ch. I, 8 in. × 7 in., signed with cipher *R.W.* bottom left. Letter "B", formed by stout man in hood, carrying a stick.

Ch. II, 11½ in. × 9 in., signed with cipher *R.W.*, bottom left. Letter "A" with a mask on either side. On the reverse an illustration to *The Pilgrim's Progress* (no. 523).

Ch. III, 8 in. × 7 in., signed with cipher *R.W. 1926*, bottom left. Letter "N", wreathed with a serpent, between lilies.

Ch. IV, 8 in. × 7 in., unsigned. Letter "T", formed by a gallows with a corpse on each arm and a crow perched on the cross-bar.

Rough Sketches for the 4 initials, pencil and Indian ink, 1 ft. 3 in. × 11 in., unsigned. On the reverse, Indian ink and wash, a drawing of Delilah clipping Samson's hair.

(3) "Gilles de Lacenaire"—2 drawings, 1 ft. 1 in. × 9½ in., unsigned. The first a pencil sketch, head and shoulders, with a sword; on the reverse, a comic design in pencil for a soup-plate (a grinning face with a spoon in the mouth). The second, pen and Indian ink, unsigned, head and shoulders of the knight in an attitude of prayer.

(4) "The Hermit of Blavet", Indian ink and wash, 11½ in. × 9 in., signed on a book to the right: *Rex Whistler, March 1926*. An aged hermit in a skull-cap, reading in a cave, with his right hand on a book and left hand supporting his head. To the left a candle on a bracket.

On Mar. 9th, 1926, in an unpublished letter, George Moore wrote to the artist: "I shall be seeing Mr. Evans about the illustrated edition of Peronnik, and it would be well that we should go throu [sic] the book together with the view of making a selection of the scenes that call for pictorial comment. . . . Please to bring the book." This was Vol. XXI of the Carra Edition of the Collected Works of George Moore (Boni and Liveright, New York, 1924), a copy emended by the author.

The following day the artist lunched with Moore and recorded in his diary, "He gave me a long, but very incoherent account of the story. Something about an *Irish poet or hermit*, & some very improper incidents, which almost choked him with glee, & caused him to stop in his narrative. All seems now agreed about the illustrations, & on parting, he invited me, kindly, to come &

lunch with him at any time & show him how they progressed." The next day Moore had doubts again, and told his publisher to ask for "several more *trial* drawings", as the artist puts it. The latter showed the letter to Tonks, who advised him to do nothing more for the present, "as I *cannot* be fairly expected to keep doing *trial* drawings for ever".

Moore finally decided against the decorations, and the first English edition of 1933 contained engravings by Stephen Gooden.   *Owner: Laurence Whistler*

520   **A BOOK OF PENSÉES**   *1926*
by Ronald Hall
Indian ink and water-colour.   *8 in. × 6½ in.*

Full-page illustrations to a book never published. Nos. 1, 2, and 3 were reproduced by Mr. Hall in his pamphlet *Heart Disease; How I Cured Myself* (Lewes Press, Lewes, 1959), with titles not anticipated by the artist.

(1) Globe Trotters. Signed, bottom right: *Rex Whistler*. Travellers on a hill-top, in knee breeches; one standing, one sitting, chin in hand. Reproduced in *Heart Disease* (opp. p. 53) with the title: "Globe Trotters with no Heart Troubles."

(2) The Master Communist. Signed, bottom right: *Rex Whistler 1926*. Death standing by a king, who lies aghast in a four-poster bed. Reproduced in *Heart Disease* (opp. p. 5) with the title: "A King with Heart Disease."   *Owner: Mr. Ronald Hall*

(3) "The Man of Destiny." Signed, bottom right: *Rex Whistler, 1926*. Bearded tramp with folded arms, against a slum background. Reproduced in *Heart Disease* (opp. p. 35) with the title: "Tramp with no Heart Disease."   *Owner: Laurence Whistler*

(4) When the Impossible Comes True. No signature. Two men in Hell observing one of the blessed who carries a sack of sovereigns (his reward for charity on earth).
    Owner: Mr. Ronald Hall

(5) "Illustration to 'Death's Precipice'." Signed, bottom right: *Rex Whistler*. A seated man holding forth. In the background another gloomily regarding himself in the mirror. The subject is humorous. One character is deploring the fact that man must suffer and die, though cast in the divine image. The other replies, "But are we really so beautiful?"   *Owner: Laurence Whistler*

(6) "A Man of Pedigree." No signature. A lackadaisical youth reclining on a sofa.   *Owner: Laurence Whistler*

521   **THE MAN WITHIN**
by Graham Greene   (*Heinemann, 1929*)

Finished drawing for dust-wrapper. Indian ink and water-colour, 7¾ in. × 6½ in., unsigned. Bottom right, the hero kneeling in terror, aware of his ghostly personae behind him. A finished design.   *Owner: Laurence Whistler*

Rough sketch for the above, 7¾ in. × 6½ in., showing the man leaning on an urn.   *Owner: Graham Greene, Esq.*

522 THE MARRIAGE OF CUPID *1932*
AND PSYCHES tr. William Adlington

The artist agreed to provide a drawn title-page, 12 full-page illustrations and 6 head- and tail-pieces for what would have been one of his most important books. Probably he produced nothing but the delicately finished title-page and 3 light pencil sketches for the full plates.

(1) *The title-page*, sepia ink and wash, 1 ft. ½ in. × 9 in. "The most pleasant and delectable tale of The Marriage of Cupid and Psyches Translated out of Latin by William Adlington Illustrated by Rex Whistler. William Heinemann Ltd. London." Used as the title-page of the present work, with printed wording substituted.

(2) *4 pencil sketches* for full plates, 1 ft. 2 in. × 10 in., with the following captions: "They bring her to the appointed Rocke of the high hill, and set her hereon and so depart." "Awakening, Psyche espied in the midst of the wood a princely Edifice." "Psyche cometh to the bed-side where she finds the most meek and sweetest of all beasts—even fair Cupid." "The rusticall god PAN sitting on the river-side, perceives Psyches in sorrowful case."

Owner: Laurence Whistler

523 THE PILGRIM'S PROGRESS *c. 1932*
by John Bunyan

Sepia ink and wash.   11½ in. × 9 in.   *Unsigned*

"Christian fights with Apollyon." One full-page drawing of Christian beaten down on his knee, defending himself against the flaming fiend with poised darts, beneath a wayside tree. A measurement suggests that this drawing was somewhere reproduced.

On the reverse (probably of earlier date), an initial letter for *Peronnik the Fool* (no. 519).   *Owner: Laurence Whistler*

524 ABOUT JOHN *n.d.*
"New Cautionary Tales" by Hilaire Belloc

Pen and Indian ink.   *Unsigned*

4 sketches:

(1) "J. V. de Q. J. was very fond of throwing stones." 3½ in. × 3¾ in. A fat boy in a sailor suit rolling up his sleeve to throw a stone.

(2) "& often chuckled wait until", etc. 3¾ in. × 3¾ in. Stout red-nosed gentleman, finger to nose, with small boy in the exact attitude of illus. (1).

(3) "& there he sank into a doze." 3½ in. × 3¼ in. Old gentleman asleep in a bath-chair, with a nurse seated in the background.

(4) "He shrieked in agonising tones." 3⅞ in. × 4¼ in. Old gentleman in bath-chair receiving a stone in his eye, the horrified nurse beside him.

Owner: Laurence Whistler

525 TWO FABLES OF AESOP *n.d.*
Pen and Indian ink.   5 in. × 3½ in.   *Unsigned*

(1) *The Satyr and the Traveller.* The interior of a cave. On the left the Traveller with a bowl of soup, on the right, at the cave entrance, the Satyr beside a fire.

(2) *The Two Springs.* On the left a tumbling waterfall; on the right a placid stream, both issuing from a hill on the skyline in the form of a human face.

The pictures were drawn for an intended verse translation of the *Fables* by the artist's mother.

Owner: Laurence Whistler

526 "THE FARMER AND HIS SONS" *n.d.*
Pen and Indian ink.   1 ft. 2 in. × 9¾ in.   *Unsigned*

Unidentified, probably for a children's story. To the left the aged farmer in bed, with his four boys round the foot of the bed, one seated.   *Owner: Laurence Whistler*

Special Decorations in Books

See also Printed Books, *The Traveller's Companion*, 1931 (no. 436). *The Next Volume*, 1932 (no. 441).

527 TITLE-PAGE DECORATION *1928*
for a copy of "The Heart's Journey"
by Siegfried Sassoon (limited edition), 1927

A large trophy of arms in Indian ink, topped by a wreathed skull and palms which form a frame to the poet's written signature. The half-title is inscribed: "Rex Whistler from an admirer of his art. Siegfried Sassoon. Xmas, 1928."

Owner: Laurence Whistler

528 PAGE DECORATION *1928*
for a copy of "The Heart's Journey"
by Siegfried Sassoon, 1928

Water-colour decoration below and around poem X,

"What is Stonehenge? It is the roofless past . . ."—one of the artist's favourite poems. The Stones at a distance, under rolling clouds. The title-page is inscribed, "Laurie from Rex 1928".   *Owner: Laurence Whistler*

529 TITLE-PAGE DECORATION *1931*
for a copy of "The Poems of Edmund Blunden",
1930

An asymmetrical rococo cartouche in sepia ink, backed by musical instruments and flowers, c. 2½ in. × 2½ in. "Nov. 13/ Laurence Whistler/Edmund Blunden/1931." Mr. Blunden inscribed his own signature.   *Owner: Laurence Whistler*

530 FLY-LEAF DECORATION *1934*
for vol. I of Shakespeare, ed. W. E. Henley, 1901
Sepia ink and wash.   1 ft. 1 in. × 8 in.   Unsigned
(Plate 80)
"To their Royal Highnesses/The Duke and Duchess of Kent/on the occasion of their/wedding/from Diana and Duff Cooper/Nov 29 – 1934." Richly flourished, with a kneeling Cupid at the top, and a vignette at the foot of Adam and Eve, holding hands, in a glade by a waterfall.
Owner: H.R.H. The Duchess of Kent

531 HALF-TITLE DECORATION *1936*
for a copy of "Fairy Tales" by Hans Andersen
Water-colour.   8 in. × 5¼ in.   (Plate 77)
The artist gave a copy of his own Hans Andersen to Lord Herbert (now Lord Pembroke) as a wedding present. Under the half-title appears a cartouche with cherubs and cornucopias, containing the words: "For Sidney with affectionate good wishes from Rex." Below is a view of the south and east sides of Wilton House, flanked by trees: "July 27th 1936" on a scroll. *Owner: The Earl of Pembroke*

532 COVERS AND END-PAPER *1938*
DECORATIONS
for a copy of "Sir John Vanbrugh"
by Laurence Whistler
(Plate 79)
Presented to H.M. the Queen (H.M. Queen Elizabeth the Queen Mother). Front cover: an asymmetrical rococo cartouche containing an "E", backed by a flag, etc., and topped by a crown: all in gold, the block being specially cut, *c.* 4½ in. × 3½ in. Also in gold: four small ciphers of "ER" in the corners, and, on the back cover, an architectural device repeated from the title-page.

Paste-down end-paper: sepia ink and wash, 10¼ in. × 6¼ in., signed bottom, *Rex Whistler 1938.* Architectural symbols: a plinth with "ELIZABETH", supporting a broken column and a medallion-portrait of "Sir John Vanbrugh". Below, a tumble of instruments, a broken cornice, skull, etc.
Owner: H.M. Queen Elizabeth the Queen Mother

533 END-PAPER DECORATION *1939*
for a copy of "Sir John Vanbrugh"
by Laurence Whistler
Indian ink and wash.   10 in. × 6 in.
Signed, lower centre: Rex Whistler
A symmetrical rococo cartouche on the paste-down end-paper, containing the words "Elsie Tritton". Trees behind and above; books and drawing instruments below; gardening tools to the right. Opposite, on the free end-paper, "Elsie with love from Rex. Christmas 1939."
Owner: Mrs. Tritton

534 DECORATION *1941*
for a copy of "Country Moods and Tenses"
by Edith Olivier, 1941
Presented to H.M. the Queen (H.M. Queen Elizabeth the Queen Mother). Edith Olivier records in her unpublished Journal for Nov. 9th: "Rex was most of the day making an exquisite decoration round the inscription I have written in a copy of my book for the Queen." Mislaid.
Owner: H.M. Queen Elizabeth the Queen Mother

535 END-PAPER DECORATION *1943*
for a copy of "Fairy Tales" by Hans Andersen
Sepia ink and water-colour.   8 in. × 5¼ in.   Unsigned
A floral wreath—containing a rococo cartouche—containing the letters P.J.P. Below, a mermaid on a rock, cherubs, a shell, etc. Drawn in a copy of his own Hans Andersen, on the free end-paper.   *Owner: Mrs. Richard Altham*

536 END-PAPER DECORATION *1943*
for a copy of "The Last of Uptake"
by Simon Harcourt-Smith
Sepia ink and wash.   10 in. × 7½ in.   Signed, bottom right:
Rex Whistler, Fonthill Gifford, 1943.
A great smoking urn of ovoid shape, with a cipher of FP in an oval medallion.   *Owner: Sir Francis Portal, Bt.*

537 COVER DECORATION *1944*
for "The Love Poems of John Donne", "Poems of Andrew Marvell", and "The Temple"
by George Herbert
Copies of the Nonesuch editions, 1923-7, in uniform special binding of orange cloth and marbled end-papers, chosen by the artist. On the front cover a central cipher of SW in a symmetrical rococo cartouche surrounded with stars, and with stars in the four corners and along the spine. All in gold, the blocks being specially cut. For the first three birthdays of his godson—the owner: Simon Whistler, Esq.

Periodicals:
Illustrations and Decorations

538   **ENGLISH LIFE**   *June–Dec. 1926*
Jan.–June 1927

Full-page illustrations to serialized novel, *Our Mr. Dormer*, by R. H. Mottram: 1. Two men in a coach at night, one firing a gun through the window. 2. Two men carrying box into a bank at night. 3. "Mr. Stephen Dormer of Doughty's Bank." 4. Man and boy in Regency dress walking in a garden while a girl descends steps of a terrace. 5. Policeman wrestling with youth on the floor, two figures standing by in horror. 6. Sleeping man in summer-house, beside whom a girl greets her lover. 7. "He mounted the old stairs." 8. Oval portrait of "Pleasance". 9. Elderly man in arm-chair sitting for his portrait. 10. Youth leaning against mantelpiece, his father haggard in an easy-chair. 11. Elderly woman enters library door on the arm of a servant. 12. Top-hatted lawyer, followed by his "man", leaving garden gates. 13. Old lady at a table by window surrounded by awed relatives. 14. Man looking out of a window at a fire, small boy and frightened old woman behind him. 15. Man in a chair at a table, a tray with glass of milk and biscuits beside him.

539   **ENGLISH LIFE**   *September–*
December 1926

Three head-pieces: (1) "English life" in a cartouche, beside which reclines an early 19th-century sportsman with a gun. (2) "English Tidings" in a similar cartouche, beside which a woman reclines under a tree with a book on her lap and a parrot perched on her right hand. (3) "The Connoisseur" on a fringed drapery with swags of flowers above, and on left and right winged cherubs, one opening a treasure-chest, the other painting a portrait. (4) June 1927. "The Theatre." A candle flanked by tragic and comic masks, and two rococo ovals ribboned "Tragedy" and "Comedy".

540   **ENGLISH LIFE**   *November 1926*

Two half-page illustrations to *Samuel Pepys at Brampton* by Professor A. E. Richardson: "Mr and Mrs Pepys in the Country", illustrating the sitting-room at Brampton; "Mr Pepys explains his theatre-goings" to his wife, very bored by the fireplace.

541   **THE SPHERE**   *January 1927*

Head-piece to *A London Newsletter*. This continued each week up to the issue of Mar. 5th, 1927. A reclining Triton holding a conch, from which flows the River Thames; in the centre a title-scroll, to the right tragic and comic masks.

Two studies for the above, pen and Indian ink, $8\frac{1}{4}$ in. $\times$ $9\frac{1}{2}$ in., unsigned. (1) In a classical frame, a scallop shell with the words "A London News Letter"; flanked by cupids, one with a sack. (2) The wording in a rococo cartouche, to be flanked by urns (one omitted).
Owner: Laurence Whistler

542   **THE EPICUREAN**   *January 1929*

An unofficial magazine at Stowe School. Cover only. An elegant youth leaning on the pedestal of an urn, reading, and with a glass of wine in his hand. A skull and a trophy of games equipment below. Pen and Indian ink on orange paper, $11\frac{1}{4}$ in. $\times$ $8\frac{1}{2}$ in., signed on the back, *Rex Whistler, 20 Fitzroy St., W.1.* Pencilled in the cartouche, "No 1, Volume 1, January 1929".

Preliminary study. Pen and Indian ink on orange paper, $4\frac{1}{2}$ in. $\times$ $3\frac{1}{4}$ in., unsigned. "Dec: 1928", and other annotations. *Owner: Laurence Whistler*

543   **VOGUE**   *January 1929*

Four illustrations to an article, *Cumberland*, by Lady Ankaret Jackson: 1. Huntsman and companion in Cumberland with cupids, one of whom is seated painting at an easel, the other flying with huntsman's cap and whip. 2. Medallion of John Peel, with sporting trophy. 3. Cumbrian wrestlers in the ring. 4. Two girls with a dog by a mountain tarn, one nude, the other taking off her shoe.

544   **THE LONDON**   *February 1929*
HOSPITAL GAZETTE

Cover only. This cover design, which is still in use, replaced one drawn by Professor Henry Tonks, who was responsible for Rex Whistler's designing the new one.

545   **THE STRAND**   *April 1930*

Two illustrations to *This or This? A Symposium* by Frank Swinnerton and others. (1) Title decoration. To the left a whiskered Victorian in smoking cap and jacket gesturing towards a Victorian arm-chair: to the right, a well-tailored modern, indicating a chromium chair. (2) A Victorian mother in a rocking-chair, holding a book, with a child at her knee, the father behind twirling his moustache.

546   **FARRAGO**   *1931*

Head-piece to poem, *The Death of Pan*, by Laurence Whistler: the dead god prone, on a rocky shore.

547   **THE RADIO TIMES**   *December 1931*

Christmas number. Cover only (colour). Three female figures with flute, trumpet, etc., and three cherubs, above a cartouche.

Study for the above. "Rough Preliminary drawing", sepia ink and water-colour, 9 in.×7 in., signed on back, *Rex Whistler.*   *Owner: Laurence Whistler*

548   **COUNTRY LIFE**   *March–*
May 1932

Decorations to *Down the Garden Path* by Beverley Nicholls, serialized. As in the published book of that year (no. 443), but reduced in size.

549   **COUNTRY LIFE**   *June 1932*

Head-piece to an article by Lord Conway of Allington, *Episodes in a Varied Life.* In the foreground, framed, *Jan Arnolfini and His Wife Joanna* by Van Eyck, with drapery across the frame. A castle to the left; two igloos to the right.

Study for the above. Sepia ink and wash, 4½ in.×9½ in., unsigned. Much as carried out, but the painting indicated is the *Tempesta* by Giorgione.   *Owner: Laurence Whistler*

550   **COUNTRY LIFE**   *January–*
June 1932

Head-piece to series, *The Traveller.* Title in Roman capitals above a rocky shore. To the left, a youth walking with a dog; to the right, classical ruins.

"Rough head-piece" for the above. Two studies, so inscribed, Indian ink and wash, 3 in.×9¼ in., signed on backs, in pencil, *Rex Whistler.* (1) Title in flourished italics across a ruin: a youth reclining, to the left, with a dog. (2) Title in Roman capitals on ruin: the youth standing, to the right, with dog.   *Owner: Laurence Whistler*

551   **NASH'S MAGAZINE** *October 1933*

Two illustrations to *Lady Blessington: Splendours & Miseries of a Gossip Writer,* by Peter Quennell.

Head-piece, a ball-room scene under a chandelier, a couple taking the floor, a flunkey entering from the left with a decanter.

Full-page colour plate: Lady Blessington, in a pink dress, reclining, her head against County D'Orsay standing behind her, looking down, beside a balustrade. Georgian façade and park in the background. Indian ink and water-colour, 10½ in.×8 in., unsigned.

Owner: Dame Adelaide Livingstone

552   **THE FINANCIAL NEWS**   *1933*
"MAP OF THE STOCK EXCHANGE"
As printed: 9¼ in.×1 ft. 1 in.

A bird's-eye view of a fanciful enclosure, shaped like the Stock Exchange, in which the various markets are humorously symbolized, e.g. for "Gilt-edged", three tail-coated worshippers kneeling to a bust with "M.N." (Montague

Norman) inscribed on it. In the four corners symbolic figures, Mercury the messenger-god, with a telegram on the end of his *caduceus*; Ceres tipping out a cornucopia; "King Midas" turning all to gold; Dame Fortune, blind, with shears; and a top-hatted Bear and Bull supporting a name-cartouche crowned with a bag marked "£".

Mr. Grahame Martin-Turner proposed a diagram of the Stock Exchange markets, and the late Lord Bracken of Christchurch (then Mr. Brendan Bracken) suggested Rex Whistler. Mr. Martin-Turner remembers that a stock-broker friend was called in to sketch the position of each market, but the artist "was not satisfied with this and came back with a request that my friend should actually pace out the various distances". He also insisted on showing the restaurants in Throgmorton St. used by members, and the Cable Office in Shorter's Court, symbolized by messenger-boys sent running by Mercury.

Published in a special supplement of *The Financial News* on the City of London, to celebrate the 50th anniversary of the paper. Also used as a calendar in 1934.

Study for the above. Sepia ink and water-colour, 9¼ in.×1 ft. 1 in., unsigned. Very much as carried out, in general; but with many inventive touches still to be inserted, e.g. the cherub, top right and the top hats of the Bear and Bull. In the final design the worshippers of "M.N." took the place of a trophy of flags and cannon.
Owner: Grahame Martin-Turner, Esq.

553   **THE FINANCIAL NEWS**   *1934*
"PROSPECT OF THE CITY OF LONDON"
As printed: 1 ft. 6 in.×1 ft. 11¼ in.

An aerial view with the streets somewhat rectified, and St. Paul's bulking very large. Labels show the habitats of "Diamonds", "Fur-skins", "London Rubber", etc. Top left, on clouds, Gog and Magog support Temple Bar and point to Dick Whittington and his cat on a medallion. In the other corners, the Arms of the City, Father Thames, and a cartouche—"Being a Map for the/Merchants, Bankers and Brokers/ & other Venturers trading into/that City. 1934." Published in a special supplement of *The Financial News* on the City of London, to celebrate the 50th anniversary of the paper.

554   **NASH'S**   *February 1934*
MAGAZINE

Illustrations to *Four Poems* by Martha Banning Thomas. (1) Head-piece to "Lament": a man with night-cap and candle. (2) Head-piece to "Unfinished portrait": a middle-aged man turning his back on a weeping cupid. (3) Head-and tail-piece to "A Yell for Recognition" (on one sheet): two men chopping a log; a man knocking at a door, with a dog. (4) Tail-piece to "Northern Travellers": crags and a river, beyond trees. Sepia ink and wash, 9½ in.×7 in., unsigned.   *Owner: Laurence Whistler*

555   **NASH'S MAGAZINE**   *July 1934*

Decorative border to the editorial, *Twenty-five Years.* Representing incidents and personalities, 1909–1934, the left-hand border Edwardian, from the Coronation (top) to the Suffragettes, the right from the First World War (top) to Hitler; the price of Nash's (in ovals round the border) rising from 6d. to 1s. Sepia ink and wash, 1 ft. 2¼ in. × 10½ in., unsigned. *Owner: Laurence Whistler*

556 **NASH'S** *December 1934*
MAGAZINE

Christmas Number. Cover (in colour). Winter landscape framed in red curtains above a rococo cartouche. Indian ink and water-colour, 1 ft. ¼ in. × 9½ in., signed on the back: *Rex Whistler*.

Preliminary study, pencil and water-colour, 10 in. × 8 in., unsigned. A pencilled landscape between two terminal figures, the left holding a half-drawn red curtain, with a title-cartouche below. *Owner: Laurence Whistler*

557 **NASH'S MAGAZINE** *1935*

Illustrations for 11 monthly articles, *The English Year*, by Hector Bolitho.

(1) *January*
Sepia ink and wash. A meet in a village, 5 in. × 6 in. Man and wife at the tea-table with dog, 5 in. × 6 in. Horseman leaving drive gates with two dogs, 6½ in. × 7½ in.

(2) *February*
Sepia ink and wash. A bishop telling a smoking-room story, 5 in. × 7¼ in. "The Pope carried in state in St. Peter's." Mother and child on the way to a corrugated iron church.

(3) *March*
Sepia ink and wash. Youth at window with a gun, 5¾ in. × 5½ in. "Dick Turpin sometimes haunts the passages of the inn"—ghost and terrified yokels, 8½ in. × 7½ in.
Sepia ink and water-colour. Cottage in a downpour, disconsolate youth in doorway, 11 in. × 9 in.

(4) *April*
Sepia ink, wash, and water-colour. Crowd watching "The Boat Race", 7¾ in. × 8½ in. The Cambridge Backs, two men in a boat. Tom Tower. Cromwell refusing drink.

May—no article

(5) *June*
Sepia ink, wash, and water-colour. Queen Anne alighting from a coach at a race-course, 8 in. × 9 in. (Reproduced in *Restoration Love Songs*, ed. John Hadfield, 1950.)
Sepia ink and wash. Queen Victoria in a carriage with two ladies in waiting, 5 in. × 5 in. "Fijian, Portuguese & a Lap, surprised at our racing customs", 5 in. × 7 in. "George IV weeping at news of death of his giraffe", 5 in. × 5 in.

(6) *July*
Sepia ink and wash. "King Henry had all the wives & the Pope all the bulls." Schoolboy between Pope and King Henry VIII, 7 in. × 10 in. (Reproduced in *Art Review for 1935* (Artist Pub. Co.).) "Oh Napoleon was only a foreigner & went about with his hands in

his pockets." Napoleon putting his tongue out at a lofty Wellington, 8 in. × 6¾ in. "Large drafty buildings with plenty of tradition and not very much plumbing." Aristocrat in a hip-bath, 5 in. × 10 in.

(7) *August*
Sepia ink and wash heightened with white. Victoria and Albert in Osborne Gardens, 10 in. × 8 in. Charles I in prison, 10 in. × 8 in.
Water-colour. Yachts at sea, 6½ in. × 10 in.

(8) *September*
Sepia ink and wash, heightened with white. "Thousands of English oysters were eaten at the great Roman feasts & even the ladies carried about with them peacock feathers and other dainty throat-ticklers", 8¾ in. × 10 in.
Sepia ink and wash. "I myself have eaten 120 oysters in a day"—table piled with oyster-shells, gentleman beneath it, 6¼ in. × 10 in. "Queen Elizabeth visiting an impoverished country gentleman", 6½ in. × 10 in.

(9) *October*
Sepia ink and wash. Victorian picnic on Scottish moors, 6 in. × 9½ in. "Informal visiting"—Queen Victoria visiting crofters, 5 in. × 8½ in. Gentleman and lady riding near Balmoral, 4¾ in. × 8¾ in.

(10) *November*
Sepia ink and wash. Children demanding pennies for their Guy, 8 in. × 10½ in. A trophy of fireworks, 8 in. × 10½ in. Guy Fawkes, surprised, 8 in. × 10½ in.

(11) *December*
Sepia ink and water-colour. Bringing the Yule Log across the drawbridge, 9½ in. × 1 ft. 3¾ in. (Double spread.)
Sepia ink and wash. Backs of three yokels carousing at a fireplace, 4 in. × 5½ in.
Sepia ink and water colour. Camel caravan on skyline, 4½ in. × 5½ in. Christmas tree with Victorian family of ten, 6¾ in. × 7 in. Reproduced in *The Saturday Book*, no. 13, 1953, on p. 17. All are unsigned.

Owner of 3rd drawing listed for January: David Higham, Esq.
Owner of the 3rd for February, and the 1st for September: Hector Bolitho, Esq.
Whereabouts unknown of the 2nd drawing listed for February and the 2nd, 3rd, and 4th for April.
Owner of remainder: Laurence Whistler.

558 **HARPER'S BAZAAR** *1935*

Five illustrations to an article, *Something Floral*, by Constance Spry. Sepia ink and wash, unsigned.
(1) 10 in. × 9½ in., three girls in evening dress with flowers in hair or on bodice. (2) 11½ in. × 9¾ in., floral chaplet dislodged by military partner. (3) 8 in. × 5¾ in., two wreaths and a detail of floral shoulder-knot, on a single sheet. *Owner: Laurence Whistler*

559 **VOGUE** *1935*

Full-page decorative frame to a photograph of King George V. Palm-trees rising from cornucopias. Sepia pen and ink, heightened with white, 1 ft. 1 in. × 9½ in., unsigned. *Owner: Laurence Whistler*

560   **THE TATLER**
November 22nd, 1935

"Winter": full-page drawing. A wintry scene with skaters on a pond in the middle distance. In the foreground, reclining on a cartouche inscribed "Winter", an aged nude man, his left arm resting on a jar from which water pours and freezes into icicles on the edge of the cartouche. A rook on a leafless bough above him. The whole in a frame twined with barren twigs. The reproduction was used by Cecil Beaton as a background for a photographic portrait of the music-hall artist, Miss Nellie Wallace, and for others.

561   **GOOD HOUSEKEEPING**
December 1935

Three illustrations to *Shops I Like*, by Osbert Sitwell: head-piece, lady in Sedan chair at "Oliver & Sons", Bury St. Edmunds; two oval decorations, "Oyster Bar of Miss Cheeseman in Brighton"; "Mr. Pollock's shop in Shoreditch, relic of a period of theatrical glory".

562   **VOGUE**   *April 1936*

Two full plates (colour), illustrating evening gowns by Eva Lutyens:

(1) Two girls, one in a yellow dress, sitting with her back turned, on a sofa, the other in a striped gown beside her.
(2) Woman in a blue dress with white stars, on a terrace in front of a group of statuary and, beyond, the lit window of a house.

Sketches for evening gowns, etc., by Eva Lutyens. Three sheets of pencil sketches, 1 ft. 3½ in. × 9¾ in., and one water-colour design, 11 in. × 7½ in., for a black striped blouse, unfinished.   *Owner: Laurence Whistler*

563   **GOOD HOUSEKEEPING** *June 1936*

Three illustrations to *The Pleasures of Picnics*, by Osbert Sitwell. 1. Head-piece: picnic in 18th-century dress, with music. 2. Robinson Crusoe on a box under tattered parasol. 3. Picnic on the edge of a precipice by Niagara Falls.

Drawing for Robinson Crusoe in (2) above, sepia ink and water-colour, 10 in. × 7 in., unsigned.
Owner: Laurence Whistler

564   **THE TIMES** *January 7th, 1937*
WEEKLY EDITION

"England in the Seventies." A double-spread commemorating the 60th anniversary of the edition. Four scenes: Hyde Park, croquet, a dinner party, a lady shopping. Sepia ink and water-colour, 1 ft. 3 in. × 1 ft. 8 in., signed bottom right: *Rex Whistler*. Top left corner missing.
Owner: Laurence Whistler

565   **NASH'S MAGAZINE**   *February–March 1937*

Four illustrations to *The Court Circle*, by Laurence Housman. (1) Interior, showing Lord Melbourne bowing to the young Queen. In a rococo cartouche, topped by a crown. (2) The Duke of Sussex tipsily approaching the Queen in a state room. To the left, the Prince Consort playing chess. (3) The Queen on a sofa with Lady Seward. (4) Lady Seward at a piano. Nos. (1) and (2), Indian ink and coloured wash, c. 9 in. × 8½ in., unsigned.   *Owner: John Teed, Esq.*

566   **VOGUE**   *April 1937*

Three drawings of the Royal Family in a coloured border with decorative titles, for an article, *Coronation Day*, by Sacheverell Sitwell.

(1) "The King and Queen with the Princesses," with two dogs on a terrace under trees. Pencil, 1 ft. 1 in. × 10 in., unsigned. Bottom left margin: "How about another basket of flowers to hide the dog's derrière?" Listed also under Portraits (no. 193).
Owner: H.M. Queen Elizabeth the Queen Mother
(2) Queen Mary and the Princess Royal on a sofa: the Duke of Windsor seated on the back of the sofa. Pencil, 1 ft. 1 in. × 10 in., unsigned.
(3) Double-spread of an imaginary picnic. The Duke of Gloucester on horse-back, the Duchess waving to him. The Duke and Duchess of Kent with the infant Prince Edward and Princess Alexandra. Pencil, 1 ft. ½ in. × 1 ft. 7 in., unsigned.   *Owner: Laurence Whistler*
Head-piece to the above. Flourished title above Royal trophy, with roses. Initial letters to paragraphs with floral sprays.

567   **HARPER'S BAZAAR**   *May 1937*

Two colour plates of Coronation Robes. Sepia ink and water-colour, 1 ft. 2 in. × 10 in., unsigned.
(1) "The correct robes for the Royal Duchesses to wear at the Coronation of their Majesties on May 12th 1937."
(2) "The correct robes for the Dukes and Duchesses. . . ."
Owner: Laurence Whistler

568   **THE RADIO TIMES**
November 12th, 1937

Woman's Broadcasting Number. Cover (colour). Maidens singing to lutes, etc., in romantic landscape of trees, cliffs, ruins, and a waterfall; three winged cupids hover about a microphone attached to the bough of a tree.

569   **THE TATLER**   *November 1937*

White Christmas. Full-page illustration of a sonnet by Laurence Whistler. Ivied trees at the edge of a snow-clad precipice, a dead tree-trunk half buried in snow across the foreground.

570   **THE TATLER**   *November 1938*

Ancien Régime. Full-page illustration to a poem by Laurence Whistler. A girl and a small boy with a drum, on a stone balcony before an open window in the snow.

571　　**ILLUSTRATED**　*December 1939*

A double-spread drawing, "Flying Visit of Truth to Berlin". On Oct. 1st/2nd, 1939, No. 10 Squadron made the first raid Berlin had ever suffered—though only a leaflet one. The drawing was made to commemorate it. It shows a perspective map of Berlin, with a winged Britannia top left, thronged about with cherubs in goggles, who drop leaflets. Opposite, bottom right, we see Hitler and Goering under a swaying Jolly Roger, brandishing their fists, Goebbels cowering behind them and Ribbentrop under the table. *Mein Kampf* has tumbled to the ground; Hitler points to it in outrage. A cartouche, top right, speaks of this "Flying Visit of No. 10 Squadron to Berlin in the form of an R.A.F. leaflet raid here fancifully depicted—but not forgetting a great many hard facts." It is adorned with the heads of Goebbels, Goering, Hitler, and the Devil.

The artist gave the drawing to A.V-M. Staton, who commanded the Squadron and had written as a stranger with a request to buy it. He then added the Squadron badge to the shield of Britannia, improving the heraldry, as he was resolved to do, by reversing the wings. Four crews took part, and three copies were presented to the pilots who returned. Indian ink and wash, 1 ft. 1½ in. ×

1 ft. 8½ in., signed in cartouche, top right: *By Rex Whistler.*
　　　　　　　　　　　　Owner: Air Vice-Marshal Staton

572　　**ILLUSTRATED**　*April 1940*

Full-page drawing of Birthday Card, tied with ribbon: "To Adolf on his Birthday—April 20th." Within a rococo frame, Hitler as a small howling boy in sash and lace collar sits on a stool, about to light the candles on a cake labelled "from the B.E.F. Best Dynamite", while birthday presents fall about him from the air—including a box of cigars ("Flor de T.N.T." "With many wishes from Winston"), a coal-scuttle containing shells ("All the best from the Royal Navy"), a bundle of leaflets in ribbon ("Greetings from the R.A.F."), a gramophone ("Love and kisses from Goebbels") and a Jack-in-the-box, making a rude face. In a cartouche beneath:

> "These gifts you get at fifty-one
> From us a card; from every Hun
> To cheer you in your state of funk
> A new edition of 'Mein Junk'."

573　　**THE LISTENER**　*December 1941*

Christmas number. Cover, St. George slaying the dragon.

Designs probably for Periodicals

574　　**"THE PARTY SPIRIT"**　*c. 1935*
　　Indian ink and pencil.　　7¼ in. × 10 in.　　*Unsigned*

A butler bearing a birthday cake, with three boys in Eton suits jumping before him, and three excited small girls with fans at a table on the right.
　　　　　　　Owner: The Estate of Mrs. Constance Spry

575　　**ELEVEN UNIDENTIFIED**　*? c. 1935*
　　　　　　　DRAWINGS
　　Sepia ink and wash.　*Average size* 10½ in. × 8¼ in.
　　　　　　　　Unsigned

(1) Urn with flowers.—"Use your *Urns* stuffed with every flower." (2) Soup-tureen with flowers.—"Use your soup-tureens." (3) Tea-urn full of corn and poppies. Shell with flowers.—"Use your *Shells* do you think? (a nasty jar at Gerald's)." (4) Classical bust, wreathed.—"Use your *Busts* wreathed in grapes and flowers." (The artist's comments may be his proposals for captions to an article.) (5) A crown on a cushion, both made of flowers. (6) A circular table with a ship centrepiece. (7) An ornamental angel holding a cornucopia full of flowers. (8) A mantelpiece with a Tudor portrait between vase of grapes and flowers. (9) Floral wreaths linking candelabra on a table. (10) A marquee, with shrubs in pots and couples waltzing. (11) A wide-brimmed straw-hat full of flowers.

Some of the above may have been drawn for Mrs. Constance Spry. Nearly all have measurements added for printer's blocks. Nos. 1, 4, and 11 were reproduced in

Georgian Love Songs, 1949 (no. 513), p. 48, frontispiece, and p. 31, respectively.　　*Owner: Laurence Whistler*

576　　**"THE TERRACES"**　*n.d.*
　Pencil, sepia ink, and water-colour.　10 in. × 1 ft. 3¾ in.
　　　　　　　　Unsigned

Regency street in perspective, towards a church resembling All Souls, Langham Place. A William IV gentleman and lady, with two children, in the foreground. Across the sky "The Terraces" in pencil, probably representing a printed title.　　*Owner: Laurence Whistler*

577　　**A MOONLIT GARDEN**　*n.d.*
　　Water-colour.　11¼ in. × 1 ft. 5 in.　*Unsigned*

On the right, a terrace and a Tudor house, with a woman in a white dress standing before the door, looking up at the full moon.　　*Owner: Ronald Fuller*

578　　**A WAR-TIME STREET SCENE**　*n.d.*
　　　　　　　AT NIGHT
　　Water-colour.　1 ft. 1 in. × 10 in.　*Unsigned*

Two soldiers and a girl about to enter a taxi, while a commissionaire shines a torch on the kerb. Possibly to illustrate an article on the First World War.
　　　　　　　　Owner: Laurence Whistler

579 FOUR GEORGIAN DRAWINGS n.d.

Sepia ink and wash.   11 in. × 8¼ in.   Unsigned

On one sheet. (1) A carriage drawn by two horses driving from the right towards a Georgian country house; three small trees to the left. Reproduced in *Georgian Love Songs*, 1949 (no. 513), p. xviii. (2) Two men with long canes, in Conversation: one raising his finger. Reproduced in *Georgian Love Songs*, opp. p. 33.

(3) Male figure in 18th-century costume. A be-wigged figure in knee-length coat, with a sword. Reproduced in *Georgian Love Songs*, opp. p. 112.

(4) Female figure in 18th-century costume. With a fan to her lips, and a handkerchief in her raised left hand. Reproduced in *Georgian Love Songs*, opp. p. 97.

Owner: The London Library

580 A ROYAL PROCESSION n.d.

Sepia ink and wash.   4 in. × 8 in.   Unsigned

King George V and Queen Mary in a carriage drawn by four horses, driving between a double line of Guards, acknowledging a cheering crowd. Possibly for a head- or tail-piece.

Owner: Laurence Whistler

581 A WINTER LANDSCAPE n.d.

Sepia ink and wash.   5 in. × 10 in.   Unsigned

A river winding through fields and distant woods. Below, a top-hatted fox's head, backed by a hunting horn and a crop.

Owner: Laurence Whistler

582 A WREATH, WITH CUPIDS n.d.

Sepia ink and wash.   8¼ in. × 11 in.   Unsigned

The wreath tied at the base with ribbon, a winged cupid to left and right. A space for wording. Reproduced in *Georgian Love Songs*, 1949 (no. 513), p. vii.

Owner: Laurence Whistler

583 A CURTAIN AND CUPIDS

Sepia ink and wash.   11 in. × 8 in.   Unsigned

To the right, a column, draped with a tasselled curtain, to which two cupids cling in alarm, while a third soars to the left of them. Reproduced (repeated in reverse) as the frame to a double page in *The Masque*, nos. 5 and 6 (cat. no. 515).

Owner: Laurence Whistler

From *HANS ANDERSEN*: 'The Marsh King's Daughter'. Cat. no. 475

Bookplates

Where notes of medium and signature are given, the original drawings survive in the possession of those for whom they were made. Printed copies may be seen at the Victoria and Albert Museum, London (a complete set), and at the Public Library, Liverpool. All were reproduced in *The Bookplates of Rex Whistler*, by Laurence Whistler, *The Connoisseur*, Oct. 1959.

584   **FOR RONALD FULLER**   *1925*
Line block. $5\frac{3}{8}$ *in.* × $3\frac{7}{8}$ *in.*

A cowled and cloaked skeleton, holding in the right hand a sword, in the left a pair of scales.—Seated above a shield inscribed "Ronald Fuller" flanked by two cherubs holding a scroll—"Ex Libris". Behind, a faun on the left and "a species of Medusa" on the right. The right-hand cherub bears a staff with a ribbon reading "A.D. 1925. Merton College Oxford". Beyond, a landscape with buildings. On encountering this early work, three years later, the artist wrote: "I almost vomitted [*sic*] when I saw the book-plate & I can't *believe* that I could have done anything *quite* so disgusting—& not so very long ago either!" Pen and Indian ink, 6 in.× $4\frac{1}{2}$ in., signed bottom right in a cipher: "RJW".

585   **FOR THE ARTIST**   *1926*
Half-tone. $4\frac{1}{8}$ *in.* × $3\frac{1}{4}$ *in.*

Two terminal figures, nymph and satyr, their inward hands raised, supporting a central torch, from which wreaths fall to their other hands. Between them "Rex J. Whistler" above a formal sun, inscribed "19—". At the bottom, a lyre, etc. The whole within a decorated border.

Sketches for the above. Pen and Indian ink, $8\frac{1}{2}$ in.× 10 in. Four studies on one sheet, evidently for the adopted design (two involving terminal figures). "Rex Whistler" or "Rex J. Whistler" in the centre space of each, with the year "1926" in the designs.

Two other designs survive. (1) In *Myrtles and Roses*, 1926, a finished drawing, involving two cherubs with spears. (2) In the 1926A Sketch-book. In her Journal for May 31st, 1925, Edith Olivier records the making of an earlier design.

586   **FOR SIR OSBERT SITWELL, Bt.** *1928*
Collotype. $4\frac{1}{2}$ *in.* × $2\frac{7}{8}$ *in.*
(*Plate 71*)

A cartouche formed by a spiral rococo staircase. At the base a dolphin, at the top, in front of a semicircular colonnade, Sir Osbert, seated with quill pen raised. In the centre "Osbert Sitwell". Reproduced in *Rex Whistler*, by Laurence Whistler, 1948, p. 89 (no. 510). Pen and Indian ink, $10\frac{1}{2}$ in.× $7\frac{1}{4}$ in., signed bottom left, *Rex Whistler 1928*. On the reverse, a trophy of arms with a draped cloth reading, "Book-plate for Osbert Sitwell Esq. . . . from Rex Whistler, A.D. MCMXXVIII." Books and an ink-pot below.

Sketches for the above. (1) "Rough sketch for Osbert's book-plate. Dec. 10th 1928." Pen and Indian ink, 9 in.× 7 in., unsigned. Very much as executed. (2) Three variant pencil studies, with features similar to the final design. $8\frac{1}{4}$ in.× 6 in., unsigned. (3) A similar design enclosed in a baroque architectural frame. Brown ink, 5 in.× $4\frac{1}{2}$ in., unsigned.   *Owner: Laurence Whistler*

587   **FOR THE DUCHESS OF**   *1930*
WESTMINSTER
Engraved by Robert Osmund. $3\frac{1}{4}$ *in.* × $2\frac{3}{8}$ *in.*
(*Plate 72*)

A carriage and pair in front of St. James's Palace, within a framework of intertwining leaves and flowers. At the top, two cherubs with trumpets, supporting a coroneted cartouche inscribed: "Loelia Westminster". At the bottom, on a cartouche, "Ex Libris." Sepia ink and water-colour, $8\frac{1}{2}$ in.× $6\frac{1}{2}$ in., signed bottom centre, *Rex Whistler*.

In the upper cartouche, "L from Victor"; in the lower, "February 20th 1930". The view delicately tinted, with a yellow coach. A soft brush drawing, freely translated by the engraver. It was a present from Mr. Victor Cazalet.

588   **FOR JOHN WALLACE, ESQ.**   *1931*
Line block. $3\frac{5}{8}$ *in.* × $2\frac{3}{8}$ *in.*

In an oval shield, backed by flags and weapons, "John Wallace".

589   **FOR KENNETH RAE, ESQ.**   *1931*
Collotype. $3\frac{1}{2}$ *in.* × $2\frac{1}{2}$ *in.*

"Kenneth Rae" inscribed on a rococo cartouche, supported by a spear, a rose, a skull, books, etc. Drawn in return for the loan of ski-ing equipment. Pen and sepia ink, c. $4\frac{1}{2}$ in.× $3\frac{1}{2}$ in., signed bottom right: *Rex Whistler 1931*.

590 **FOR ALFRED DUFF COOPER, ESQ.**
AND LADY DIANA COOPER   *1931*
Engraved by Robert Osmund.   7 *in.* × $5\frac{5}{8}$ *in.* and
$5\frac{5}{8}$ *in.* × $3\frac{7}{8}$ *in.*

A vine-clad rococo cartouche with a flourished "Duff Cooper". At the top, a portrait bust of "Diana", with bow and arrows. Beneath the cartouche, bottles of champagne, rolled documents, and despatch boxes.

591 FOR THE LORD ROTHSCHILD *c. 1931*
Engraved by Robert Osmund. 4¼ in. × 3⅝ in.

A medallion carved with a head and shoulders of "Jonathan Swift". It rests on a pile of books over which falls a scroll reading: "Victor Rothschild".

592 FOR MR. AND MRS. HENRY *1932*
McLAREN (Lord and Lady Aberconway)
Collotype. 4⅛ in. × 3⅜ in. (*Plate 74*)

The interior of a library with a winged cupid to the right, drawing aside the curtain of an arch. Beyond, in a glimpsed garden, is a Neptune fountain with sea-horses. Above the arch, a musical trophy; to left and right, above bookcases, busts with "C" and "H" on their plinths. Below, a rococo cartouche reading "Christabel and Henry McLaren". Pen and sepia ink, 6 in. × 4⅝ in., signed bottom right: *Rex Whistler 1932*.
Owner: Christabel Lady Aberconway
Studies for the above. (1) Sepia ink and wash, 8½ in. × 7 in., unsigned. Much as executed, but with details of cartouche and garden different. (2) Pencil, 9 in. × 7 in., unsigned. Two sketches on one sheet, with features similar to those in the final design. *Owner: Laurence Whistler*

593 FOR DAME ADELAIDE *1933*
LIVINGSTONE
Collotype. 4½ in. × 3 in.

An open window, on the sill of which stands a smoking urn hung with a wreath and flanked with books and flowers. To the left, a tasselled curtain with a view of the sea. Below, a parchment: "Adelaide Livingstone." Symbols of her New England origin (a ship), of her love of flowers, reading and climbing, and of the chase (a horn). Sepia ink and wash with coloured ruled border, 10 in. × 8 in. Signed, bottom right: *Rex Whistler 1933*. Reproduced on the title-page of Geoffrey Handley-Taylor's *John Masefield, O.M., Poet Laureate: a Bibliography and Eighty-First Birthday Tribute* (The Cranbrook Tower Press, London, 1959).

594 FOR PATRICK LAWRENCE, ESQ.
1934
Collotype. 4¾ in. × 3¾ in.

A bust of Minerva and cricket implements above a wreathed cartouche reading: "Terence Patrick Lawrence". To the right, a drawn curtain revealing a glimpse of a cricket match in front of Mr. Lawrence's house.

595 FOR MISS VALENCIA *1936*
LANCASTER
Collotype. 2 in. × 2¾ in.

Within a wreath of leaves and flowers, tied at the bottom with a ribbon, the initials "C.V.L." Sepia ink with coloured

ruled border, 6¾ in. × 7½ in., signed bottom right: *Rex Whistler*. The ruled border, with its green band, was omitted in the reproduction.

596 FOR MRS. BRIAN *1936*
MACARTNEY-FILGATE
Line block. 6 in. × 4 in.

A simple wreath in a ruled border containing the cipher of "MF", and beneath it "Ethel Macartney-Filgate". Sepia ink, and green ink (line in ruled border), 6 in. × 4½ in., unsigned.

597 FOR THE BOOK SOCIETY *1936*
Half-tone. 3⅞ in. × 2½ in.

Within an oval wreath, surmounted by crossed quills and a ribbon reading "The Book Society", the interior of a library, with a man seated at the window in an easy-chair, reading. Below, as if carved on a stone plaque, "Ex Libris". Sepia ink and wash, 6¼ in. × 4½ in., signed bottom centre: *Rex Whistler*.

598 FOR THE HON. MRS. A. E. *1939*
PLEYDELL BOUVERIE
Lithograph in colour. 5¼ in. × 3¾ in.

Cupid in the arms of a naked reclining Venus beneath a tree. A distant landscape. "Audrey Pleydell Bouverie" in the centre, across the sky. Water-colour, 5¼ in. × 3¾ in. Sent by the artist to atone for forgetting a dinner party. Green and blue, with notes of yellow. Inscribed "from Rex, to ingratiate himself (if still possible)".

599 FOR MRS. ROBERT TRITTON *1940*
Engraved by G. T. Friend. 4⅞ in. × 3⅞ in.

A large rococo cartouche containing the name "Elsie Tritton", backed by banners and a flaming torch, and resting on a pedestal; on which is seated to the right a winged cherub. A background of trees. Sepia pen and ink, *c.* 5½ in. × 4½ in., signed bottom right: *Rex Whistler 1940*.

600 FOR WILLOUGHBY NORMAN, *1941*
ESQ.
Engraved by G. T. Friend. 4⅝ in. × 3¾ in. (*Plate 73*)

At the bottom, a rococo cartouche backed by flowers and fruit, and inscribed "Willoughby Norman". To the left a ruined Corinthian arch, and in the distance a domed classical pavilion behind a fountain. Sepia ink and wash, 9½ in. × 7½ in., signed bottom left: *Rex Whistler 1941*.

601 *1940*
In December 1940 the artist made, for Mr. Francis Egerton, a rough sketch of a bookplate—now temporarily mislaid. The printed plate, engraved by another hand, shows the crest: a lion rampant, etc. It does not suggest the artist's manner.

Unused Designs for Bookplates

602 FOR SIR GEORGE SITWELL

(1) *c.* 1930. Ink and wash, 8½ in. × 7 in., unsigned. The crest of a lion on a helmet with rich mantling, and the motto "Ne Cede Malis" on a ribbon, drawn as if carved in relief on stone. At the bottom a pencil note by the artist (probably in 1932): "The first rough sketch made a year or two ago." Reproduced in *Noble Essences*, by Sir Osbert Sitwell (Macmillan, 1950), opposite p. 277.

(2) 1932. Sepia ink and wash, 7 in. × 6 in., signed bottom right: *Rex Whistler 1932*. Finished drawing for the above, with hatched background (no effect of carved stone) and a ruled border by the artist.

Owner: Sir Osbert Sitwell, Bt.

602A FOR THE EARL OF UXBRIDGE *1936*

Sepia ink and wash, 7 in. × 5½ in., signed in margin, bottom right: *for Henry with love from Rex. 1936*. A rococo cartouche containing the family arms, backed by musical instruments, a torch, a pink rose, etc. Below, another cartouche containing "George, Charles, Henry, Victor/Marquis of Anglesey" (the last three words in a subsequent paste-on, by another hand).

Owner: The Marquis of Anglesey

MEMBERSHIP **CARD**. For Stowe School. Cat. no. 604

603 MENU CARD *1928*
Sepia ink and wash. 8 in. × 5½ in. Unsigned

For a farewell dinner to Professor Bernard Ashmole, when ceasing to be head of the British School at Rome, on June 19th. Thick paper, folded. On the front cover an urn under a weeping willow with *Addio* on the pedestal, and lamenting cherubs; the British School to the right, a departing steamer to the left. Left, inside, a broken column. Right, inside, the Bill of Fare written out by the artist: below, a cartouche; above, an urn, etc. On the back cover, luggage, pram, bird-cage, golf-clubs, etc.

Owner: Professor Bernard Ashmole

604 "THE VITRUVIANS" *1929* MEMBERSHIP CARD
Pen and Indian ink. 5½ in. × 4¼ in. Unsigned.
(See page 96)

Cover design: Vitruvius and two cupids with architectural instruments, beneath a cartouche—"The Vitruvians"; Stowe School in the background. Head-piece for interior of folded card, right-hand page, over member's name: a medallion head of Vitruvius.—"The Vitruvians. Being the Stowe School Architectural Society." Rex Whistler was an associate-member of the Society in the spring of 1930. He framed the cover-design himself, and presented it to the School with this inscription on the back of the frame: "To the *Vitruvians* of Stowe from Rex Whistler, Dec. 1929." On the reverse of the drawing is a pencil study for the head-piece. Mislaid. *Owner: Stowe School.*

Owner of the head-piece drawing: Laurence Whistler

605 CHRISTMAS CARD FOR *1929* 601 SQUADRON
As printed: 6¾ in. × 4¾ in.

A winged Britannia holding a shield with a crest and ribbon reading "601 Squadron": a lion at her feet, and a glimpse of an aerodrome beyond. For Sir Philip Sassoon.

Studies for the above, pencil, 7 in. × 4½ in., unsigned. (1) A winged Britannia pointing to the clouds, leaning on a cartouche, inscribed: "R.A.F. 601". Without the lion or aerodrome. On the reverse, four gesturing studies for Britannia. (2) Rough sketch for Britannia with shield.

Owner: Laurence Whistler

606 CHRISTMAS CARD FOR *1929* MESSRS. FABER & FABER
As printed: 9 in. × 6 in.

Between (left) a vase of flowers and (right) a tree, a trophy of arms above a rococo cartouche: "With all good Wishes for Christmas & the New Year from Faber and Faber."

Studies for the above. Pencil, 7 in. × 4½ in., unsigned. Two rococo cartouches, one on each side of paper. The lettering sketched. *Owner: Laurence Whistler*

607 CHRISTMAS CARD FOR *1929* MRS. TOWERS SETTLE
As printed: 7¼ in. × 5¼ in.

Cover: a rococo cartouche supporting a flaming urn: to the left, a female figure; to the right, a man with a guitar. *Inside page:* in decorative border, "To wish you well in 1930 from Mrs. Towers Settle Editor of Vogue." Beneath, a cake on a stand.

608 ENVELOPE FOR NATIONAL *1930* TRUST
As printed: 4 in. × 6 in.

View of a castle beside a lake, with two figures to the right, under trees. Enclosed within oval masonry frame, twined with a ribbon inscribed "Properties of", and below, in a cartouche, "The National Trust". For the front of envelopes. Reproduced in *The National Trust Report 1929–1930.*

Study for the above. Pencil, 8 in. × 10 in., unsigned. Much as executed. *Owner: Laurence Whistler*

609 INVITATION CARD TO THE *1932* LEWIS CARROLL EXHIBITION
As printed: 6 in. × 7½ in.

Figures from the two "Alice" books bordering, to right and left, an invitation to the Lewis Carroll Centenary Exhibition on June 28th at "The Old Court House (J. & E. Bumpus Ltd) 350 Oxford Street W.1".

610 CHRISTMAS CARD FOR *1932* MR. CROOKS RIPLEY
As printed: 6 in. × 7 in.

On the left, part of a church porch, towards which, through the churchyard, a Georgian congregation walks. Distant buildings. Urn and tomb, bottom right. The style strongly suggests an earlier work, used for this occasion.

611 CHRISTMAS CARD FOR *1932* SIR PHILIP SASSOON
As printed: 7 in. × 5½ in.

The plan of Port Lympne, as painted by the artist on the wall of the dining-room. Reproduced with this addition: "P Christmas 1932 S".

612 COVER FOR A DANCE *1933*
PROGRAMME
As printed: 10 in. × 7½ in.

An oval cartouche, with the words: "The League of Nations Union/The International Ball/June 20th/Grosvenor House/MCMXXXIII". Peace at the top blowing a trumpet; War to the right casting away his torch. Background, the countries of the world in a bird's-eye view. The original drawing was auctioned at the Ball.

613 INVITATION CARD TO A *1933*
CHRISTMAS PARTY
As printed: 4 in. × 6 in.

On the back of an invitation to a Christmas party from The Sunshine Home, Shoeburyness, and The Children's Hospital, Ballam St., a decoration of a sea-horse drawing a scallop-shell crowded with children, a dolphin beside it.

614 DANCE PROGRAMME COVER
"Dorchester House, July 3rd, 1934"
As printed: 10 in. × 7½ in.

A classical archway topped by crossed flags and a cartouche, from each side of which depend vertical decorations of flowers and tassells. Reproduced in *Rex Whistler*, by Laurence Whistler, 1948, p. 66.

615 DANCE PROGRAMME COVER
"The Masked Ball at the Austrian Legation,"
Dec. 13th, 1934
As printed: 7½ in. × 6¼ in.

A rococo cartouche backed by a drum, trumpet, etc., in which is a masked woman in a crinoline.

616 RENISHAW *c. 1934*
LETTER-HEADING
Sepia pen and ink.   5 in. × 7½ in.   Signed, bottom right:
Osbert with love from Rex

The house in diminishing perspective to the right, at the end of the curving drive, flanked by trees.

Reproduced as frontispiece to *Two Generations*, by Osbert Sitwell (Macmillan, 1940), and in *Rex Whistler*, by Laurence Whistler, 1948 (no. 510), p. 78.
Owner: Sir Osbert Sitwell

617 CHRISTMAS CARD FOR *1935*
THE PIONEER HEALTH CENTRE
As printed: 5½ in. × 8 in.

A map of the approach to the Centre, with "Hygea" on a cloud, a cupid with a compass, and another cupid holding (left) a scroll of directions: "How to get to the Pioneer Health Centre."

618 DANCE PROGRAMME COVER *1935*
FOR MISS J. HORNE
Red and black inks on white scraper-board.   4¼ in. × 3 in.
Signed, bottom right: R.W.

For the dance given by Lady Horne and Mrs. Ulick Verney at 26 Belgrave Square, on May 21st, for Miss J. Horne. A red trophy of musical instruments, hanging from a black bird, in a black wreath wound with red ribbon. "J" on the drum and in the four corners. On the paper pasted below: "May 21st 1935. Dance." Printed by the Curwen Press for a dance catered for by Messrs. Fortnum and Mason.
Owner: Laurence Whistler

619 ST. VALENTINE'S DAY *1935*
GREETINGS TELEGRAM
As printed: 6½ in. × 8½ in.

A wreath of palms flanked by winged cherubs, from whose hands drop vertical swags containing fruits, a torch, a bow and arrow, etc. In colour.

The first of its kind. Nearly 49,000 were sold on the day. (New designs were made for St. Valentine's Day 1937–9 by other artists.) Shown at the Victoria and Albert Museum's "Exhibition of Modern Commercial Typography", Sept. 1936. Reproduced in *The English Festivals*, by Laurence Whistler, 1947, opp. p. 100.

620 GREETINGS TELEGRAM *1936*
As printed: 6½ in. × 8½ in.

"Post Office Greetings Telegram" in a heavy cartouche, backed by agricultural tools, Pan-pipes, etc., and with two cornucopias from which flowers and fruit pour vertically. In colour. Used between June 29th and Dec. 14th. The printed form conveys little of the delicacy of the original design: sepia ink and water-colour, 8¼ in. × 10 in., unsigned. Annotated—"The official P.O. Crown and 'Post Office' in Roman print—all in the deep rose colour".
Owner: The G.P.O.

621 CHRISTMAS CARD FOR *1936*
PEARN, POLLINGER & HIGHAM Ltd.
As printed: 6¼ in. × 5½ in.

"Best wishes from Pearn Pollinger & Higham Ltd. Christmas 1936." In a rococo cartouche, flanked at the base with books, and topped with crossed quills and a scallop-shell inscribed with a cipher of "PPH".

622 CHRISTMAS CARD FOR *1940*
THE WELSH GUARDS
Sepia ink and wash.   5 in. × 7 in.   Unsigned

For "The Welsh Regiment of Foot Guards". The Royal Arms, between sprays ribboned with the battle honours of the Regiment.
Owner: The Welsh Guards

623 CHRISTMAS CARD FOR *1941*
THE WELSH GUARDS
Indian ink and water-colour.   6 in. × 5 in.
Signed, bottom right: Rex Whistler

Within a border of leaves ribboned with battle honours, the crest of the Regiment backed by flags. Below, guns, ammunition, etc., and a scroll with drawing of a Cruiser Tank.
Owner: The Welsh Guards

624 CHRISTMAS CARD FOR *1943*
THE GUARDS ARMOURED DIVISION
As printed: 7¾ in. × 6¼ in.

A hen-pecked General "under orders", laden with purchases and followed by his fearsome wife "in support", vainly attempting to halt a furious taximan. Surrounded by current military catch-phrases, under the general heading "Standing orders (or 'Nobody Ever Tells Me Anything')". A copy coloured by the artist is in the possession of Terence Young, Esq.

625 DESIGN FOR A LABEL *n.d.*

For Messrs. Faber and Faber. A rococo cartouche, backed by a spray of leaves and lilies, with scrolls reading (above), "Faber & Faber Ltd." and (below), "24 Russell Square. London, WC.". A blueprint of the design exists (with the artist's name and address pencilled in the cartouche), but apparently it was not used.

Original design, pen and Indian ink and white paint, 6 in. × 9 in., signed bottom left: *Rex Whistler*. Converted to his own use: the scroll reading (above), "From Rex Whistler" and (below) "No. 20 Fitzroy St. London, W.I." and white with stars added on the cartouche.

Owner: Laurence Whistler

Special Decorations on Stationery

626 DECORATED INVITATION *1927*
CARD

Water-colour. *4 in. × 5 in.* *Signed:* Rex Whistler
(in frieze of portico)

The printed card for the opening of the Tate Gallery Refreshment Room on Nov. 30th, embellished by the artist with allusions to the buildings and characters in the murals. Inscribed by him: "Miss Jean Turnbull."

Owner: Mrs. Eldridge

From *THE LORD FISH*. Cat. no. 454

Advertisements

(Excluding Posters)

The artist stipulated that his advertisement drawings should not be signed. He made an exception of those few with which he was content to be publicly connected: e.g., the Reversible Faces.

Shell

Owner: Shell-Mex and B.P. Ltd., except where otherwise stated.

627 **"SHELL PETROL IS DIFFERENT" SERIES** *1929*

(1) The Boat Race. Pen and Indian ink, 5¼ in. × 6¼ in., unsigned. Neptune and mermaids in a paddle steamer.
(2) The Royal Academy. Pen and Indian ink, 4½ in. × 6¾ in.
(3) The Cup Final. Pen and Indian ink, 5¼ in. × 6¼ in., unsigned.
(4) The Grand National.
(5) Wimbledon.
(6) Summer Weather. A disconsolate ice-cream man, and crowds sheltering from the rain.
(7) The Election. Pen and Indian ink, 5¼ in. × 6¾ in., unsigned. A deaf old lady in a bath-chair listening to an orator.
(8) Trafalgar Square. Pen and Indian ink, 5½ in. × 7¼ in., unsigned. A whale in the fountain.
(9) A Difference worth Getting up for. Indian ink and wash, 5¼ in. × 6¼ in., unsigned. A man in pyjamas greeting the sunrise.
(10) Two (very different) Dancing Partners. Pen and Indian ink, 5¼ in. × 6¼ in., unsigned.
(11) Unidentified. (?) For this series. Two men standing in the same attitudes, fingering their moustaches: one elegantly top-hatted, the other with his dress-suit in rags.
Owner: no. 8. Mrs. Jack Beddington; the remainder, Shell-Mex and B.P. Ltd.

628 **"THAT'S SHELL—THAT WAS!" SERIES** *1929*

(1) Two gentlemen astonished by the speed of a departing car. Water-colour, 1 ft. × 8½ in., unsigned.
(2) Two men and a dog astonished by a departed car.
(3) Group, including sandwich-man, *ditto*.
(4) Unused design: pencil and Indian ink, *c.* 1 ft. × 9 in., unsigned. Back view of an ice-cream vendor, his head drawn facing both ways, to indicate the speed of a passing car.

629 **THE QUICK START** *1929*

(1a) Pen and Indian ink, 5 in. × 6 in., unsigned. Workmen smiling down from a fence at a little crowded car.
Owner: Mrs. Jack Beddington
(1b) The car vanished, leaving workmen astonished.

1930
(2) "And above all, George, beware of those quick-starting Shells!" Old lady's advice to aged husband.

1930
(3) "Now Albert I'll pretend to be that quick-starting Shell, so 'old tight." Little boy with baby brother in wheeled cart.

630 **QUICK STARTING** *1930*

Pen and Indian ink, 10½ in. × 8 in., unsigned. Two old ladies left in the air by the quick departure of the car in which they were seated. Reproduced in *The English Comic Album*, by Leonard Russell and Nicholas Bentley (Michael Joseph, 1948).

? 1930

Sepia ink and wash, 1 ft. 2 in. × 10 in., unsigned. A petrol pump as a mother, with an armful of five infant pumps, each labelled, "Economy", "M.P.G.", etc. She looks fondly at the sixth who is running away, labelled "Quick Starting". Also a sheet, 3¾ in. × 3½ in., to superimpose, with the mother-pump as two-way-facing. "Personally to me there seems no point in the *two* heads for this picture." A very similar drawing was made for Shell by J. S. Goodall, in 1935, but without the run-away pump.

631 **"YOU CAN BE SURE OF SHELL!"** *1930*

Pen and Indian ink, 1 ft. 1½ in. × 9½ in., unsigned. Text with mixed metaphors, illustrated in a border all round. "We may not be sure of our metaphors, but you can be sure of Shell."

632 **SHELL OIL** *1930*

Pen and Indian ink, 1 ft. ½ in. × 8¾ in., signed bottom centre: *Rex Whistler*. Border all round and very elaborate flourishing to printed lettering by another hand, cut out and arranged by the artist.

1930

Mock-Tenniel head-pieces to parodies of *You are old, Father William*, each with different verses, no. 3 in French.

(1) Pen and Indian ink, *c.* 5 in. × 6½ in., unsigned. Father William seated, holding a can of Shell oil: the boy leaning on the table.

(2) Pen and Indian ink, *c.* 5 in. × 6½ in., unsigned. Father William standing: the boy enveloped in exhaust smoke (from bad oil).

(3) *Tu es vieux, père Guillaume.*

1931

Pen and Indian ink, 6¾ in. × 10 in., unsigned. An elegant lady, pouring out for a gentleman, from an oil-can. To a parody of Hood's poem, *I remember, I remember*. Reproduced in *The English Comic Album*, by Leonard Russell and Nicholas Bentley (Michael Joseph, 1948).

Owner: Mrs. Jack Beddington

633   **REVERSIBLE FACES** *1931–1932*

When these drawings were published in *¡OHO!* with rhymes by Laurence Whistler, 1946 (no. 507), all but one were redrawn from printed advertisements, original drawings, or sketches. Eight of the originals have since come to light, together with three unused originals, average size 10 in. × 7 in. (The *¡OHO!* names are given in brackets.)

(1) Midshipman X Admiral (Midshipman X Commodore). Signed: *Rex ɹǝʅʇsıɥM*.

(2) Age X Youth (ditto). Signed as in no. (1).

★(3) (Patrolman X Policeman). Unsigned.

★(4) (Headmaster X Chauffeur). Unsigned.

(5) (Doris X Bert). Unsigned.

★(6) (Tripper X Taximan). Signed as in no. (1).

(7) Nobleman X his Duchess (Lord Littleray X Lady Cardigan). Unsigned.

(8) Bookmaker X Backer (Mrs. Habakkuk X Ernie). Signed as in no. (1).

★(9) (Mad Wife X Farmer). Sepia ink and water-colour. Unsigned.

★(10) (Manchild X Old Man). Signed as in no. (1).

(11) Two Motorists (Troubled Pilot X Happy Pilot). Unsigned.

★(12) (Intellectual X Pugilist). Water-colour. Unsigned.

(13) Mayor X Mayoress (Madame Mayor X Mr Mayor). Signed as in no. (1).

(14) Householder X Fireman (Ditto). Unsigned.

(15) Patient X Nurse (Ditto). Signed as in no. (1).

★ Owner of six originals so marked, Indian ink wash (except where otherwise stated), average size, 9½ in. × 7 in.: *Laurence Whistler*.

Three Reversible Faces Unused

Sepia ink and wash.   *Average size 1 ft. × 7½ in.*

Unsigned

(16) Learned Counsel X Defendant. Unsigned. Very similar to no. (7).

(17) Sailor X Nursemaid. Unsigned. Full-face, one eye winking: flapping collar X cap.

(18) Scotsman X Donkey. Unsigned. Profile. Huge moustache X donkey's ears.

1931

Reversible Face Unused. Pencil and water-colour, 9¼ in. × 7 in., signed: *Rex Whistler, Nov 15, 1931*. ? Darby X Joan. Smiling old man X woman, in profile, with red cap X scarf. *Owner: Laurence Whistler*

16 Sketches for Reversible Faces. Pencil and Indian ink or sepia ink wash, on small pieces of paper, including one envelope postmarked, Sept. 25th, 1931. Studies for the printed faces, with others. *Owner: Laurence Whistler*

634   **ARCHITECTURAL SUBJECTS** *1933*
                 FOR SHELL

Possibly for use in the serious weeklies.   *(Plate 78)*

(1) "The Gray Memorial at Stoke Poges." Sepia ink and wash, 1 ft. 1½ in. × 10 in. Signed bottom right: *Rex Whistler*. Perspective view of the monument with a seated male figure reading aloud to a reclining female. *Owner: Mrs. Jack Beddington*

(2) "Temple Bar." Sepia ink and wash, heightened with white, 7 in. × 7 in. Unsigned. The arch in perspective, seen in shadow, with sunlight passing through from behind: heightened with white where the light strikes up from below on projections. A tree and a rustic to the left. *Owner: Laurence Whistler*

(3) The interior of a classical chapel: two figures looking at a great 18th-century tomb; an old man sweeping.

635   **MISCELLANEOUS**   *1934*

Indian ink and red ink, 9 in. × 7 in., unsigned. A Shell petrol pump saluting, and holding up the nozzle. Probably unused.

1934

Indian ink, 9 in. × 6½ in., unsigned. "Bees in the Bonnet" —"But Shell in the Tank." A cross-eyed lunatic in a veteran car escaping at speed from an asylum. Unused.

1934

Indian ink, *c.* 1 ft. × 8 in., unsigned. A bust of John Stuart Mill resting on four volumes: one, "Mill on Liberty".

? 1934

Four drawings, Indian ink and wash, 1 ft. ½ in. × 9 in., unsigned. Each a border to a missing text, evidently based on a catch-phrase. (1) ? Watch Your Step: a man about to walk into a man-hole. (2) ? Toad-in-the-Hole. (3) Fly in the Ointment. (4) Cat on Hot Bricks. The four are mounted on black paper in book-form. Unused.

? 1935

Summer Shell. Sepia ink and wash, 9½ in. × 7¼ in., signed bottom right: *R.W.* A mock Maypole Dance round a petrol pump. *Owner: Laurence Whistler*

? 1935

Winter Shell. A take-off of a child's barometer. "Miss Summer" yawning inside the little house, holding a notice

"Summer Shell". "Mr. Winter" cheerfully advanced, holding the nozzle at the ready, and a notice, "Winter Shell".

In 1935, J. S. Goodall made several drawings for Shell in a similar style, showing petrol pumps with faces.
See also Posters: The Vale of Aylesbury (no. 656).

B.P. Ethyl

636 "I AM A PLAIN . . ." SERIES *1933*
Sepia ink and wash.   Unsigned
(1) "I am a Plain Games-Mistress, 5 in. × 5 in.
(2) "..........Intellectual Woman", 8 in. × 6½ in.
(3) "..........Stockbroker", 4 in. × 3½ in.
(4) "..........Pugilist", 9 in. × 7 in.
(5) "..........Wife", 6½ in. × 5¼ in.
(6) "..........Housemaster", 9 in. × 7 in.
(7) "..........Man", 4¾ in. × 3¾ in.
(8) "..........Subaltern", 5 in. × 3¾ in.
(9) "..........Doctor", 10 in. × 7 in.
(10) "..........Society Beauty", 5 in. × 5 in.
(11) "..........Connoisseur", 10 in. × 7 in.
(12) "..........Lady Golfer", 9 in. × 7 in.
(13) "..........Globe-trotter", 9 in. × 7 in.
(14) "..........Cook", 9 in. × 7 in.

Unused
(15) "I am a Plain Chauffeur", 9 in. × 7 in.
(16) "..........Puritan", 9 in. × 7 in.
(17) "..........Bandmaster", 5 in. × 4 in.
(18) "..........Gangster", 9 in. × 7 in.
(19) "..........Pessimist", 9 in. × 7 in.
(20) "..........Punter", 10 in. × 7 in.
(21) "..........Person of Private Means", 9 in. × 7 in.
(22) "..........? Colonel", 4½ in. × 3½ in.
(23) "..........Undertaker" (proof only examined).
(24) "..........Bridge-Player", 7 in. × 7 in.

Also a pencil sketch for no. 24: "Is this your idea of a Bridge-player? I haven't gone further with it until I know if this is on the right lines. R.W."

(25) "I am a Plain Ad. Man". Water-colour, 8½ in. × 6½ in. unsigned. Printed in monochrome as a private joke, with a caricature of the late Mr. Jack Beddington, who arranged the series, holding a telephone to his left ear.
Owner: Mrs. Jack Beddington

"I AM A PLAIN . . ." SERIES: MINIATURE DRAWINGS

Indian ink, unsigned. Several were included in the text of each advertisement, showing comic figures, faces, cars, etc. They were drawn four or five to a sheet, and some so remain. Most have been cut out individually on fragments of paper, *c.* 1 in. × 1 in.; and most, but not all, of these have subsequently been mounted in appropriate sets. 16 sheets survive, average size 9 in. × 8 in.; and 9 cut-out miniatures.

637 "THE ORDINARY MOTORIST" *1933*
—"AND HIS GIRL-FRIEND"
Three drawings.   Sepia ink and wash.   c. 9 in. × 7 in.
Unsigned

Head and shoulders. Two are alternatives for the girl in a beret: one full-face, one facing half-right.

Simpkin Marshall Ltd.

638   "THE BEST BOOKS OF THE SEASON"   1932
9¾ in. × 7½ in.
Cover only, frame in brown, and landscape in green.

Fortnum and Mason

639   CHRISTMAS *1932-1936*
CATALOGUES
Covers only: for the five years indicated (the inside decorations being by Hendy). Sketches for 1934 and 1935, sepia ink and water-colour, *c.* 8½ in. × 6¼ in., unsigned.
Owner: Laurence Whistler
(The inside decorations of the 1937 Christmas Catalogue, like those of Coronation Commentary and Special Hampers for the Coronation, both of 1937, are in a style closely imitating the artist's, and are thought to have been by Kendal.)

640   STORES FOR SCOTLAND *1936*
8 in. × 4 in. Cover and four double-spreads in black and red.

641   "ENTERTAINING MADE *1935-*
EASY" SERIES *1936*
7½ in. × 4½ in.
(1) Apr. 1935. Cover design and 6 vignettes, all in colour.
(2) Sept. 1935. Cover design and 5 vignettes, all in colour.
(3) Apr. 1936. Cover design and 5 vignettes, all in colour.

Imperial Airways

642   TWO LEAFLETS   1934

Decoration and lettering of cover in black and red.

(1) "Week-end Services: London & Le Touquet." 8¾ in. × 4 in.

(2) "Comfort and convenience." 5½ in. × 3½ in.

643   CORONATION DESIGN FOR   1937 IMPERIAL AIRWAYS LTD.

Sepia ink and water-colour.   1 ft. ½ in. × 9 in.
Unsigned

Sketch. A slender draped archway topped with the Royal Standard: to contain the wording (sketched in pencil). Out of the base of it, cavalry march through troop-lined crowds. Aeroplanes fly above.   *Owner: Laurence Whistler*

Arthur Guinness, Son & Co. Ltd.

644   SONGS OF OUR GRAND-   1936 FATHERS RE-SET IN GUINNESS TIME

9½ in. × 6 in.

A humorous booklet containing parodies of traditional songs, with a cover and 24 decorations, all in colour. Some of these decorations were enlarged to be used as separate advertisements. Indian ink and water-colour. The cover signed, bottom centre: *Rex Whistler*.
Owner: Arthur Guinness, Son & Co. Ltd.

645   THE 88th BOAT-RACE   1936

"Have a Guinness on the stroke of Eight!" Pen and Indian ink, 9 in. × 1 ft. 6 in., unsigned.
Owner: Arthur Guinness, Son & Co. Ltd.

646   "I PASSED BY YOUR   1937 WINDOW . . ."

Two decorations to comic verse. Indian ink and wash, unsigned.   *Owner: Arthur Guinness, Son & Co. Ltd.*

647   "SUPPER FOR MR. DISRAELI"   1937

Illustrated quotation from a letter of Disraeli's, 1837. Water-colour, 5½ in. × 5¼ in., signed bottom right: *Rex Whistler*.   *Owner: Arthur Guinness, Son & Co. Ltd.*

Souvenir Booklet

648   "THE ASSEMBLY ROOMS,   1938 BATH," SOUVENIR BOOKLET

October 19th

9 in. × 7 in.

Cover only. Cherubs right and left of a coat of arms, holding back curtains above a rococo cartouche, flanked by candelabra. In a smaller cartouche below, a ballroom scene. Reproduced in *The Masque*, no. 7.
Owner: The Mayor and Corporation of Bath

Wiggins, Teape, & Alex Pirie (Sales) Ltd.

649   CALENDAR   1939

Commissioned in 1939, the 12 oil paintings were produced as a large-scale Calendar, published from Apr., 1940–41. Size as printed: 1 ft. 2½ in. × 11 in. No. 10 was printed as a Christmas card of the Welsh Guards, 1955.

Oil on canvas.   1 ft. 6 in. × 1 ft. 1¾ in.   Unsigned

Original Designs:

1. *April:* Young shepherd and shepherdess by a stream.
2. *May:* Old man fishing with a boy; inn beyond bridge.
3. *June:* Young mother with two children under a garden statue.
4. *July:* Fat Nanny picknicking with three children.
5. *August:* Young mother, naked, with two children by a pool.
6. *September:* Two harvesters eating and drinking, with a boy.
7. *October:* Man and boy by a twilight fire, with a caravan.
8. *November:* A meet at the King's Head.
9. *December:* Father Christmas arrives with the Christmas tree.
10. *January:* Skating party with a sledge on a country house lake.
11. *February:* Tea-time: a young man at his fireside.
12. *March:* A gale in Salisbury High Street. In the distance the archway to the Close and the Cathedral spire.

Nos. 4, 6, and 7 are badly damaged.
Owner: Laurence Whistler

650

In 1940 Messrs. Rothmans of Pall Mall, London, began to commission drawings from the artist as a policy of keeping their name before the public until the normal market should be restored. The following 29 unsigned drawings in pen and Indian ink are in the possession of Messrs. Rothmans.

1. 10 in. × 7 in.: A musical evening. 2. 8 in. × 8½ in.: "Officer's Notice Board Scene". 3.★ 11 in. × 10 in.: A lady and gentleman recognizing a friend in a hansom cab. 4. 1 ft. × 10 in.: Headmaster catching a boy smoking in an easy-chair. 5. 8 in. × 6 in.: Sportsman in tobacconist's shop showing his top-hatted friend how he shoots. 6. 10 in. × 7 in.: Elegant 19th-century figures strolling past the Duke of York's column. 7.★ 10 in. × 8 in.: A hansom stands opposite "Rothmans Five Pall Mall", while two top-hatted gentlemen pass by. 8. 8½ in. × 8 in.: 18th-century sailor and shipmaster on a quay, with masts visible behind. 9. 10 in. × 7 in.: A man smoking a pipe at a book-strewn table; a youth in uniform beside him. 10. 1 ft. × 10 in.: A bishop and his wife glance furiously at two smokers. 11.★ 11 in. × 9½ in.: A mother surprises her daughter in the act of accepting a cigarette from her young man. Later given the title: "Caught in the Act 1900". 12.★ 11 in. × 9½ in.: Two men in top hats, one with an eye-glass, standing under street lamps. 13. 10 in. × 7 in.: Mechanical Smoking—a gentleman using a primitive lighter for his cigar to the astonishment of his companion. 14. 10 in. × 7 in.: Sherlock Holmes and Dr. Watson. 15. 10 in. × 7 in.: Romantic smokers—apparently on the Stage. 16. 10 in. × 7 in.: Young man addressing mounted lady in Rotten Row. 17. Period 1900. Cigarette holder scandal. 18.★ 9 in. × 8 in.: Elderly gentleman in smoking cap piercing his cigar. 19. 1 ft. 2 in. × 10 in.: A Colonel and subaltern entering Rothmans, a boy behind with news-placard: "Kitchener Wants You!" 20. 9 in. × 7½ in.: Young hopeful—a schoolboy buying cigars. 21. 9 in. × 6½ in.: Early Victorian dandies taking snuff. 22. 10½ in. × 8½ in.: Top-hatted gentleman buying cigars in a tobacconist's. 23. 10 in. × 7 in.: A 1914 subaltern talking to his father at the fireside. 24. 10 in. × 7 in.: Pleasant journey! —overdressed gentleman with cigar about to board a train. 25. 10 in. × 8¼ in.: Smoke of battle, Crimean officers by a tent watching the smoker of a paper cigar. 26. 9 in. × 6½ in.: Two ladies with muffs in a 1900 motor-car, while the chauffeur stands by, smoking. 27. 9 in. × 7 in.: A man singing on a music-hall stage, while the audience wave tankards and cigars. 28. 10 in. × 7 in.: In the theatre. The villain twirls his moustache, the hero points to the door, the heroine swoons. 29.★ 9 in. × 1 ft.: Rothmans' van stands by the kerb, while a lady and gentleman recognize an old gentleman bowing from a hansom beyond.

★ Issued in 1950 for the Diamond Jubilee of Messrs. Rothmans, in a portfolio, with colouring not proposed by the artist.

Some of J. S. Goodall's drawings for Rothmans are in a similar style.

From *THE LORD FISH*. Cat. no. 454

Posters

(See also under Plays)

---

651   TWO REVOLUTIONARY   *1926*

"Drew all day at the 2 posters for Countess Rubra . . . to stick on the walls of a scene in a film she is helping to produce. They had to be very 'revolutionary in sentiment' and bold black and white to photograph well." Diary for Mar. 17th.

SKETCH FOR THE ABOVE   *1926*
Charcoal.   6¾ in. × 5 in.   Unsigned

A Bolshevik kneeling as a pavement artist, holding out a hand for a bag marked "£", a knife in the other hand behind his back. "Famine" and "Bloodshed" are propped against the wall, and "All my own work" is written on the pavement. (Two days before, the artist had drawn pavement pictures in coloured chalks outside the entrance to the Slade School, to surprise the students coming out. "Collected quite a sum for the Slade Centenary fund!" he recorded.)   *Owner: Archie Balfour, Esq.*

652   THE LONDON MUSEUM   *1928*

A brightly-coloured poster of Britannia in a yellow and black hansom cab with Union Jack wheels, driven by the Lion and drawn by the Unicorn. Above a cartouche, supported by comic cherubs: "Britannia visits the London Museum."

A policeman doffs his helmet to her, and various statues, including Nelson on his column and Charles I on his horse, bow from a distance. A cherub in the foreground offers her a Guide to the London Museum. In the background St. Martin-in-the-Fields and St. Paul's Cathedral.

Copies in the British Museum and the Victoria and Albert Museum. A sketch for this poster was exhibited at the Imperial Institute, Mar. 1931.

653   THE TATE GALLERY   *c. 1928*

A humorous reflection of the artist's own murals in the Restaurant (no. 2). Two elderly ladies up from the country are having tea, with umbrella, parcel and Tate Gallery Catalogue, unaware that the distinction between painted wall and actual floor has disappeared and the characters in the mural are close behind them, trying to attract their attention. Cupid's bicycle is reflected in the parquet floor, the snake is sliding out into the room. If dimly aware, the ladies show only distaste. Copies are in the British Museum and the Victoria and Albert Museum.

SKETCH FOR THE ABOVE   *1928*
Water-colour.   1 ft. 6 in. × 1 ft. ½ in.   Unsigned

The two ladies taking tea, bored, and unaware that the huge right-hand glutton of the Entrance Arch is humorously observing them. No attempt, here, to blend the two planes of illusion.

On the reverse, a pencil sketch of the poster as executed.
Owner: Laurence Whistler

EARLY SKETCH FOR THE ABOVE   *1928*
Water-colour.   10½ in. × 6¾ in.   Unsigned

Possibly the initial idea, on a page of the 1928 Rome Sketch-book (no. 296). To the right, a parson and his wife at a tea-table, surprised by the unicorn of the murals advancing towards them, reined-in by a figure. Below and on the opposite page, pencil sketches for the poster, all embodying the notion of characters emerging from the mural.   *Owner: Laurence Whistler*

654   THE FOUR GEORGES   *1930*
EXHIBITION
(Feb. 23rd–Mar. 30th, 1931)

A cartouche backed by flags, with this wording: "In aid of the Royal Northern Hospital/The Four Georges Loan Exhibition/of pictures (Gainsborough, Reynolds etc)/and Furniture etc: of these 4 Reigns./Open Daily 11 till 7/ Sundays included/Open Feb. 23rd until Mar. 30th/Admission 5/– at 25 Park Lane." In the corners four coins with profile portraits of the four Georges. Indian and sepia ink and water-colour, 2 ft. 5 in. × 1 ft. 6 in., signed, bottom right: *Rex Whistler 1930*. Raffled for the benefit of the Royal Northern Hospital Fund at the Exhibition at Sir Philip Sassoon's house, 25 Park Lane, and won by E. Assheton-Bennett, Esq.

2 studies for the above, pencil, 7 in. × 4½ in., unsigned. (1) Indication of the cartouche, flags and medals: without wording. (2) Sketches of the four Georges. On a sheet of writing paper, 29 Bury St., S.W.1.
Owner: Laurence Whistler

655   THE AGE OF WALNUT   *1932*

For an Exhibition of art treasures in aid of the Royal Northern Hospital, 25 Park Lane, London.

King William and Queen Mary sitting crowned, with interlinked arms, under a domed canopy surmounted by ostrich feathers, on either side of which a cupid blows a trumpet with attached banners: "King William" and "Queen Mary." In the space on either side of the canopy are the words: "The Age of Walnut. 1660–1714"; in a scroll to right and left of the royal pair: "In aid of the Royal/Northern Hospital". Below them a large cartouche which reads: "Loan Exhibition/of Furniture, Pictures, Silver, etc./Daily 11 till 7/(Sundays included)/Open Feb 23rd./until Apl. 4th./Admission Five Shillings". In a small acanthus device beneath, "25 Park Lane".

The design was also used for the cover of the Catalogue of the Exhibition, identical except that the words on either side of the canopy and in the scroll are omitted, and the cartouche reads simply: "Loan Exhibition. The Age of Walnut." Sepia ink and water-colour, 1 ft. 2 in. × 9 in., signed bottom right: *Rex Whistler 1932*.

Owner: Major D. James

A copy is in the Victoria and Albert Museum, London.

SKETCH FOR THE ABOVE
Pencil.   8 in. × 5 in.   Unsigned

Very much as finally carried out, but with minor differences in the wording of the cartouche. On a sheet of writing-paper bearing the address: "25 Park Lane, W."

Owner: Laurence Whistler

656   **THE VALE OF AYLESBURY**   *1932*
Oil on canvas.   1 ft. 10 in. × 3 ft. 2 in.
Signed, bottom right: Rex Whistler

The view is from the top of the field in the grounds of the artist's home, Bolebec House, Whitchurch, Bucks. Across the valley are the roofs and church tower of Aylesbury, with the Chiltern Hills beyond. Seated under the tree in the right foreground is the artist's brother, Laurence. Painted for Shell-Mex and reproduced as a poster with the above title, also as a Christmas card.

A copy of the poster is in the Victoria and Albert Museum, London.   *Owner: Shell-Mex and B.P. Ltd.*

657   **EXHIBITION OF ENGLISH**   *1934*
WOMEN'S CLOTHING IN THE 19th
CENTURY (In Aid of the Pioneer Health Centre)
May 25th–June 18th.   15 Portman Sq., W.1

In the centre a circular wreath of roses and columbines enclosing a picture of two ladies at a dressing-table. Copies of the poster are in the Witt Library, The Courtauld Institute, and in the Bethnal Green Museum.

From *THE LORD FISH*. Cat. no. 454

Jeux d'Esprit

658   **THREE LEAVES FROM A**   *c. 1932*
SKETCH-BOOK

Pencil. $10\frac{1}{2}$ in. × $8\frac{1}{4}$ in.   *Unsigned*

A letter pasted on to the back of the frame of no. 2 describes how, on a wet afternoon at Wilsford, the artist amused his fellow guests with rapid sketches, showing them impersonating the characters in famous pictures—*The Boyhood of Raleigh, Primavera,* etc. Most do not appear to be direct caricatures, but to have been made, possibly, in connection with charades.

(1) On the front 4 sketches; on the reverse 6 sketches.
(2) 5 sketches.
(3) On the front and back, caricatures of Mrs. Sacheverell Sitwell, Mr. Cecil Beaton, and Mr. Brian Howard, etc.

Owner: Christabel Lady Aberconway

659   **CIRCUS BEDROOM AT**   *? c. 1934*
ASHCOMBE

Oil on wall-surface.   *c. 6 ft.* × *2 ft. 6 in.*   *Unsigned*

Several artists contributed to the decoration of this bedroom. Rex Whistler painted a Fat Woman with right arm raised and left foot on a little stool. Painted over by a subsequent occupier. (Photograph in *Ashcombe,* by Cecil Beaton (no. 512), opp. p. 52.) He also designed the "circus bed" (*Ashcombe,* p. 48; photographs opp. p. 45). It was carried out by Savage's, the Roundabout-makers of King's Lynn.

660   **ORGY TO MUSIC ON THE**   *c. 1935*
THAMES

Indian ink and wash. $8\frac{1}{2}$ in. × $9\frac{1}{2}$ in.   *Unsigned*

A high-prowed boat with figure-head and single sail, full of drunken merry-makers, and musicians in the stern. Air-borne cherubs. Floating bottles, etc. Drawn for a Charity party on the Thames, organized by Lady Mary Dunn.   *Owner: Mrs. Jeremy Sandford*

661   **TWO PAVEMENT**   *c. 1935*
DRAWINGS

Chalk on cardboard.   *2 ft. 1 in.* × *1 ft. 2 in.*   *Unsigned*

(1) "Happy and Glorious." A caricature of King George V, passed off as typical work of the pavement. Head and shoulders, facing right, in lurid mauve, pink, and green.
(2) "Still Life." A classical bust, in white chalk, facing left.

These, and other drawings on the pavement itself, one day appeared outside the lodgings of Lady Caroline Paget and Mr. David Parsons, in Wellington Square, Oxford. They were satisfactorily taken in by the unshaven and seedy artist sitting cross-legged beside them, who begged them to spare a copper for a poor man. Two at least were purchased.   *Owner: David Parsons, Esq.*

662   **BIRTHDAY SCROLL FOR**   *1936*
MRS. SACHEVERELL SITWELL

Water-colour on vellum.   *Approx. 1 ft. 5 in.* × *1 ft.*

Signed: Rex

In a head-piece the Eye of God beams down on Good Samaritan and victim. Below is an inscription perhaps partly composed by the artist: "Whereas Mrs Sacheverell Sitwell has this day, the Eighth of July in the Year of Our Lord, nineteen hundred and thirty-six, attained the Thirtieth Anniversary of her Birthday, We, the undersigned, representative body of loyal Friends in divers walks of life, beg humbly to congratulate her.

"Inasmuch as she has by her PIETY and VIRTUE endeared herself to them, the aforesaid loyal friends hereby express the hope that she may long continue to be a COMFORT to them in adversity—but more often in prosperity—and a prop to them in their declining years.

Signed by: Osbert Sitwell, Edith Sitwell, Cecil Beaton, Christabel Aberconway, Loelia Westminster, David Horner, Rex."

(The artist's first use of vellum was at Haileybury in 1920, when, at the age of 15, he inscribed a scroll presented to the returning hero, Field-Marshal Lord Allenby. He was then alarmed because each of the pieces provided—two, in case of accident—cost 10s. 6d.)

Owner: Mrs. Sacheverell Sitwell

663   **POLITICAL CARTOON**   *? 1939*

? Water-colour.   *c. 13 ft. 6 in.* × *7 ft. 6 in.*

Winston Churchill and Duff Cooper snowballing Neville Chamberlain, whose umbrella has turned inside out. Statues of the raped countries of Europe in perspective, under a dark sky. Hitler, Sir Thomas Beecham, and Lady Cunard were also apparently shown: probably Goering and Goebbels. Drawn for Charity, and bought by Sir Adrian Baillie. (Description supplied.) Lost in transit, *c. 1946.*   *Owner: Lady Baillie*

664   **PRECONCEPTION OF AN**   *1941*
EPIDIASCOPE

Black ink and red chalk.   *7 in.* × $4\frac{1}{2}$ in.   *Unsigned.*

(*See page 108*)

On first hearing of this apparatus, while training with the Guards Armoured Division, the artist assumed it to be a self-propelled, tracked vehicle for measuring bishops. Apparatus in black: bishop, erect, in red.

Owner: Richard Sawrey-Cookson, Esq.

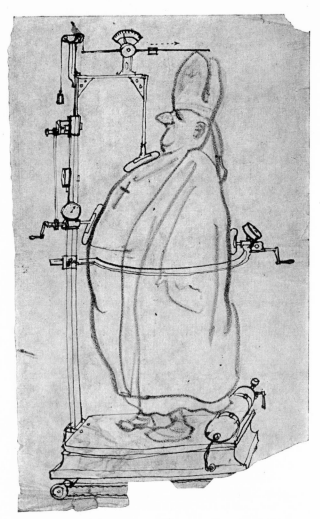

PRECONCEPTION OF AN EPIDIASCOPE. Cat. no. 664

decorated the rooms occupied by his fellow-officers or men. Most of these *jeux d'esprit* were obliterated by later occupants, but *thirteen* paintings, which appeared to hang from silk cords, in gold frames, round the walls of the ante-room at Codford, were rescued and are now at Regimental Headquarters, Wellington Barracks. They are only a residue; for Richard Whiskard wrote, in a letter of May 10th, of "a most realistic fish in a glass case, a very fine Holbein of Henry VIII", and of other "Old Masters", now lost.

(1) 8½ in. × 10¾ in. Night raid on London. Searchlights beyond a railway signal and a gasometer outlined against the sky.

(2) 8½ in. × 10¾ in. A skull, a bone, a rose.

(3) 10½ in. × 1 ft. 4 in. A Georgian prize-fight in a ring outside an inn.

(4) 1 ft. 4½ in. × 1 ft. 11 in. A Poussin. A shepherdess dancing to a piping shepherd near a ruined arch. A reminiscence of one of the *trompe l'œil* engravings at 90 Gower St. (no. 8).

(5) 11½ in. × 9¼ in. Perspective of a curving French street. Unfinished.

(6) 1 ft. 11 in. × 1 ft. 4½ in. A Titian. A sleeping Venus with right arm above head, and a bowl of fruit.

(7) 1 ft. 4½ in. × 1 ft. 11 in. A Titian. A Bacchanalia, with two flying cupids, top right.

(8) 1 ft. 10 in. × 1 ft. 3 in. A regimental portrait. A crimson-faced elderly Blimp, half-length, in full-dress uniform with medals.

(9) 1 ft. 3 in. × 1 ft. 10 in. Still Life. A tray of drinks and a loaf of bread on a table. Head of the same officer flush with the table-cloth, eyeing the drinks.

(10) 1 ft. 10 in. × 1 ft. 3 in. A flower-piece, clutched by the hands of the same officer—whose face appears within it, enraged by a butterfly perching on his forehead.

(11) 11½ in. × 9¼ in. A pastoral. A shepherd and shepherdess beneath a tree.

(12) 10¼ in. × 1 ft. A romantic landscape. A rock with a ruined castle. To the left a balloon.

(13) 1 ft. 1 in. × 1 ft. 4½ in. Surrealist landscape, after Dali. A tilted rock, supporting, half-way up, a grand piano. The whole is twined with a serpent, one end of which flies the Union Jack, while the other issues from an ant-covered face, half-buried in the sand. Three crooked water-taps in the desert. In the distance a burning tank—in allusion to the war in the desert. Painted in answer to a challenge. But in the new moon which is also a golf-ball, and in the pince-nez, etc., the artist could not resist those natural touches of humour which are fatal to the solemnity of Surrealism.

Owner: The Welsh Guards

---

665   **"BACCHUS AND ARIADNE**   *? 1941*
          AFTER TITIAN"

Blue ink.   7 in. × 8¾ in.   *Unsigned.*   (*See page* xxiv)
Bacchus and Ariadne leaping from the chariot in pursuit of the horrified painter, who drops his brushes and makes off.   *Owner: Richard Sawrey-Cookson, Esq.*

666   **DRAWING IN AN ALBUM**   *1941*
     Sepia ink and water-colour.   10 in. × 10 in.
       Signed, bottom right: Rex Whistler

Drawn for Mrs. V. M. G. Cripps on the page recording the visit of her Mobile Cinema. "4th Dec. Visit to 2nd Armoured Battalion, Welsh Guards, Codford." A struggling mass of soldiers fighting their way across a street and in at a door. "*Not* an invasion scare—only the Battalion rather keen to get into the Queensbury Cripps Cinema in the wool store." See also no. 668.

Owner: The Hon. Mrs. V. M. G. Cripps

667   **PAINTINGS FOR THE**   *1942*
   2nd BN. THE WELSH GUARDS
        Oil on boarding.   *Unsigned*

Wherever the artist was stationed with his regiment he

668   **DRAWING IN AN ALBUM**   *1942*
     Sepia ink and water-colour.   10 in. × 10 in.
       Signed on rim of plate: Rex Whistler

Drawn on the page recording the second visit of Mrs. Cripps's Mobile Cinema: to Fonthill Giffard, Wilts. The face of a Welsh Guardsman, with enormous grinning mouth containing the words: "With very many thanks for yet another delightful performance, from the 2nd

Bn. Welsh Guards who are *hungry for more*". The guardsman holds knife and fork at the ready, and is backed by other regimental grotesques. See also no. 666.

Owner: The Hon. Mrs. V. M. G. Cripps

669 BEFORE-AND-AFTER DRAWINGS *c. 1942*

Sepia ink and wash.   Approx. 10 in. × 1 ft. 1 in.
Unsigned.   (Plates 89 and 90)

Proposals for improving the comfort of the Welsh Guards 2nd Bn. Officers' Mess at Codford St. Mary, Wilts.

(1) The Dining-Room as it was: a scene of hideous discomfort with tables too narrow ("resulting in knee-trouble") blazing top lights which dazzled the diners, and mess-waiters falling over one another, etc.

(2) As it might be: with wider tables and table-lights. Soft illumination, "Service with a Smile", great comfort, "better conversation".

(3) The Ante-Room as it was: unspeakable discomfort from top lights, and tables too small: causing contortions in officers reading, playing games, etc.

(4) As it might be: side-lights, more tables, palpable ease and luxury.   *Owner: The Welsh Guards*

670 A TROMPE L'ŒIL IN A BLIND *1943* WINDOW Pakenham Vicarage, Suffolk

Oil on wall surface.   Unsigned

Painted when the 2nd Bn. the Welsh Guards was stationed at Thetford, and the artist was visiting friends in this Vicarage, the Rev. and Mrs. M. S. Douglas. He noticed a blank upper window facing the drive and proposed to paint in it the head of an 18th-century parson, as if in the room. Ladders were erected, the white glazing bars were painted out, and he completed the picture in about an hour and a half, partly beneath an umbrella held up for him during heavy rain. He thought that in the benign wigged head, reading a little book beside an extinguished candle, one was glimpsing the incumbent of about 1740. He forgot the exact position of the obliterated glazing bars, the lowest horizontal of which would have cut right across his painted head, if repainted where it had been. Hence the slightly irregular spacing now: the lower panes being taller.

671 8 IMAGINARY FAMILY *1943* PORTRAITS

Body colour
Nos. 1 and 8: 1 ft. 8¼ in. × 2 ft. 7 in.
2–7: 2 ft. 7 in. × 1 ft. 8¼ in.
(These measurements include imitation gold frames painted by the artist.)   Unsigned

To decorate the ballroom for a dance given at Breccles Hall, Norfolk, by Mrs. Edwin Montagu.

(1) A mock Pastoral scene: a swarthy man in a crimson cloak, piping to an ample nude.

(2) Half-length of a man in 18th-century costume and wig, leaning on his right elbow.

(3) Head and shoulders of a woman in a flower-trimmed hat and considerable décolleté.

(4) Head and shoulders of an elderly man, scowling, in early 19th-century costume, with a yellow waistcoat.

(5) A chinless Guardee in uniform, half-length, against a crimson drapery.

(6) Head and shoulders of a man in a tall-crowned hat and Puritan-type costume.

(7) Head and shoulders of a Colonel Blimp in full-dress uniform, with eye-glass.

(8) A plump reclining Venus, with Cupid and a bowl of fruit: a background of blue hills.

Owner: Peter Hughes, Esq.

In another place he painted a fat Bacchus, or Silenus, seated astride a barrel, laughing, vine-wreathed, a glass of champagne in the left hand: very similar to the one soon afterwards painted at the Old Ship Club, Bosham (no. 673).

Owner: Peter Hughes, Esq.

672 NUDE IN A NISSEN HUT *1943*

Coloured wax pencils on wall-board.   ? 3 ft. high.
Unsigned

Nearly full length, resting on the right elbow, wearing one stocking. Drawn above Lt. Freddy Shaughnessy's bed at Riddlesworth Camp, Thetford, Norfolk; and inscribed by him on leaving: "This nude was drawn by Rex Whistler. Please look after her." (Or in similar words.)

Photographed. Probably destroyed

673 MURAL SKETCHES AT THE *1944* OLD SHIP CLUB, BOSHAM, SUSSEX

Charcoal, blue and red pencil, on wall.   Main wall:
3 ft. 9 in. × 9 ft. 4 in.   Signed, bottom right on main wall:
Rex Whistler

In late May and June, when the 2nd Bn. Welsh Guards was waiting to take part in the invasion, officers used to visit this Club, then owned by Mr. and Mrs. Moorhouse. One evening the artist drew on a partition wall in the dining-room a laughing Bacchus, or Silenus. Clad in nothing but a ribbon saying "The Ship", he sits astride a barrel of beer and holds aloft in his right hand a thyrsus, and in his left a glass of champagne. The next evening he began on the longer wall with a naked nymph, thereafter adopting the suggestions of his audience—that she should be tied to a stake, that a fawn should be added beside the pool. (Misunderstanding this, he drew at the right end a charming faun with a bunch of grapes.) When Mrs. Frogbrook ("Froggie" behind the bar) asked to be included, a frog's head appeared emerging from the pool. Round the hatchway at the extreme left there are heads leering at the girl. These reveal by their amateurishness and lack of scale that they were drawn by another, or by others, in the party; though he evidently touched up the two grotesque faces on the right of the group.

On leaving the Club, Mrs. Moorhouse removed the Bacchus.

Owner of remaining murals: Ralph Gordon-Smith, Esq.

Caricatures

See also the following: no. 287 (L. Whistler); no. 636 (25) (Mr. J. Beddington); no. 658 (Mrs. S. Sitwell, Mr. C. Beaton, Mr. B. Howard); no. 661 (King George V).

674   **RONALD FULLER**   *1923*

Indian ink.   *9 in.× 7 in.*   *Signed, bottom right:*
Rex Whistler

Begun as a serious portrait: head, left profile. But later a diminutive body was added, with the right hand raised, holding a daisy, and the left foot stepping over a cliff. "R.W.D. composing an 'ode to a daisy'."

Owner: Ronald Fuller

675   **PROFESSOR TONKS**   *? c. 1925*
AND A PROMISING PUPIL

? Pencil and water-colour

To the left, the elongated Slade Professor with eyes and hands raised, in mock homage before the drawing held up for his inspection, horizontally above the head of the squat, dowdy, wholly satisfied girl-student. Reproduced in *The Artist*, Nov. 1935, and *The Daily Express*, Nov. 2nd, 1959.

676   **MISS SUSAN LOWNDES**   *c. 1928*
(D. Susan Lowndes Marques)

Pencil.   *7 in.× 4½ in.*

Full length, with diminished body.

Owner: D. Susan Lowndes Marques

677   **THE SITWELLS**   *1929*

Pencil.   *c. 7¼ in.× 3¾ in.*   *Unsigned*

Drawn at Haus Hirth, Untergrainau, Bavaria, for Herr Walter Hirth, who had not met the three authors.

(1) MISS EDITH SITWELL (Dame Edith Sitwell)
Full length, full-face, head tilted to the right with hands extended.

(2) OSBERT SITWELL, ESQ. (Sir Osbert Sitwell, Bt.)
Full length, left profile, a cigar held in the right hand.

(3) SACHEVERELL SITWELL, ESQ.
Full length, facing half-left, hat and coat on arm, a rococo door behind him: the indefatigable sight-seer.

Owner: Prince Ludwig von Hessen

678   **SIR PHILIP SASSOON**   *? c. 1936*

Pencil.   *4 in.× 2 in.*   *Unsigned*

Head and shoulders, left profile; pasted into a scrapbook.

Owner: Cecil Beaton, Esq.

679   **SIR WINSTON**   *? c. 1939*
CHURCHILL

Pencil.   *1 ft. 3¼ in.× 10 in.*   *Unsigned*

The head of a top-hatted bulldog, facing half-right, with cigar. An indication of arms folded, and the clothes of John Bull.   *Owner: Laurence Whistler*

680   **COLONEL ANDREW GRAHAM** *1940*

Blue ink and red chalk.   *9½ in.× 7½ in.*

Signed, bottom right: Rex Whistler

Full length, left profile, in a Welsh Guard's cap; with diminished body. Extending a hand to a dowager, who curtsies low, décolleté.—"A fine pair of Charlies."

Owner: Col. Andrew Graham

681   **LIEUT. J. G. JENKINS**   *c. 1942*

Ink and wash.   *Unsigned*

When the artist was in charge of the Bn. Photograph Album, he framed a snapshot of this brother-officer pictorially. Above, quantities of food. Each side, a bull. Below, a caricature of Mr. Jenkins as a cave-man, morosely carrying off a reluctant girl.   *Owner: The Welsh Guards*

682   **CECIL BEATON, Esq.**   *n.d.*

Pencil and water-colour.   *7 in.× 4½ in.*   *Unsigned*

A slender figure standing with arms and legs crossed, casually swinging a camera from his right hand, a cigarette in the left. "Cecil Beaton." In the background, pencil only, a larger camera and a jar of lilies. On buff writing-paper.

On the reverse: "Empire day"—a civilian Blimp waving a small Union Jack.   *Owner: Laurence Whistler*

683   **"SIR WILLIAM EDEN**   *n.d.*
PAINTING IN ST. PAUL'S"

Pencil.   *8 in.× 5 in.*   *Unsigned*

Elegantly dressed, seated on a tiny camp-stool, facing left under Corinthian pilasters: with brush poised and rapt expression.   *Owner: Laurence Whistler*

684   **CHALIAPINE**   *n.d.*

Pencil, on Port Lympne writing-paper: evidently enclosed in a letter

(1) On stage, probably as Prince Igor, crowned and distinguished. (2) Plump, amiably grinning, with a glass of champagne. "I was terribly disappointed in Chaliapine 'in the flesh'. He looked practically like this I thought while he was toasting Emerald Cunard!"

Owner: Christabel Lady Aberconway

For Children

685 FEMALE NUDE AS A   *c. 1933*
            LANDSCAPE GARDEN

Sepia ink and wash.   7¾ in. × 10 in.   Unsigned.
                      (*Plate 70*)

When asked by Hugo Philipps, about four years old, to draw a garden, the artist drew one in the form of a supine woman, with swelling mounts and wandering paths, twin-domed pavilions, a circular basin mid-way; also appropriate boskage, at the head, etc. For similar conceptions, see *The Next Volume*, by Edward James, 1932 (no. 441), tail-piece no. 10; also *The New Keepsake*, 1931 (no. 435), head-piece no 14.

Owner: Miss Rosamond Lehmann

686 15 PRETENCE CIGARETTE- *c. 1934*
            CARDS

Sepia ink and water-colour.   Each 2⅝ in. × 1½ in. on a sheet
      10¾ in. × 1 ft. 1¾ in.   Unsigned

To illustrate *The Tinder Box*, by Hans Andersen. Numbered 1–15, no. 1 having the title of the story. Now pasted on a sheet.   *Owner: Billy Wallace, Esq.*

687 FIVE REVERSIBLE FACES *c. 1935*
Sepia ink and water-colour.   c. 7 in. × 4¾ in.   Unsigned

"Cinderella" X "Fairy Godmother"—used on the covers of *¡OHO!* by Rex and Laurence Whistler (no. 507), and reproduced in *Rex Whistler*, by Laurence Whistler, 1948 (no. 510), p. 62. "Mr Bun In a bad temper" X "Mrs Bun in a good temper". "Robin Hood" X "Sherlock Holmes" (the artist has marked the first as "1", the other as "2"). "A Viking" X "Old Gentleman jumping" (the artist has marked the first as "1", the other as "2" —a grotesque figure, not merely a head). Bluebeard X Fatima.   *Owner: Mrs. Herbert Agar*

688 REVERSIBLE FACE   *c. 1935*
Water-colour.   8½ in. × 6 in.   Unsigned

"A Professor and his newly engaged Cook." Very similar to the pair reproduced in *¡OHO!* (Lane, 1946) as Lord Littleray of Sunshine X Lady Cardigan Fitz Baddeley, but without the coronet X pearl necklace. All round the page: "John Julius from Rex."

Owner: The Viscount Norwich

689 "TRAGEDY IN 3 ACTS" *? c. 1935*
Sepia ink and wash.   5 in. × 7½ in.   Unsigned

(1) "Act 1." Three sailors in a rowing-boat serenely approaching an apparent rock.

(2) [Act 2.] The sailors appalled to find the rock a fearsome monster, about to swallow their boat.
(3) [Act 3.] The monster, with contented expression, crunching up sailors, boat, and all.

Owner: The Lady Elizabeth Clyde

690   LITTLE MISS MUFFET   *? 1936*
Oil on wood.   1 ft. 2 in. × 1 ft.   Signed, bottom right:
                  Rex Whistler

Miss Muffet is shown as an early 19th-century child in a mob cap looking down at her bowl; but the eyelids are painted on pieces of wood visible through holes in the face. When a tassel at the bottom of the picture is pulled, the lids are lifted, to reveal alarmed eyes looking sideways at a Spider, which appears on a thread to the right. The mechanism at the back appears to have been made by the artist himself. Exhibited in the Paintings for Children Exhibition at 56 Brook St. June 1936.

Owner: Colonel Reggie Cooper

691   REVERSIBLE FACE   *1938*
Pencil and water-colour.   5¼ in. × 4¼ in.
Signed on the mount: Rosina [*sic*] with love
                      xǝᴚ ɯoɹℲ

Henry VIII X Anne of Cleves: he eyeing her askance with great disrelish; she grimacing hideously back. Brought as a present to Rosanagh Crichton, aged 6, when painting her portrait (no. 131).   *Owner: The Baroness Michael Raben*

692   BATHROOM AT   *c. 1938*
   LAVINGTON PARK, SUSSEX

Oil on wall-surface.   Now approx. 3 ft. 3 in. × 4 ft. 8 in.
   Originally 4 ft. 8 in. × 7 ft.   Unsigned

Painted for the bathroom of Mr. Billy Wallace, when a child, to induce him to go to bed. Above the bath, Neptune in a choppy sea, ogling a lovely mermaid seated on the end of the bath.

When the house was requisitioned during the war and the owner proposed to safeguard the painting by boarding it up, the billeting Major replied: "Don't bother, Mrs. Agar. My troops have seen lewder things than that!" Lavington Park is now a boys' school. Neptune survives, though with face obliterated. The alluring mermaid has been painted out.

693   A JACOB'S LADDER   *1940*
Oil on wood.   1 ft. 5 in. × 7½ in.

Six slats of wood painted on both sides: so bound together with tapes as to flop over at a twist of a handle at the top, and reveal the picture on the other side. On one side "Lucifer", on the other "Michael". On the one side "Made by Anne", on the other "Painted by Rex".

Owner: Dr. Anne McLaren

694   JACK THE GIANT-KILLER   *1941*

Pen and sepia ink.   8¼ in. × 6¾ in.   Unsigned

A vast giant in hat, coat, and breeches, standing up behind distant hills, with a walking-stick. A minute Jack on the church spire firing at him. Drawn—to be sent to Jeanne and Coralie Portal in S. Africa—while he was "puzzling over the answer to one of the questions in our gunnery exam". (Letter from their father on reverse of frame.)

Owner: Mrs. Richard Altham

695   THE NAUGHTY BOY AND   *1943*
THE MONSTER

Pencil and coloured chalks.   8 in. × 1 ft. ½ in.   Unsigned

For Juliet Nissen when a little girl: the story in three pictures—nos. (2) and (3) on one sheet—of a naughty boy who goes to sea in his father's dinghy; is gobbled up by an appalling sea-serpent; and rescued from its very jaws by an angel.

(1) Happily picnicking. Monster approaching from the rear.

(2) Helpless in the gap between the prominent front teeth. (Angel with flaming sword coming down from afar.)

(3) Flying away safe in angelic arms. The monster burnt out. The bottle of ginger-beer in the angel's pocket.

Owner: Miss Juliet Nissen

696   THE STORY OF A BOY AND   *1943*
A MAN

Thirteen sketches in pencil.   Average size 3¼ in. × 3½ in.
Unsigned

For Juliet Nissen when a little girl: the story in pictures of a boy who dreams of a curious man, whom he follows up the chimney, and with whom in the end he takes a hot bath. Inserted in a sketch-book, 7 in. × 5 in., with a narrative written by the owner: Miss Juliet Nissen.

697   CHRISTMAS CARD TO   *1943*
"MISS JEANNE PORTAL"

(1) Envelope. Sepia ink and water-colour, 4 in. × 5¾ in., unsigned. A flourished address in a wreath.

(2) Card. A folded sheet, 7 in. × 3¼ in., sepia ink and water-colour.

Front.—A large, bright-coloured Father Christmas, seated on a stool and supporting a sack labelled "Presents for Jeanne". "Happy Christmas to Jeanne" across his yellow waistcoat.

Inside, right-hand page.—A mermaid on a rococo cartouche: "With love and all good wishes from Rex Whistler." The artist had never met Jeanne and Coralie Portal (see below), who were in South Africa, the children of a brother-officer.   *Owner: Mrs. Richard Altham*

698   CHRISTMAS CARD TO   *1943*
"MISS CORALIE PORTAL"

(1) Envelope. Sepia ink and water-colour, 4 in. × 5¾ in., unsigned. A flourished address among sprays of roses and stars.

(2) Card. A folded sheet, 7 in. × 3¼ in., sepia ink and water-colour.

Front.—The huge, bright-coloured head of Father Christmas, with "Happy Christmas to Coralie" inside the laughing mouth.

Inside, right-hand page.—The Fairy Queen saucily perched on a rococo cartouche: "With love and all good wishes from Rex Whistler 1943."

Owner: Miss Coralie Portal

699   DECORATIONS IN THE   *1943*
MEMORIAL HALL, PICKERING, YORKS

Oil on boarding

When the 2nd Bn. the Welsh Guards was stationed at Pickering, the artist suggested, and himself largely devised, a mammoth Christmas Party for nearly 300 children of the town (as described in *Rex Whistler*, by Laurence Whistler, p. 37). On each side of the proscenium arch he painted "an enormous guardsman (10 or 11 ft. high) in full dress, bearskin and all", and on a side wall the heads of three children, wolfing cakes. The last-named painting remains in place; the two guardsmen, distracting in serious concerts, have been moved to the back of the hall.

700   AUNT SALLY   *n.d.*

Oil on ply-wood.   2 ft. 9 in. × 2 ft. 5¼ in.   Unsigned

For a children's party. With open mouth, blue outraged eyes, and a green cap.   *Owner: Laurence Whistler*

Works in National Collections

LONDON

THE TATE GALLERY

Self-portrait. Oils. 1926. (No. 107.)
"The Pursuit of Rare Meats." Murals in the Refreshment Room. 1927. (No. 2.)
Ten illustrations to *Königsmark*. Sepia ink and wash, with water-colour. 1941. (No. 516.)

THE NATIONAL PORTRAIT GALLERY

Portrait of Sir William Walton. Pencil. 1929. (No. 172.)
Self-portrait. Oils. ?1934. (No. 116.)

THE BRITISH MUSEUM

Special decoration in copy of *The Next Volume*. (No. 441.)

THE VICTORIA AND ALBERT MUSEUM

Copies of seventeen book-plates, 1925–1941. (No. 584 *et seq.*)
Copies of posters for The Tate Gallery, 1928; The London Museum, 1928; The Age of Walnut, 1932; The Vale of Aylesbury, 1932; Exhibition of English Women's Clothing, 1934 (Bethnal Green). (No. 652 *et seq.*)
Copies of Christmas cards, stationery, etc.
Copies of advertisements for Fortnum and Mason, Guinness, and Rothman.

THE COURTAULD INSTITUTE

Copy of poster for Exhibition of English Women's Clothing, 1934.

BATH

THE ART GALLERY

"The Foreign Bloke." Oils. *c.* 1935. (No. 66.)

BRIGHTON

THE ROYAL PAVILION

"Allegory", and medallion of George IV. Oils. 1944. (No. 15.)

LIVERPOOL

THE PUBLIC LIBRARY

*A collection of book-plates (printed copies).

OXFORD

THE ASHMOLEAN MUSEUM

"Samson Destroying the Philistines." Pen and sepia ink. 1928. (No. 238.)
Design for dust-wrapper of *Cannibal Coryton*. 1930. (No. 433.)
"An Encampment in a Ruined Temple." Pen and sepia ink, with water-colour (*n.d.*). (No. 280.)

WORKSOP

THE PUBLIC LIBRARY AND MUSEUM

"The Palladian Bridge, Wilton." Water-colour (*n.d.*). (No. 281.)

NATIONAL TRUST PROPERTIES

DORNEYWOOD, BUCKS.

Mural. 1928–9. (No. 3.)

MOTTISFONT ABBEY, HANTS.

Murals. 1938–9. (No. 14.)

ASCOTT, BUCKS.

Creslow Hall, Bucks. Oils. *c.* 1935. (No. 65.)

U.S.A.

METROPOLITAN MUSEUM OF ART, NEW YORK

Designs for *The New Forget-Me-Not*. (No. 419.)

From *THE NEW KEEPSAKE*. Cat. no. 435

Bibliography

of the principal books and articles on Rex Whistler, and printed references to him.

BOOKS

Aberconway, Christabel: *The Story of Mr. Korah* (Michael Joseph, 1954). Introduction.

Ambrose, Kay: *A Balletomane's Sketch-Book* (A. & C. Black, 1941).

Asquith, Lady Cynthia: *Haply I May Remember* (Barrie, 1950).

Bax, Clifford, and Stewart, Meum: *The Distaff Muse* (Hollis & Carter, 1949). Contains a poem by Dorothy Wellesley on the artist.

Beaton, Cecil: *Ashcombe. The Story of a Fifteen-Year Lease* (Batsford, 1949).

Beaumont, Cyril, W.: *The Sadler's Wells Ballet* (Beaumont, 1946).

Bland, David: *The Illustration of Books* (Faber, 1953).

Charques, R. D.: *Footnotes to the Theatre* (Peter Davies, 1938). Contains an article by the artist, "Problems of the Stage Designer".

Cochran, C. B.: *A Showman Looks On* (Dent, 1949).

Cooper, Diana: *The Light of Common Day* (Hart-Davis, 1959).

Ellis, Major L. F.: *The Welsh Guards at War* (Aldershot, 1946).

Feibusch, Hans: *Mural Painting* (A. & C. Black, 1946).

Haskell, Arnold: *Ballet Panorama* (Batsford, 1938). *Ballet Since 1939* (British Council, 1946). *Gala Performance* (Collins, 1953).

Leeper, Janet: *English Ballet* (Penguin, 1944).

Manchester, P. W.: *Vic-Wells: A Ballet Progress* (Gollancz, 1942).

Mander, Raymond, and Mitchenson, J.: *A Picture History of the British Theatre* (Hulton Press, 1957).

Masque, The (Curtain Press, 1947–8): Nos. 2, 4, and 7, as follows: No. 2—"Designs for the Theatre by Rex Whistler," Part I, by Laurence Whistler and Cecil Beaton. No. 4—Part II, by James Laver. No. 7—Part III, by Laurence Whistler. Collected in *The Masque Library*, ed. Lionel Carter, 1950.

Olivier, Edith: *In Pursuit of Rare Meats*. The Tate Gallery Restaurant Murals (Tate Gallery, 1954).

Sitwell, Sir Osbert: *Noble Essences or Courteous Revelations* (Macmillan, 1950). Chapter 10 is on Rex Whistler.

Turner, W. J.: *The English Ballet* (Collins, 1944).

Wellesley, Dorothy: *Selected Poems* (Williams & Norgate, 1949). Contains a poem, *For Rex Whistler*.

Whistler, Laurence: *Rex Whistler, His Life and His Drawings* (Art & Technics, 1948). *Rex Whistler: The Königsmark Drawings* (Richards Press, 1952).

PERIODICALS

Architectural Review, The, June 1931: "The Royal Academy."

Artist, The, Nov. 1935: "Artists of Note, No. 9: Rex Whistler."

Curl, Peter: "Designing a Book-Jacket" (*Studio*, 1956).

Davis, Elidir: "Murals in England" (*Decoration*, no. 32, Summer, 1939).

Easton, Malcolm: "The Book Jacket in Modern Book Production" (*Bookseller*, Mar. 17th, 1937). "The Art of the Book Jacket" (*Artist*, Sept. 1937).

Englefield, W. A. D.: "Check List of Rex Whistler Book-wrappers" (*Book Collector's Quarterly*, no. XVII, April–June 1935).

Hill, Oliver: "Mr. Rex Whistler at Port Lympne" (*Country Life*, Feb. 4th, 1933).

Hussey, Christopher: "Paintings at 36 Hill St." (*Country Life*, Mar. 25th, 1939). "The Rex Whistler Room at Plas Newydd' (*Country Life*, Feb. 22nd, 1946). "Mottisfont Abbey" (*Country Life*, May 6th, 1954).

Laver, James: "The Evolution of Theatrical Décor" (*Artist*, Feb. 1937).

Leeper, Janet: "Stage Designers II: Rex Whistler" (*Ballet*, June 1948).

Newdigate, Bernard: "The Art of the Book" (*Studio*, Autumn, 1938).

Olivier, Edith: "Memories of Rex Whistler" (*Country Life*, Sept. 1st, 1944).

Sitwell, Sir Osbert: "This Strange Country" (*Architectural Review*, July 1929). "Ex Libris" (Rex Whistler's book-plates) (*Harper's Bazaar*, Sept. 1937).

Steegman, John: "The Artist and the Country House" (*Country Life*, 1949).

Studio, The, Vol. 100 (1931): "Modern Book Illustration."

Whistler, Laurence: "Rex Whistler" (*Everybody's*, Oct. 1948). "The Bookplates of Rex Whistler" (*Connoisseur*, Oct. 1959). "A Portrait in the Guards" (a poem) (*Listener*, Nov. 20th, 1958).

Index

CAPITALS denote works by the artist. *Italics* are used for the titles of Plays, Ballets, Operas, Revues and Revue-sketches; also for the titles of printed Books and Periodicals, and of Articles and Poems in Periodicals, decorated by him.

Red earthenware? 'frills' along roof ridges.

Bright yellow variegated Privet bushes

Geraniums

Stone or Terracotta